# ELECTRICAL RESISTANCE
# OF METALS

# THE INTERNATIONAL CRYOGENICS MONOGRAPH SERIES

*General Editors*

Dr. K. Mendelssohn, F. R. S.
*The Clarendon Laboratory*
*Oxford, England*

Dr. K. D. Timmerhaus
*University of Colorado*
*Boulder, Colorado*

| | |
|---|---|
| H. J. Goldsmid | *Thermoelectric Refrigeration, 1964* |
| G. T. Meaden | *Electrical Resistance of Metals, 1965* |

*Volumes in preparation*

| | |
|---|---|
| D. H. Parkinson and B. Mulhall | *Very High Magnetic Fields* |
| J. L. Olsen and S. Gygax | *Superconductivity for Engineers* |
| A. J. Croft and P. V. E. McClintock | *Cryogenic Laboratory Equipment* |
| G. K. Gaulé | *Superconductivity in Elements, Alloys, and Compounds* |
| E. S. Raja Gopal | *Specific Heats at Low Temperatures* |
| M. G. Zabetakis | *Cryogenic Safety* |
| F. B. Canfield | *Low-Temperature Phase Equilibria* |
| W. E. Keller | *Helium-3 and Helium-4* |
| S. Ramaseshan | *Low-Temperature Crystallography* |
| P. Glaser and A. Wechsler | *Cryogenic Insulation Systems* |

# ELECTRICAL RESISTANCE OF METALS

### George Terence Meaden
M.A., D.Phil. (Oxon), A.Inst.P., F.R.Met.S.

*Centre de Recherches sur les Très Basses Températures*
*Faculté des Sciences*
*Université de Grenoble*
*France*

Ⴔ

PLENUM PRESS

NEW YORK

1965

Library of Congress Catalog Card Number 64-23243

©1965 Plenum Press
A Division of Consultants Bureau Enterprises, Inc.
227 West 17th Street • New York, N. Y. 10011

Printed in the United States of America

This book is dedicated
affectionately
to my parents

# Preface

This book has been written chiefly in mind of the needs of scientists and engineers who require a full and current presentation of the experimental facts together with a relatively concise account of the modern theory of the electrical resistance of metals and alloys. While all the essential groundwork on the behavior of the resistance of metals has been covered in this treatment, no pretense is made that any part of the theory is exhaustively covered; resistance measurements on metals embrace many broad fields and fringe on so many others that without much difficulty all the chapters of the present book could easily have been expanded into extensive volumes in their own right. In particular, to those reviewers who may claim that Chapters 5 and 6 are perhaps too condensed, I say at once that whole books, fine review articles, and conference proceedings already exist on such subjects as imperfections in metals, magnetic-field and pressure effects, and the irradiation damage of metals. Also, the section on superconductivity has been deliberately kept short because a companion monograph on this topic is presently being prepared by Dr. Gygax and Professor Olsen.

In brief, this book may be said to be an introduction to the subject of electrical resistance in metals that can be understood by anyone with a university science degree who has made some study of solid state and atomic physics, and can be used by anyone who seeks to obtain experimental resistivity data tabulated herein on the pure metals or who desires to make resistivity measurements for himself.

One especial aim has been to scour thoroughly all results published in the literature on the electrical resistivity of the metallic elements up to room temperature, to review the most interesting and relevant of the data, and to tabulate systematically the best and most accurate of the data. In following the good example set by White and Woods,[M10] Dugdale and Gugan,[137,139,141] and regrettably very few others in their clear data tabulation of resistivity results, it is hoped that we shall have played a small part in establishing more uniformity in the future publication of data. Too often in the past the results of precise and productive experimental work have been published most unsatisfactorily in the inadequate form of one or two small-scale graphs without inclusion of any tables of actual figures.

Next, because this book has been written for a series of monographs on cryogenics, consideration has mostly been given to effects and results pertaining to low and ordinary temperatures—only with respect to theory has the discussion reached into the realms of higher temperatures. Indeed, on account of the cryogenic aspect and because this is essentially a practical book, we have even digressed slightly from the main theme on a few occasions to include some related issues of interest to low-temperature research and development workers. For example, there are sections on low-temperature thermocouples, semiconductor resistance thermometers, and calibration procedures.

I now wish to record my thanks to Dr. R. H. Romer, Associate Professor of Physics at Amherst College, Massachusetts, for reading and criticizing helpfully a number of the chapters, and to others of my colleagues for discussions of several points. I am also grateful to Prof. L. Weil, Centre de Recherches sur les Très Basses Températures, Université de Grenoble, who provided various laboratory facilities that made my work of writing this book while in France rather easier, and to Dr. K. Mendelssohn, F.R.S., whose unrelenting enthusiasm has stimulated and developed my love for low-temperature physics. Finally, my thanks are due to Drs. J. S. Dugdale (National Research Council, Ottawa), R. W. Powell (National Physical Laboratory, Teddington), and R. Reich (Centre National de la Recherche Scientifique, Vitry-sur-Seine) for correspondence and for supplying me with unpublished material, and to Mlle Anne Jacqueline Cheyroux for typing my final manuscript *d'une manière si impeccable*.

G. T. MEADEN

Parana Lodge
Victoria Road
Trowbridge, England
*April 1965*

# Acknowledgments

The author acknowledges the permission granted by the following publishers and societies to make use of figures that have appeared in their publications: Academic Press, Inc. (*Solid State Physics Series*), American Institute of Physics (*Physics Review, Physics Review Letters, Review of Scientific Instruments, Soviet Physics JETP*), Johann Ambrosius Barth Verlag (*Annalen der Physik, Handbuch der Experimentalphysik*), Elsevier Publishing Co. (*Journal of the Less-Common Metals*), Heywood and Co., Ltd. (*Cryogenics*), Interscience Publishers, Inc. (*Journal de Physique*), National Research Council (*Canadian Journal of Physics*), North-Holland Publishing Co. (*Physics Letters*), Oxford University Press, Pergamon Press, Ltd. (*Progress in Nuclear Energy*), Physica Foundation (*Physica*), Physical Society of Japan, The Royal Society (*Proceedings* and *Philosophical Transactions*), Springer-Verlag (*Handbuch der Physik*), and Taylor and Francis, Ltd. (*Philosophical Magazine*).

# Contents

xi

**Chapter 3      The Theory of the Electrical Resistance of Metals**

**Chapter 4      Methods of Evaluating $\theta_R$**

# List of Tables

*Chapter 1*

# The Meaning of Electrical Resistance and Its Importance

## 1.1. INTRODUCTION

A ready ability to conduct electricity is one of the most characteristic and important features of a metal. It is due to the presence of large numbers of quasi-free electrons which under the action of an applied electric field are able to flow through the metallic lattice.* Were it not for the presence of disturbing influences within the metal, infinite conductivity would result, but such influences are invariably present, and they can be very diverse and numerous.† They impede the free flow of electrons, scattering them and giving rise to a resistance called the *electrical resistance*. If the dimensions of the metal sample are known, a specific electrical resistivity for the metal can be calculated. This resistivity is characteristic of that particular metal, and it is dependent on the temperature and pressure at any instant as well as on the chemical and physical state of the metal.

By *chemical state* of a metal we mean the types and relative proportions of the foreign-impurity atoms that are present. However, their effect on the resistivity will depend not only on their quality and quantity, but also on how they are distributed within the lattice— for example, whether they are in solid solution, ordered in sublattices, or present in clusters or as compounds. Even if the metal can be considered chemically pure, localized strains may be present in the lattice, as from dislocations, vacancies, or interstitial atoms. This is what we mean by its *physical state*, and it will be dependent

---

* The direction of flow is contrary to that of the field because electrons are negatively charged.

† The low-temperature phenomenon of superconductivity is ignored for the purposes of this discussion.

1

on the previous history of the metal, including, for instance, any cold-work, irradiation, and annealing treatments to which it has been subjected. The effect of temperature, too, is more than just that of modifying the extent of the lattice vibrations and interatomic distances, since crystallographic phase changes and magnetic transitions or other order–disorder phenomena may also result.

In short, it is the object of this book to discuss all such behavior concerned with the electrical resistivities of the metals of the periodic system at and below room temperature (295°K).* Dilute alloys will be covered, too, but nondilute alloys will be considered only to a limited extent (Sections 5.3 and 5.4). In some cases the discussion of metals does extend to above room temperature. This is done principally in order to include the abnormal nonlinear effects found in Pd, Pt, Yb, Np, etc. (Section 3.12), the effects of melting on Ga and the alkalis (Section 3.13), and the antiferromagnetic transition in Cr at 312°K. Otherwise, for experimental information on electrical resistivity at high temperatures, the reader is referred to the reviews of Gerritsen [M1] and Grüneisen. [M2]

During the course of this book it will become clear how important a property the electrical resistivity of a metal really is, for it will be shown repeatedly that a knowledge of its value, especially as a temperature-dependent parameter, can have many immediate theoretical and practical consequences. Its theoretical importance will be most apparent in Chapters 3, 4, and 6, and the chief practical applications will appear in Chapters 5, 6, and 8. It is convenient to summarize here some of these practical uses.

First, we cite electrical-resistance strain gauges because they are so widely used in industry and research for determining the states of strain at the surfaces of large and small structures. These gauges are flat-wire or foil resistance elements, often made from Cu-Ni alloys, and are held firmly against the surface of interest. The action of these gauges depends on the sensitivity of the gauge resistance to its own state of strain (Section 6.1.2), and applications have been found up to 1100°K on the one hand and down to 0.06°K on the other.[66a] Next, since the electrical resistivity of a metal is also very sensitive to its degree of purity, simple resistance measurements on a specimen are often made at 4°K and at room temperature when information concerning its purity is sought (Section 1.4). Rather less good for this

---

* The most convenient scale of temperature for low-temperature research is the Kelvin absolute scale. For the sake of uniformity and to avoid possible ambiguities, we have used degrees Kelvin throughout the entire work. Thus, following White and Woods[M10] and others,[139,141,291] we have taken 295°K to represent room temperature, rather than 293.15°K ( $\equiv$ 20°C). Conversion tables relating °K, °C, °F, and °R are to be found in the Appendix (Table XVI).

purpose, but helpful all the same, are determinations at room temperature only of the absolute resistivity and the temperature coefficient of resistivity of the specimen. Then again, we can mention that carefully constructed platinum resistance-wire elements are employed as basic thermometers over the temperature range between 10 and 1600°K. In fact, high-precision ones are used for the establishment of the International Temperature Scale from 90 to 900°K (Section 8.3).

Another application of electrical-resistance measurements lies in the detection of the presence or absence of ordered lattice structures in alloys (such as in Cu-Au alloys, for example [M4]) (Section 5.3), while again from resistive data it is usually possible to make reasonable predictions of thermal conductivities by means of the Wiedemann–Franz law and other formulas both at low[384,440] and high[364,366] temperatures. One can also use magnetoresistivity measurements on high-purity Cu or Bi as the basis of a continuous-reading instrument for magnetic-field determinations at low temperatures.[281] Finally, there is the great ease with which phase and magnetic transitions (Chapter 2) and defect production and migration (Sections 5.5 and 5.6) can be studied, to say nothing of the purely theoretical uses of electrical-resistivity data (Chapters 3, 4, and 6). Undoubtedly, electrical resistivity owes much of its overall importance to the relative ease with which such experiments can be carried out, for, compared to the thermal conductivity or the specific heat, where even crude estimates are difficult to obtain, the precise measurement of electrical resistance as a function of temperature rarely presents any great experimental problems.

## 1.2. THE METALS OF THE PERIODIC SYSTEM

We shall begin by studying the way in which metals and good and poor conductors are distributed within the periodic system of the elements.

There are now 104 elements forming the periodic table, 82 of which can be considered to be metals. The remaining elements are semiconductors, insulators, the halogens, and the so-called permanent gases. These nonmetals are signified by an asterisk in the periodic table given in Table I. It is seen that the typically semiconducting elements, Si, Ge, and Se, for example, lie adjacent to the metals on the right-hand side of the table. Electronic conduction occurs in semiconductors as well as in metals, but the mode of transport is quite different. They will therefore be dealt with here only sufficiently to demonstrate the contrast that they provide with the metals. For

## Table I. Electrical Resistivities of the Elements at 295°K (residual resistivities have been subtracted)

| 1A | 2A | 3A | 4A | 5A | 6A | 7A | 8A | | | 1B | 2B | 3B | 4B | 5B | 6B | 7B | 8B |
|---|---|---|---|---|---|---|---|---|---|---|---|---|---|---|---|---|---|
| $^1$H * | | | | | | | | | | | | | | | | | He * |
| $^3$Li 9.32 | Be 3.25 | | | | | | | | | | | B * | C * | N * | O * | F * | Ne * |
| $^{11}$Na 4.75 | Mg 4.30 | | | | | | | | | | | Al 2.74 | Si * | P * | S * | Cl * | Ar * |
| $^{19}$K 7.19 | Ca 3.6 | Sc 46.8 | Ti 43.1 | V 19.9 | Cr 12.9 | Mn 139 | Fe 9.8 | Co 5.8 | Ni 7.0 | Cu 1.70 | Zn 5.92 | Ga 14.85 | Ge * | As 29 | Se * | Br * | Kr * |
| $^{37}$Rb 12.5 | Sr 21.5 | Y 58.5 | Zr 42.4 | Nb 14.5 | Mo 5.3 | Tc ~14 | Ru 7.4 | Rh 4.8 | Pd 10.5 | Ag 1.61 | Cd 7.27 | In 8.75 | Sn 11.0 | Sb 41.3 | Te * | I * | Xe * |
| $^{55}$Cs 20.0 | Ba 39 | $^{57}$La 79 | Hf 30.6 | Ta 13.1 | W 5.3 | Re 18.6 | Os 9.1 | Ir 5.1 | Pt 10.4 | Au 2.20 | Hg 95.9($l$) | Tl 16.4 | Pb 21.0 | Bi 116 | Po 46 | At * | Rn * |
| $^{87}$Fr ? | Ra ? | $^{89}$Ac ? | 104 ? | 105 | 106 | 107 | 108 | 109 | 110 | | | | | | | | |

| Lanthanide elements | Ce 81 | Pr 67 | Nd 59 | Pm ? | Sm 99 | Eu 89 | Gd 134.1 | Tb 111 | Dy 90.0 | Ho 77.7 | Er 81 | Tm 62 | Yb 26.4 | Lu 53 |
|---|---|---|---|---|---|---|---|---|---|---|---|---|---|---|
| Actinide elements | Th 15.2 | Pa ? | U 25.7 | Np 118.5 | Pu 143 | Am ? | Cm ? | Bk ? | Cf ? | Es ? | Fm ? | Md ? | (No) ? | Lw ? |

The ruled lines enclose the superconducting elements (refer to Section 2.19 and Table IV).
* Nonmetals.
? Resistivity unknown.

articles on conduction in semiconductors, reference may be made to such books as those by Ziman, [M12] Ehrenberg, [M16] and Smith. [M32]

All metals conduct electricity very well compared to the semiconducting elements. They have specific resistivities lying in the range 1.5 to 150 $\mu\Omega$-cm at room temperature, and the resistivities increase roughly in proportion to the temperature. Also, the effect of adding small amounts of impurities is to add a more-or-less temperature-independent contribution to the resistivity. The situation is entirely different with semiconductors, though, since their conductivities are $10^6$ or even $10^{12}$ times lower than for metals. Moreover, it is the rule that the resistivity *decreases* with rising temperature and with the addition of impurities. Thus it does not suffice to say that semiconductors are simply poorer conductors than metals; their behavior is in every way in direct contrast to that of metals. We will anticipate the fuller explanation given in Chapter 3 by stating here that such differences are consequent upon the different shapes and locations of Fermi surfaces and Brillouin zones in the two cases. It is because the whole Fermi surface happens to fall in the energy gap between rather widely spaced Brillouin zones in Si, Ge, Se, and Te that these polyvalent elements chance to be semiconductors, while others adjacent to them are good metallic conductors. This will be discussed further in Chapter 3, and we now return to the periodic system in Table I in order to comment on the arrangement of good and poor conductors among the metallic elements. In studying this table it should be noted that the room-temperature resistivities given are not actual measured values, because the resistivity remaining as the temperature nears absolute zero (the residual resistivity) has already been subtracted in each case in order to provide values for hypothetically pure metals. This is in accordance with Matthiessen's rule, to be discussed later in Sections 1.4 and 3.8, which is generally applicable when the residual resistivities are small fractions of the measured room-temperature resistivities, as they are here. Typical residual resistivities for pure, strain-free samples of the various metallic elements are also included in Table II.

We see that, as judged by the room-temperature resistivities, the best conductors are to be found among the noble metals and the simpler alkalis (all monovalent), and that the resistivities of the adjacent divalent metals are distinctly higher. Many of the transition metals have still higher resistivities, while as a group the rare-earth metals are the worst conductors of all.

Quantitatively, modern theories of conduction apply only to the monovalent metals, but in a qualitative way it can be understood why transition metals and rare earths should have much higher resistivities, although very little can be treated analytically at the present time. The details of the temperature variation of the lattice resistance at low temperatures are also imprecisely understood even in some of the simpler metals, though some approximate and helpful solutions of the problem have been obtained. In brief, it is all too evident that the current situation regarding the theory of the resistance of metals is still rather poor, but at least in one important branch, namely, superconductivity, much encouraging progress has been made during the last ten years. However, before discussing existing theories of electrical resistance in Chapter 3, we shall first present the experimental results on all of the metals in some detail (Chapter 2). The reader will then have a clearer idea of the variety of phenomena and behaviors that occur and which therefore require explanation.

We shall not carry the treatment of superconductivity very far in this book, because the subject forms an extensive field itself, and there exists a companion volume in this series, by Gygax and Olsen, [M18] which deals with it. Consequently, we shall consider only those few aspects of the subject that are of greatest relevance to our own needs (Section 2.19). The remaining sections of the present chapter are chiefly taken up with definitions and explanations of a number of terms that will prove helpful before continuing to the aforementioned chapter on experimental results.

### 1.3. OHM'S LAW, ELECTRICAL RESISTANCE, AND ELECTRICAL RESISTIVITY

Ohm's law is the experimental observation that at constant temperature the ratio of the current density $\mathbf{J}$ within a metallic conductor to the electric field $\mathbf{E}$ is a constant.

This may be expressed by

$$\frac{\mathbf{J}}{\mathbf{E}} = \frac{1}{\rho} \quad \text{or} \quad \frac{\mathbf{J}}{\mathbf{E}} = \sigma \tag{1.1}$$

where $\rho$ and $\sigma$ are known as the specific electrical resistivity and conductivity, respectively.

Applying this to a conductor of uniform cross-sectional area $A$ and length $l$ in which a voltage $V$ between its ends is produced by a current $I$, we have the relations

$$\mathbf{E} = \frac{V}{l} \qquad \mathbf{J} = \frac{I}{A} \tag{1.2}$$

Substituting in equation (1.1), we obtain

$$\frac{V}{I} = \frac{\rho l}{A} \tag{1.3}$$

$\rho l/A$ is called $R$, the electrical resistance of the conductor, so that we have as an alternative expression of Ohm's law

$$V = IR \tag{1.4}$$

With $V$ in volts and $I$ in amperes, $R$ is measured in ohms. The electrical resistivity $\rho = RA/l$ is then given in ohm-centimeters if $A$ is in square centimeters and $l$ in centimeters.

## 1.4. IMPURITY RESISTIVITY, IDEAL RESISTIVITY, AND MATTHIESSEN'S RULE

The measured resistivity $\rho_T$ is generally a function of temperature, but on approaching absolute zero it comes to assume a constant residual value, known as the residual resistivity $\rho_0$. The quantity $\rho_0$ arises from the presence of impurities, defects, and strains in the metal lattice. However, in pure annealed metals it is only a small fraction of the total resistivity at room temperature. A specification of $\rho_0$ and the total room-temperature resistivity $\rho_{295}$ for a given specimen provides a ready indication of the specimen's state of purity and freedom from strain. But it is instead more accepted practice to determine for this purpose either the resistance or the resistivity at the ice-point and at $4°K$ (or less) and to calculate and quote the ratio $R_0/R_{273}$ or $\rho_0/\rho_{273}$. A glance at Table II will show that ratios smaller than $10^{-3}$ have been obtained for more than twenty different metals and smaller than $10^{-2}$ for most others excepting the magnetic rare earths. The lowest such resistivity ratio of all to date appears to be $4 \times 10^{-6}$ for Sn.[455]

Subtraction of $\rho_0$ from the measured resistivity gives a value of the resistivity appropriate for a perfectly pure, strain-free specimen. In the case of a nonmagnetic metal the temperature-dependent resistivity thus obtained is called the ideal or intrinsic resistivity (Section 3.4). It is designated by $\rho_{iT}$ at temperature $T$, and it is caused by the interaction of the conduction electrons with the thermal vibrations of the ions of the lattice (Sections 3.6 and 3.7).

The separation of the total resistivity $\rho_T$ into temperature-dependent ($\rho_{iT}$) and temperature-independent ($\rho_0$) contributions in this way is known as Matthiessen's rule, which may be written

$$\rho_T = \rho_0 + \rho_{iT} \tag{1.5}$$

This is not the form in which Matthiessen's original statement in 1860 was expressed, for it was then based on and applied to alloys in only the room-temperature region[298] (this was still many years before the first liquefaction of the permanent gases*). Matthiessen's original statement (in German) was to the effect that the increase in resistance due to a small concentration of another metal in solid solution is in general independent of the temperature. This is equivalent to saying that the addition of small amounts of impurity atoms does not modify the thermal vibrations of the ions of the host lattice, so that the impurity contribution to the resistivity may be considered apart from the ideal or thermal contribution. This subject will be treated in some detail in Chapters 3 and 5.

Another important contribution to the resistivity occurs only in ferromagnetic and antiferromagnetic metals below their magnetic transition temperatures and is due to scattering from disordered spin arrangements. The magnitude of this effect varies according to the element, but it is very great indeed in Mn and many of the rare earths, and is largely responsible for their huge resistivities. This magnetic disorder term ($\rho_{mT}$), temperature-dependent below the Curie or Néel temperature, may to a first approximation be considered additive to the residual and ideal resistivities in these metals. Thus

$$\rho_T = \rho_0 + \rho_{iT} + \rho_{mT} \tag{1.6}$$

These and other points mentioned above will be discussed more fully in later chapters.

## 1.5. RESISTIVITY IN ANISOTROPIC METALS

A metal with a cubic crystal structure has the same resistivity whether in polycrystalline or single crystal form, apart from a small extra contribution in a polycrystal that may sometimes arise because of grain boundaries. But in a single crystal of a noncubic metal the resistivity is often very anisotropic, its value depending on the direction of the flow of current. Likewise, polycrystalline specimens of such metals, if preferentially oriented, as by rolling or drawing, for instance, will have direction-dependent resistive properties. It is therefore important with polycrystalline samples of such metals to remove any preferred orientation by means of adequate annealing, and with single crystals to remember that statements of the resistivity have no exactness unless the directions in the crystal along which the resistivity is measured are also specified.

It is also useful to be able to derive from single-crystal data mean resistivity values that would be appropriate for polycrystalline specimens of the same material. The chief noncubic metallic crystals are

---

* Liquid oxygen: (1877, Pictet) 1895, Linde and Hampson. Liquid hydrogen: 1898, Dewar. Liquid helium: 1908, Onnes.

those with the close-packed hexagonal, rhombohedral (trigonal), tetragonal, and orthorhombic structures. A partial list is given in Table III.

Let $\rho_{\parallel}$ be the electrical resistivity parallel to the principal crystalline axis and $\rho_{\perp 1}$, $\rho_{\perp 2}$ the resistivities along the two orthogonal axes. Let $\bar{\rho}$ stand for the resistivity of an isotropic polycrystalline sample of the same metal, and $\sigma_{\parallel}$, $\sigma_{\perp 1}$, $\sigma_{\perp 2}$, and $\bar{\sigma}$ represent the corresponding electrical conductivities.

We begin by working in terms of the conductivities and consider the most general case, in which $\sigma_{\parallel} \neq \sigma_{\perp 1} \neq \sigma_{\perp 2}$. With the direction of the applied field **E** making angles with the crystal axes as shown in the diagram (Fig. 1), the resulting current density relative to this direction may be shown to be given by[82]

$$J = (\sigma_{\parallel} \cos^2\phi + \sigma_{\perp 1} \cos^2\psi \sin^2\phi + \sigma_{\perp 2} \sin^2\psi \sin^2\phi)E \qquad (1.7)$$

(In anisotropic metals **J** is not necessarily parallel to **E**, unless directed along a crystal axis, for example.) Writing $\sigma(\phi, \psi) = J/E$, one then obtains for the conductivity in the direction of **E**

$$\sigma(\phi, \psi) = \sigma_{\parallel} \cos^2\phi + \sigma_{\perp 1} \cos^2\psi \sin^2\phi + \sigma_{\perp 2} \sin^2\psi \sin^2\phi \qquad (1.8)$$

If, therefore, $\sigma(\phi, \psi)$ is measured for a large number of single crystals of known orientation, the axial conductivities themselves may be calculated from the simultaneous equations obtained by the use of equation (1.8). This was the procedure followed by Pascal,

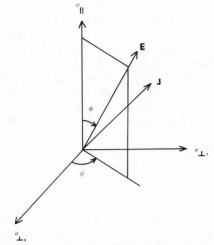

Fig. 1. General case of an anisotropic single crystal in which the axis of the specimen does not coincide with any of the principal crystal axes.

Morin, and Lacombe for orthorhombic U.[346] (See also Powell's work on orthorhombic Ga.[361])

For most close-packed hexagonal (cph) crystals, and for rhombohedral Bi as well, the problem is simpler since it has been established by experiment that $\sigma_{\perp 1} = \sigma_{\perp 2}$ (Table III). That is, there is rotational symmetry of the conductivity about the major axis. Therefore, with $\psi$ equal to 0, equation (1.8) reduces to

$$\sigma(\phi) = \sigma_{\parallel} \cos^2\phi + \sigma_{\perp} \sin^2\phi$$

$$= \sigma_{\perp} + (\sigma_{\parallel} - \sigma_{\perp}) \cos^2\phi \tag{1.9}$$

Averaging over the entire solid angle, we find

$$\bar{\sigma} = \sigma_{\perp} + \tfrac{1}{3}(\sigma_{\parallel} - \sigma_{\perp})$$

$$= \tfrac{1}{3}(2\sigma_{\perp} + \sigma_{\parallel}) \tag{1.10}$$

which may alternatively be expressed by

$$\bar{\rho} = \frac{3\rho_{\perp}\rho_{\parallel}}{2\rho_{\parallel} + \rho_{\perp}} \tag{1.11}$$

Equations (1.10) and (1.11) are due to Voigt,[430] and for many years they have been used fairly generally for the determination of $\bar{\sigma}$ or $\bar{\rho}$ from single crystal axial conductivities or resistivities.[M1] In fact, they have always been considered to give satisfactory-enough agreement with direct observations made on polycrystals, but Alstad, Colvin, and Legvold[46] have shown that Voigt's equations do not work out well with the experimental results of Hall, Legvold, and Spedding[202] on rods of cph Y. This metal has a particularly large anisotropy ratio ($\rho_{\perp}/\rho_{\parallel} = 2.1$ at 300°K) and consequently provides equation (1.11) and other proposed formulas with a very stringent test by revealing differences not so clearly seen when $\rho_{\perp}/\rho_{\parallel}$ is close to unity. These authors found that the best equation for obtaining $\bar{\rho}$ was that which Nichols[329] had already discovered to be perfect for the case of cph Mg (thick bars). This equation is

$$\bar{\rho} = \tfrac{1}{3}(2\rho_{\perp} + \rho_{\parallel}) \tag{1.12}$$

and is derived in a manner analogous to the derivation of equation (1.10), except that $\phi$ is taken as the angle between the principal axis and the direction of current flow.[329,82] It thus recognizes that in some experiments, as with wires or rods of anisotropic crystals, it is the current density rather than the electric field which is in a specified direction. Equation (1.12) has also been used quite satisfactorily with many of the cph rare-earth metals. (See, for example, Ho, Section 2.17.11.)

For further discussion of the above and other formulas, reference should be made to Boas and Mackenzie,[82] Grüneisen,[M2] Meissner, [M26] and the other references cited in this section.

*Chapter 2*

# Experimental Data on the Resistivity of Metals

## 2.1. ARRANGEMENT OF MATERIAL

In this chapter, data are presented and discussed on the electrical resistivities of 66 of the 82 metals of the periodic system. Those for which no resistive data have so far been obtained are Tc (atomic number 43), Pm (61), Fr (87), Ra (88), Ac (89), Pa (91), and the ten trans-Pu elements (95 to 104). In the case of Po (84), experiments on films have been performed but none yet on the bulk metal. These 17 radioactive elements are not found in nature and only very small quantities have ever been prepared in metallic form. Nevertheless, enough metal has been gathered, though usually just a few milligrams, in the cases of Tc, Ra, Ac, Pa, Am, and Cm for their melting points and the densities and crystal structures of some principal phases to be determined (Table XV). But with Pm, Fr, and the trans-Cm elements there is to date no experimental knowledge of their metallic states.

For ease of presentation the metals are arranged in homologous groups in the following order: the alkalis (Li, Na, K, Rb, Cs, Fr), the noble metals (Cu, Ag, Au), the alkaline-earth metals (Be, Mg, Ca, Sr, Ba, Ra), and the metals of group IIB (Zn, Cd, Hg), IIIB (Al, Ga, In, Tl), IVB (Sn, Pb), VB (As, Sb, Bi), and VIB (Po). Then follow the transition metals (starting with Sc and Y, after which they are grouped in columns of three, Ti, Zr, Hf, etc.), the rare-earth or lanthanide series (La to Lu inclusive), and the actinide series (Ac to Lw inclusive). This arrangement is not without some weaknesses, such as the locations of La, Lu, and Ac (discussed in Section 2.17) and the splitting of the iron group metals (Fe, Co, Ni), but is otherwise the most natural and convenient.

12

For many polyvalent metals more than one crystal structure is possible, the range of stability of any one phase being dependent on the temperature and the pressure. At normal atmospheric pressure several metals have three different temperature-dependent forms, while in Mn and Ce there are four and in Pu as many as six. Phase changes even occur in two of the simplest metals, monovalent Na and Li, although in these, owing to the low temperatures involved ( < 75°K), the transformation never goes to completion (Section 2.2). As a rule, crystallographic phase changes are high-temperature phenomena, but even so, high-temperature phases can sometimes be studied at room temperature and below by means of quenching methods and without resorting to the use of alloys. Major examples include $\beta$-Mn and $\beta$-Pu (the Greek letter $\alpha$ is normally given to the lowest-temperature phase, $\beta$ to the next highest, and so on). In this book all data, if not otherwise specified, refer to the phase normally stable at room temperature. Other crystal modifications receive mention only if they are low-temperature forms or if it has proved possible to stabilize high-temperature forms at or below room temperature by quenching, as in $\beta$-Mn and $\beta$-Pu, or by other means (for example, $\gamma$-Mn, $\beta$-La, and $\beta$-Hg), and thus to study their resistivities.

By making a close study of the literature we have compiled what we consider to be the most recent and reliable published data on resistivity as a function of temperature for all of the metallic elements in their purest and most strain-free states. The most important features of the resistive behavior are discussed, and often also given in graphic form. The data are assembled and summarized in Table II, where resistivities at the useful temperatures of 20, 80, 273, and 295°K together with some at intermediate temperatures can be found. All values given in this table have had residual resistivities $\rho_0$ subtracted. Typical residual resistivities for specimens in good condition are therefore also listed, because these are not by any means always small and represent minimum values that should be added to the tabulated readings in order to provide a truer idea of the resistivities to be expected under experimental conditions. Finally, axial resistivities for anisotropic single crystals are listed in Table III, and the chapter ends with a short discussion on superconductivity, with the transition temperatures of the superconducting metals collected and grouped together in Table IV.

Since, in many instances, a plethora of data by different authors has been reported for the same metal and because this is not intended to be a historical survey, only selected data considered to be among the most satisfactory have usually been discussed. This has meant passing over a lot of older work, including several long-accepted results. Particularly in the transition and rare-earth elements, specimen quality has been improved greatly in recent years and this has led to remeasurement and at the same time more extensive investigation of their properties. White and Woods and collaborators [M10] have covered most of the transition metals, and Ames Laboratory workers, directed by Professors Legvold and Spedding, the rare earths. Examples of outstanding individual experiments on other metals that replace all previous work are those of Dugdale and Gugan on the alkalis and of Powell on Ga. Old papers not mentioned here may be traced by referring to Gerritsen, [M1] Grüneisen, [M2] the International Critical Tables, [M21] and the Landolt–Börnstein tables. [M23]

In order to produce a uniform table, some adjustment of published figures has been necessary at times. Not all authors have obtained ice-point readings, and room-temperature readings have ranged from 288 to 300°K. Many workers who have made low-temperature studies have published relative, not absolute, values of the resistivity, frequently normalizing to unity at 273°K or some other nearby temperature. In a number of instances, residual resistances were never determined and little indication of purity supplied; also, some experiments were limited to only four or five measurements at low temperatures and a large gap left between 90 and 273°K.

In our opinion, absolute ideal resistivities of the following common metals in a pure state at room temperature have still not been well determined: Ca, Sr, Ba, and La; and some confusion exists as to which are the best values for Al and Sb. Between 90 and 273°K, data are extremely sparse and inadequate for the metals Zn, Cd, Pb, As, and the alkaline earths (apart from Be), though in all these metals the resistivity is at least approximately linear in temperature. For La and Ce the resistivities of the various pure phases require determination at all temperatures.

## 2.2. THE ALKALIS (Li, Na, K, Rb, Cs, Fr)

These monovalent metals are body-centered cubic (bcc) at ordinary temperatures and are noted for their low melting points and small densities. Because of their softness and chemical reactivity, considerable care is required in their preparation and handling. Despite the difficulties, the simpler ones at least have been much studied in the past because of the expectation that, of all metals, they should most closely conform to the concepts of the free-electron theory.

## Table II. General Table of Electrical Resistivities at Room Temperature and at Selected Low Temperatures (deg K, in $\mu\Omega$-cm)†

| | 20 | 50 | 80 | 100 | 150 | 200 | 250 | 273.15 | 295 | $\dfrac{\rho_0}{\rho_{273}} \times 10^3$ | $\rho_0$ |
|---|---|---|---|---|---|---|---|---|---|---|---|
| **Alkali Metals (IA)** | | | | | | | | | | | |
| 3 Li (nat) | (0.015) | (0.27) | 0.995 | 1.714 | 3.708 | 5.704 | 7.613 | 8.494 | 9.32 | 2 | 0.02 |
| 6Li | | | | | | | | 8.370 | 9.21 | | |
| 11 Na | 0.0165 | 0.317 | 0.805 | 1.145 | 1.994 | 2.874 | 3.821 | $4.28_9$ | $4.75_0$ | 0.3 | 0.001 |
| 19 K | 0.1074 | 0.719 | 1.389 | 1.836 | 3.005 | 4.281 | 5.720 | 6.447 | 7.19 | 0.8 | 0.005 |
| 37 Rb | 0.433 | $1.57_3$ | $2.70_0$ | $3.46_1$ | $5.46_6$ | $7.64_8$ | 10.01 | $11.2_5$ | $12.5_1$ | 1 | 0.01 |
| 55 Cs | $0.88_2$ | $2.65_5$ | $4.42_4$ | $5.63_5$ | $8.78_0$ | 12.22 | 16.06 | $18.0_0$ | $19.9_6$ | 2 | 0.04 |
| 87 Fr | No data for this metal | | | | | | | | | | |
| **Noble Metals (IB)** | | | | | | | | | | | |
| 29 Cu | 0.0008 | 0.050 | $0.21_5$ | $0.35_0$ | $0.70_5$ | 1.06 | 1.40 | 1.55 | 1.70 | 2 | 0.03 |
| 47 Ag | 0.0038 | 0.11 | $0.29_0$ | $0.42_0$ | $0.73_5$ | 1.04 | 1.34 | 1.47 | 1.61 | 0.5 | 0.001 |
| 79 Au | $0.012_5$ | 0.20 | $0.46_0$ | $0.63_0$ | 1.04 | 1.44 | 1.83 | 2.01 | 2.20 | 0.5 | 0.001 |
| **Alkaline-Earth Metals (IIA)** | | | | | | | | | | | |
| 4 Be* | 0.0004 | 0.0077 | $0.038_9$ | $0.090_7$ | 0.436 | $1.15_1$ | $2.15_6$ | 2.71 | 3.25 | 2 | 0.005 |
| 12 Mg* | $0.008_5$ | $(0.1_2)$ | 0.55 | $0.8_9$ | | (2.6) | | 3.94 | 4.30 | 1 | 0.004 |
| 20 Ca | See text | | | | | | | | 3.6 | See text | |
| 38 Sr | 0.48 | 2.5 | 4.6 | 6.3 | | (14.1) | | 19.8 | 21.5 | 90 | 2.0 |
| 56 Ba | 0.73 | 3.5 | 7.8 | 10.7 | | (25) | | 36 | 39 | 7 | 0.25 |
| 88 Ra | No data for this metal | | | | | | | | | | |
| **Group IIB** | | | | | | | | | | | |
| 30 Zn* | 0.052 | 0.49 | 1.16 | $1.6_2$ | $2.7_2$ | $3.8_4$ | $4.9_3$ | 5.45 | 5.92 | 1 | 0.005 |
| 48 Cd* | 0.13 | 0.87 | 1.7 | 2.3 | 3.6 | 4.9 | 6.2 | 6.73 | 7.27 | 0.01 | 0.0001 |
| 80 Hg* | 1.24 | $3.9_5$ | $6.6_3$ | 8.6 | 13.3 | 18.4 | 92.2(l) | 94.1(l) | 95.9(l) | 1 | 0.03 |

† For a general explanation of this table refer to the notes at the end.

**Table II.** *Cont'd*

| | 20 | 50 | 80 | 100 | 150 | 200 | 250 | 273.15 | 295 | $\dfrac{\rho_0}{\rho_{273}}\times10^3$ | $\rho_0$ |
|---|---|---|---|---|---|---|---|---|---|---|---|
| **Group IIIB** | | | | | | | | | | | |
| 13 Al | 0.0006 | 0.05 | 0.25 | 0.47 | $1.0_6$ | $1.6_5$ | 2.24 | 2.50 | 2.74 | 0.03 | 0.0001 |
| 31 Ga* | 0.09 | | $2.7_3$ | $3.9_5$ | 6.8 | $9.5_5$ | 12.3 | 13.65 | 14.85 | 0.03 | 0.0005 |
| 49 In* | 0.16 | $0.9_4$ | $1.8_0$ | $2.3_8$ | $3.8_4$ | $5.4_3$ | $7.1_5$ | 8.0 | $8.7_5$ | 0.02 | 0.0002 |
| 81 Tl* | 0.42 | 2.0 | 3.6 | 4.7 | 7.5 | $10.3_5$ | 13.5 | 15 | $16._4$ | 0.3 | 0.005 |
| **Group IVB** | | | | | | | | | | | |
| 50 Sn* | 0.10 | $0.9_5$ | $2.1_5$ | $2.9_5$ | $4.9_5$ | 7.0 | 9.1 | 10.1 | 11.0 | 0.01 | 0.0001 |
| 82 Pb | 0.56 | 2.76 | 4.97 | 6.5 | 10.2 | $13._9$ | $17._6$ | 19.3 | 21.0 | 0.02 | 0.0004 |
| **Group VB** | | | | | | | | | | | |
| 33 As* | $0.2_9$ | $1._9$ | $4._5$ | $6._4$ | | | | 26 | 29 | 12 | 0.3 |
| 51 Sb* | $0.4_2$ | 3.2 | 7.2 | 10.0 | 17.9 | 25.9 | 34.0 | 37.6 | 41.3 | 1 | 0.05 |
| | | | $5._8$ | $8._4$ | | $22._5$ | | 32.0 | (35) | | |
| **Group VIB** | | | | | | | | | | | |
| 83 Bi* | 5.8 | 19 | 30 | 37 | 55 | 74 | 96 | 105 | 116 | 4 | 0.4 |
| 84 Po | | | | | | | | 42 | 46 | | |
| **Transition Metals—Group IIIA** | | | | | | | | | | | |
| 21 Sc* | 0.16 | 2.9 | 8 | $11._2$ | 20.7 | 29.8 | $38._8$ | 42.9 | 46.8 | 200 | 10 |
| 39 Y* | $0.3_6$ | 4.8 | $11._2$ | 15.4 | $26._6$ | $37._6$ | $48._6$ | 53.7 | 58.5 | 40 | 2 |
| For La, Lu, and the lanthanides, see under "rare earths" | | | | | | | | | | | |
| **Group IVA** | | | | | | | | | | | |
| 22 Ti* | $0.02_0$ | 1.4 | $4.8_5$ | 7.9 | 16.6 | 25.7 | 34.8 | 39.0 | 43.1 | 0.7 | 0.03 |
| 40 Zr* | $0.09_0$ | $2.2_5$ | $6.4_0$ | $9.5_5$ | 17.6 | 26.1 | 34.6 | 38.6 | 42.4 | 6 | 0.25 |
| 72 Hf* | $0.10_5$ | 2.1 | 5.4 | 7.6 | 13.3 | 19.3 | 25.3 | 28.0 | 30.6 | 60 | 1.7 |
| **Group VA** | | | | | | | | | | | |
| 23 V | $0.03_7$ | $0.7_5$ | $2.6_5$ | 4.3 | 8.6 | 12.9 | $16.6_5$ | 18.3 | 19.9 | 35 | 0.7 |
| 41 Nb | 0.08 | $0.9_7$ | $2.6_8$ | $3.9_5$ | $6.9_5$ | 9.8 | 12.3 | 13.5 | 14.5 | 2 | 0.03 |
| 73 Ta | $0.05_1$ | $0.9_5$ | $2.5_0$ | $3.5_5$ | 6.1 | 8.6 | 11.0 | 12.1 | 13.1 | 15 | 0.2 |

**Table II.** *Cont'd*

| | 20 | 50 | 80 | 100 | 150 | 200 | 250 | 273.15 | 295 | $\frac{\rho_0}{\rho_{273}} \times 10^3$ | $\rho_0$ |
|---|---|---|---|---|---|---|---|---|---|---|---|
| **Group VIA** | | | | | | | | | | | |
| 24 Cr | $0.007_2$ | $0.16_5$ | $0.8_1$ | $1.6_2$ | $4.5_5$ | $7.7_5$ | $10.9_5$ | 12.1 | 12.9 | 5 | 0.1 |
| 42 Mo | $0.005_6$ | $0.11_3$ | $0.51_5$ | 0.92 | $2.0_5$ | $3.1_8$ | $4.3_2$ | $4.8_4$ | $5.3_3$ | 14 | 0.07 |
| 74 W | | $0.15_1$ | $0.60_0$ | 1.02 | 2.10 | 3.22 | $4.3_2$ | $4.8_2$ | $5.3_3$ | 0.5 | 0.003 |
| **Group VIIA** | | | | | | | | | | | |
| 25 α-Mn | 49 | 123 | 127.5 | 127.5 | 132 | 135.5 | 138 | 138.5 | 139 | 35 | 5 |
| 43 Tc* | No data for this metal | | | | | | | | | | |
| 75 Re* | $0.16_5$ | $0.7_7$ | $2.5_3$ | $3.9_5$ | $7.6_5$ | $11.4_5$ | 15.2 | 16.9 | 18.6 | 0.7 | 0.01 |
| **Group VIIIA** | | | | | | | | | | | |
| 26 Fe | $0.00_7$ | $0.13_5$ | 0.64 | 1.24 | $3.1_3$ | 5.3 | $7.5_5$ | 8.7 | 9.8 | 1 | 0.01 |
| 44 Ru* | | $0.10_5$ | 0.64 | $1.2_5$ | 2.80 | $4.3_8$ | $5.9_6$ | $6.6_9$ | $7.3_7$ | 2 | 0.015 |
| 76 Os* | | 0.26 | 1.10 | 1.90 | 3.85 | $5.7_0$ | $7.5_0$ | $8.3_5$ | $9.1_3$ | 10 | 0.09 |
| 27 Co* | $0.006_6$ | $0.14_5$ | 0.54 | 0.91 | $2.0_2$ | $3.2_3$ | $4.5_0$ | $5.1_5$ | 5.80 | 12 | 0.06 |
| 45 Rh | $0.001_8$ | $0.10_5$ | 0.51 | $0.8_9$ | $1.9_1$ | $2.9_2$ | $3.9_0$ | $4.3_6$ | 4.78 | 2 | 0.008 |
| 77 Ir | $0.005_0$ | 0.20 | 0.72 | $1.1_0$ | $2.1_7$ | $3.2_0$ | $4.1_9$ | $4.6_5$ | $5.0_7$ | 10 | 0.05 |
| 28 Ni | 0.009 | 0.15 | 0.55 | $1.0_0$ | $2.2_3$ | $3.7_2$ | $5.4_0$ | $6.2_0$ | $7.0_4$ | 3 | 0.02 |
| 46 Pd | 0.036 | 0.58 | $1.7_2$ | $2.6_0$ | $4.7_6$ | $6.9_0$ | $8.8_2$ | $9.7_0$ | $10.5_5$ | 0.5 | 0.005 |
| 78 Pt | 0.0359 | 0.719 | $1.90_9$ | $2.74_2$ | 4.78 | 6.76 | 8.70 | 9.59 | 10.42 | 0.4 | 0.004 |
| **Rare-Earth Metals** | | | | | | | | | | | |
| 57 La* | 3.3 | 17 | 29 | 36 | $49._5$ | 61 | 71 | 75 | 79 | 12 | 1.0 |
| 58 Ce | See text | | | | | | | 79 | 81 | 70 | 6 |
| 59 Pr* | | $8._5$ | 23 | 36 | 46 | 54 | 61 | 64 | 67 | 12 | 0.8 |
| 60 Nd* | $8._3$ | 17 | 25 | $29._5$ | $38._5$ | 46 | 53 | $56._5$ | 59 | 90 | 5 |
| 61 Pm | No data for this metal | | | | | | | | | | |
| 62 Sm* | 14 | 33 | 52 | 64 | 73 | 82 | 91 | 95 | 99 | 60 | 6 |
| 63 Eu | 8.5 | 33 | 61 | 78 | 75 | 78 | 83 | 86 | 89 | 6 | 0.5 |
| 64 Gd* | 1.0 | $12._5$ | $29._7$ | $41._2$ | $69._0$ | $95._6$ | $119._0$ | 127.5 | 134.1 | 18 | 2.4 |

## Table II. *Cont'd*

| | 20 | 50 | 80 | 100 | 150 | 200 | 250 | 273.15 | 295 | $\frac{\rho_0}{\rho_{273}} \times 10^3$ | $\rho_0$ |
|---|---|---|---|---|---|---|---|---|---|---|---|
| 65 Tb* | 0.9₅ | 12.₅ | 27 | 38 | 64 | 93 | 108 | 109 | 111 | 30 | 3.5 |
| 66 Dy* | 1.1 | 11.₈ | 26.6 | 40.3 | 72.₅ | 81 | 85 | 87.₅ | 90.0 | 25 | 2.4 |
| 67 Ho* | 3.4 | 15 | 31 | 43 | 56 | 64 | 71 | 74.5 | 77.7 | 70 | 3 |
| 68 Er* | 4.₅ | 24 | 39 | 42 | 52 | 63 | 73 | 77 | 81 | 60 | 5 |
| 69 Tm* | 2.1 | 21 | 25.₅ | 29 | 38 | 46 | 55 | 58 | 62 | 80 | 5 |
| 70 Yb | 1.₃ | 6.₃ | 10.₈ | 13.₃ | 17.₉ | 21.₅ | 24.₄ | 25.₅ | 26.₄ | 80 | 2.2 |
| 71 Lu* | 0.7₃ | 6.₀ | 11.₉ | 16 | 26 | 36 | 45 | 49 | 53 | 30 | 1.5 |
| **Actinide Metals** | | | | | | | | | | | |
| 89 Ac | No data for this metal | | | | | | | | | | |
| 90 Th | 0.19 | 1.67 | 3.34 | 4.4 | 7.2 | 9.9₄ | 12.7 | 14.0 | 15.2 | 15 | 0.2 |
| 91 Pa* | No data for this metal | | | | | | | | | | |
| 92 U* | 0.52 | 4.54 | 7.4 | 9.4 | 14.0 | 18.3 | 22.3 | 24.1 | 25.7 | 30 | 0.75 |
| | 0.76 | 4.79 | 8.4 | 10.7 | 16.0 | 21.1 | 25.8 | 27.9 | 29.8 | 35 | 1.0 |
| 93 Np* | 1.91 | 24.2 | 49.8 | 63.1 | 87.3 | 102.5 | 112.7 | 116.0 | 118.5 | 25 | 3.5 |
| 94 α-Pu* | 20 | 116 | 153 | 156 | 153 | 148 | 145 | 144 | 143 | 45 | 7 |

In practically all cases, the electrical resistivities have already had residuals subtracted (exceptions Ca, Ce, and Po). Thus, for nonmagnetic metals the resistivity indicated is the ideal or lattice resistivity.

The figures given in column 11 for the resistivity ratio $\rho_0/\rho_{273}$ represent values to be expected of well-annealed high-purity specimens. The figures for the residual resistivity $\rho_0$ given in the last column represent approximately what are the lowest values published to date for the various elements. It will be noted that for certain transition metals and most rare earths these values are by no means small.

\* The asterisk denotes noncubic metals. The resistivities for these elements relate to measurements on polycrystalline specimens or to values deduced from single crystal measurements. Additional information is to be found in Table III.

(*l*) The resistivities given for Hg at 250, 273.15, and 293°K refer to the liquid state. Extrapolation of the solid state data as far as the ice-point gives $\rho_{273}$ as about 26 μΩ-cm. The residual resistivity ratio of $10^{-3}$ is based on this.

Supplementary information for this table including references is provided in the text of Chapter 2.

### 2.2.1. Lithium (atomic number 3)

The low-temperature behavior of Li is complicated by a martensitic change to a cph phase that commences on cooling through 75°K. At 4°K possibly as much as 90% has transformed to this second phase. On heating again, reversion to the bcc structure does not begin until 90°K and is only complete at 160°K. A strain-induced face-centered cubic (fcc) phase can also be obtained and investigated at low temperatures.

The first study of the effect of these transformations on the electrical resistivity was made by Dugdale and Gugan.[138] They could not give actual resistivity values for the various phases in the way they had previously done for Na, but listed values for the bcc phase only at 10°K intervals between 80 and 320°K.[141] In this latter publication, data for Li consisting of over 99% $^6$Li were also tabulated (see Table II). Natural Li has about 7% $^6$Li; the rest is $^7$Li. Similar work on the resistivity of Li isotopes has been done by Leffler and Montgomery,[264] who have in addition given a table of normalized ideal resistivities for six different isotopic compositions. All the above authors[141,138,264] worked with bare-rod specimens; earlier workers had contained theirs within tubes.

The temperature dependence of the resistivity of natural Li below 100°K has been measured by MacDonald, White, and Woods.[291] Their values at 20 and 50°K, suitably scaled to $\rho_{273}$, have been used in Table II, although their specimens consisted of mixed phases in unknown proportions. (Differences in the resistivities of the two phases are less than 1%;[141] the effects of purity and cold-work are much more important.) Below 15°K, the intrinsic or ideal resistivity is proportional to $T^5$.

### 2.2.2. Sodium (atomic number 11)

Of all the metals of the periodic system, Na is the one which the quasi-free electron model describes the best. For this reason it is often studied, but it is only recently that any account has been taken of the effect on the resistivity at low temperatures of the martensitic transformation which occurs below 40°K on cooling. Dugdale and Gugan[137] have tabulated measurements between 16 and 52°K of the resistivities of the separate bcc and cph phases, and in a second paper[139] have given data for the range 50 to 295°K for the bcc phase. Their reading at the ice-point was almost identical to the long-accepted one of Hackspill.[197] In addition, they give separate lists of their results corrected to constant-density conditions.[139]

The results of previous investigations at lower temperatures are not reliable, however, because of the presence of two-phase

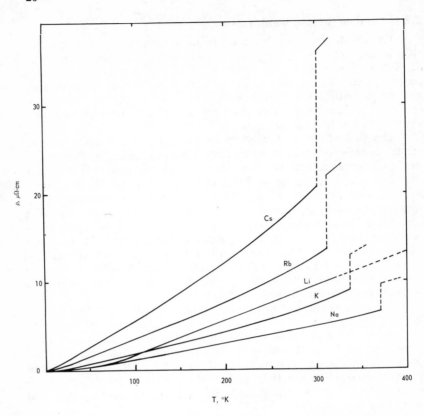

Fig. 2.  Ideal electrical resistivities of the alkali metals as far as their
melting points (except for Li, which melts at 454°K).[86,137,139,141,142]

mixtures in undetermined amounts and because glass tubes were
used for casting and supporting the specimens, a procedure criticized
by Dugdale and Gugan.[140] The best of the earlier work is that of
Bradshaw and Pearson[86] (78 to 372°K), Woods,[452] and MacDonald,
White, and Woods[291] (below 20°K). The latter obtained $\rho_i \propto T^5$
between 8 and 15°K and $T^6$ between 4 and 9°K.

### 2.2.3.  Potassium (atomic number 19)

Potassium is bcc at all temperatures.  The best work over the
widest temperature range is again that of Dugdale and Gugan,[139]
who have tabulated in model fashion, both under normal pressure
and constant-volume conditions, their accurate data obtained on

specimens of extruded bare metal between 8 and 295°K. They ascribe higher values and certain anomalies reported by some earlier experimenters to constraining effects of capillary tubes, and conclude that tubes are unsatisfactory for accurate work.[139,140]

The ideal resistivity of K, as of Na and Li, also follows a $T^5$ law at low-enough temperatures but only below 8°K.[291]

### 2.2.4. Rubidium (atomic number 37)

The recent experiments of Dugdale and Phillips[142] on bare-rod specimens give 11.25 $\mu\Omega$-cm as the ideal resistivity at the ice-point (Table II). This compares with the old Hackspill value of 11.6 $\mu\Omega$-cm for the total resistivity[197] and 11.3 $\mu\Omega$-cm due to Kurnakow and Nikitinski.[256] Much higher figures have been given by Guntz and Broniewski[193] and MacDonald, White, and Woods.[291] The latter found that the ideal resistivity decreased as $T^5$ below 5°K.

No low-temperature martensitic transformation occurs in Rb, and the supposed transition at 180°K, first reported by MacDonald,[286] is now considered to result from constraints imposed by the tube that contained his specimen.[140] Dugdale and Phillips give a table of the ideal resistivity at normal atmospheric pressure from 2 to 300°K and also a second table, up to 230°K, in which the data have been corrected to constant-density conditions.[142]

### 2.2.5. Cesium (atomic number 55)

For this metal Dugdale and Phillips,[142] working with bare-rod specimens, give $\rho_{i273} = 18.0 \mu\Omega$-cm (Table II), which is close to Hackspill's old value.[197] Their results, both at constant pressure and at constant density, extend down to 2°K. At temperatures below 20°K the resistivity has also been studied by MacDonald, White, and Woods.[291] They found that the proportionality of $\rho_i$ with $T^5$ held only below 3.1°K.

The anomalous behavior and hysteresis effects reported earlier by MacDonald and Mendelssohn[287] and others between 90°K and room temperature were probably due to the casting of specimens in glass tubes.[140]

### 2.2.6. Francium (atomic number 87)

There is no information concerning this unstable radioactive alkali metal. The half-life of the most stable isotope is only 22 minutes!

## 2.3. COPPER (29), SILVER (47), AND GOLD (79)

The noble metals are fcc at all temperatures. Like the alkalis, they are monovalent and their properties have been well investigated both experimentally and theoretically. They are less simple than Na and K, and it is known that their Fermi surfaces touch the centers of the faces of the first Brillouin zone. They are the best of electrical conductors at ordinary and high temperatures, yet they do not rank among the 30 elements which under suitable circumstances can become superconducting at very low temperatures.

The most satisfactory work on the temperature dependence of the resistivity is that of White and Woods.[M10] Because of the small diameters of their wire samples the form factors could not be calculated very precisely; they therefore normalized their results using reliable values for $\rho_{i273}$ taken from Gerritsen's monograph.[M1] It was discovered that for a limited range of temperature above 10°K $\rho_i$ varied as $T^{5.1}$ for Cu, $T^{4.7}$ for Ag, and $T^{5.1}$ for Au.

In some specimens of these metals, shallow minima in the low-temperature resistivities are found. The phenomenon is caused by trace impurities of transition elements and it is discussed in detail in Section 3.9.

## 2.4. GROUP IIA OR ALKALINE-EARTH METALS (Be, Mg, Ca, Sr, Ba, Ra)

These low-density metals of poor ductility prove awkward to prepare in a pure condition and at the same time in a suitable shape for accurate resistivity work. Be, Mg, and Ca have high conductivities besides, which make precise resistance measurement rather less straightforward. Be and Mg are hexagonal metals, the others cubic.

### 2.4.1. Beryllium (atomic number 4)

The most comprehensive study of the resistivity at normal and high temperatures is that of Powell,[362] who also gives a full critical account of all earlier work. He demonstrated the important effect that annealing near 1000°K has on the resistivity; for his best polycrystalline specimen $\rho_{293}$ was lowered from 6.7 to 3.2 $\mu\Omega$-cm by such treatment. Much earlier work was clearly based on unannealed specimens, some also of low purity. Both Lewis[265] and MacDonald and Mendelssohn[288] have given comparative values at a few low temperatures, but $\rho_0/\rho_{273}$ was of the order of 25%. Judging by Grüneisen's measurements at 20°K, he had single-crystal specimens that were of exceptional purity.[185,186] Data for these single crystals at 273 and 293°K are given in Table III; for these specimens $\rho_0$ was about

0.005 $\mu\Omega$-cm. White and Woods[436] have made low-temperature measurements on two unannealed specimens each having $\rho_{295}$ at about 5 $\mu\Omega$-cm and $\rho_0$ at 1.2 $\mu\Omega$-cm.

The data given in Table II are those obtained by Reich, Quang Kinh, and Bonmarin[377] for their best specimen, which had $\rho_0 = 0.034$ $\mu\Omega$-cm.* $\rho_{i295}$ and $\rho_{i273}$ are very similar to values estimated from Powell's paper. They observe that the resistivity was proportional to $T^4$ between about 50° and 130°K and had not become linear even at 500°K. They also state that there was some degree of preferred orientation in the $10\bar{1}0$ direction. From their results $\theta_R$ was evaluated as 1240°K, which is much closer to the specific-heat value of 1390°K[177] than the figure of 650°K calculated by MacDonald and Mendelssohn. A general discussion of the significance of $\theta_R$ values is given in Chapter 4.

### 2.4.2. Magnesium (atomic number 12)

Using Nichols's published resistivity data on high-purity single crystals,[329] we calculate $\bar{\rho}_{295}$ and $\bar{\rho}_{273}$ to be 4.30 and 3.94 $\mu\Omega$-cm, respectively (Table III), which values are identical to those of Grüneisen [M2,118] for ideal resistivities at the same temperatures. A low $\rho_0$ for all these specimens is indicated, and is probably of the order of 0.01 $\mu\Omega$-cm.[208] The above figures have been used as ideal ones in converting Meissner and Voigt's [M5] comparative data to absolute resistivities (Table II).

The resistance minimum phenomenon, apparent in Meissner and Voigt's results, shows clearly in all four specimens of MacDonald and Mendelssohn,[288] and we reproduce their graph in Figure 3. For a discussion on this subject reference should be made to Section 3.9.

### 2.4.3. Calcium (atomic number 20)

There is considerable doubt concerning the best resistivity values for this metal. Different room-temperature resistivities have been given and the few experiments done at helium temperatures have shown high residual resistivities.

The old value is that of Rinck,[379] which is 4.3 $\mu\Omega$-cm at 289°K, whereas Frank and Jeppesen[157] have more lately obtained a "room-temperature" measurement of 3.60 $\pm$ 0.03 $\mu\Omega$-cm. Such a large difference can readily be ascribed to differences in the qualities of the specimens used, i.e., in the purities and amounts of anneal. This is further supported by the big residual resistivity ratios found by

---

* The actual figures for Be given in Table II were kindly communicated to me by R. Reich.

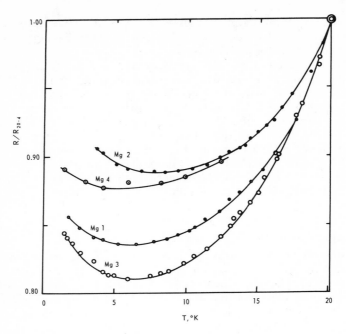

Fig. 3. Reduced electrical resistances of four Mg samples below 20°K, showing the resistance minimum (MacDonald and Mendelssohn[288]).

MacDonald and Mendelssohn[288] and Meissner and Voigt, [M5] namely, 15 and 28 %, respectively, for $\rho_0/\rho_{273}$. Under the circumstances, we suggest the use of Frank and Jeppesen's absolute room-temperature value for which $\rho_0$ was possibly quite small. No other data are given in Table II but we append here some of MacDonald and Mendelssohn's low-temperature figures for $\rho_T/\rho_{290}$: 14.4 % at 4°K, 15.4 at 20°K, 25.8 at 50°K, and 37.9 at 80°K.

### 2.4.4. Strontium (38), Barium (56), and Radium (88)

The value of 23.5 $\mu\Omega$-cm for $\rho_{295}$ of Sr was taken from a graph given by Rinck[381] for the temperature range 280 to 920°K. Meissner and Voigt's specimen[M5] had a residual resistivity ratio of 0.093, which is much lower than that of MacDonald and Mendelssohn[288] and we have accordingly used the former's values in Table II.

For Ba, Rinck[380] mentions 36 $\mu\Omega$-cm at 273°K and 40 at 291°K. Justi and Kramer's specimen[233] had the low residual resistivity ratio of 0.0068, so for the purposes of Table II we have combined their data with Rinck's ice-point resistivity.

Almost nothing is known of the physical properties of Ra, of which the most stable isotope has a half-life of 1622 years.

## 2.5. THE GROUP IIB METALS (Zn, Cd, Hg)

### 2.5.1. Zinc (atomic number 30)

We have used $5.45\,\mu\Omega$-cm for $\rho_{i273}$ as given by Grüneisen. [M2] Zinc is cph and Bridgman[90] has given $5.59\,\mu\Omega$-cm for $\rho_{\parallel}$ and $5.39$ for $\rho_{\perp}$ at $273°$K. Several authors[312,188,42] have measured $\rho_{\parallel}$ and $\rho_{\perp}$ down to $20°$K, but in Table II we have used the data of Tuyn and Onnes[426] on polycrystalline specimens. The ratio of the axial resistivities shows increasing anisotropy as the temperature is reduced. The behavior of Cd is very similar.[188,42] Below $14°$K $\rho_i \propto T^5$, as in Cd also.[42]

### 2.5.2. Cadmium (atomic number 48)

For the ice-point resistivity we have taken the value of $6.73$ $\mu\Omega$-cm [M2] deduced from $\rho_{\parallel} = 7.73$ and $\rho_{\perp} = 6.35\,\mu\Omega$-cm obtained on a single crystal (Cd, like Zn, is cph). Measurements at low temperatures on high-purity single crystals have been made by Meissner,[312] Grüneisen and Goens,[188] Meissner and Voigt, [M5] and Aleksandrov and D'yakov.[42] The values given in Table II refer to polycrystalline samples and are based on the results of Holborn[215] (20°K to room temperature) and Meissner (2 to 80°K), which are in agreement in the region of overlap.

### 2.5.3. Mercury (atomic number 80)

Mercury has a rhombohedral crystal structure and its melting point of $234.3°$K is the lowest of all metals. For the solid state we have employed Sckell and Grüneisen's value [M2] of $21.2\,\mu\Omega$-cm at $227.6°$K, obtained from measurements on single crystals, for which $\rho_{\parallel}$ was $17.8$ and $\rho_{\perp}$ was $23.5$ at this temperature. The resistance–temperature results of Onnes and Holst,[339] which extend up to $200°$K, have been normalized using this value and are given in Table II. The fourfold increase in resistivity that occurs on melting is unusually large for a metal.

At the ice-point the resistivity in the liquid state is $94.08\,\mu\Omega$-cm. This has been measured with precision on several occasions because at one time the resistance of Hg formed the basis of the definition of the international ohm. The ohm was defined as being equal to the resistance, at the temperature of melting ice, offered to an unvarying current by a column of Hg of uniform cross section and of length

106.300 cm weighing 14.4521 g. This definition has since been super-
seded because manganin resistors, which are more reproducible, are
now used instead of Hg.

Mercury has an alternative body-centered tetragonal modification that is stable below 79°K. It is formed under stress, as for
instance in extrusion, and is known as $\beta$-Hg. At 79°K its resistivity
is 1.70 times smaller than that of rhombohedral $\alpha$-Hg.[388] Both forms
become superconducting below 4°K.


## 2.6. THE GROUP IIIB METALS (Al, Ga, In, Tl)

### 2.6.1. Aluminum (atomic number 13)

The value 2.50 $\mu\Omega$-cm is the widely quoted ice-point resistivity
of Grüneisen and Goens.[189] We have used this in conjunction with
the low-temperature data of Aleksandrov and D'yakov[42] for Table II.
Their specimen had a residual resistivity of $10^{-10}$ $\Omega$-cm.

For Alcoa high-purity aluminum there is a "standard value"
of 2.6548 $\mu\Omega$-cm at 293.15°K.[418] With this one obtains 2.42 at the
ice-point and 2.675 at 295°K.


### 2.6.2. Gallium (atomic number 31)

This element has an orthorhombic crystal structure with $c : a : b =$
1 : 0.99868 : 1.69257; it displays greater anisotropy in its resistive
properties than any other metal. The best and most complete study
is that of Powell.[361] His experiments were performed by growing a
crystal within a single length of glass tubing bent to form twelve
distinct sections each of which consequently contained a single crystal
of known orientation. Each section had previously been equipped
with platinum electrodes to allow measurement of the resistance. It
was found that the resistivities along the directions of the principal
axes $c$, $a$, and $b$ at 293.15°K are 55.5$_3$, 17.2$_7$, and 7.85 $\mu\Omega$-cm, respectively, that is, the conductivities are in the ratio 1 : 3.2 : 7. A
value of 14.7$_7$ $\mu\Omega$-cm for polycrystalline Ga was deduced from this.
Careful measurements at the melting point (302.9°K) gave 15.4 $\mu\Omega$-cm
for the solid and 25.7 for the liquid. The liquid metal is easily super-
cooled and liquid state measurements were taken down to 273°K.

Experiments on the solid were carried out down to 90°K (see
Figure 4) and the axial conductivity ratios given above remained
almost unchanged and the resistivities linear. Measurements at still
lower temperatures[338] showed that the axial anisotropy increases as
helium temperatures are approached. Between 5 and 12°K $\rho_i \propto T^{4.45}$
and between 12 and 20°K $\rho_i \propto T^{3.9}$.

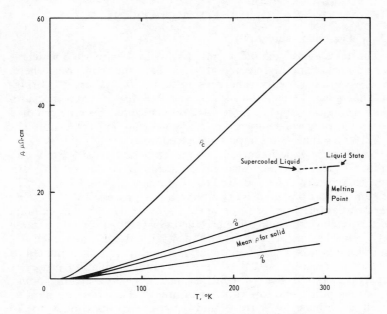

Fig. 4. Powell's resistivity data on Ga displayed graphically.[361]

Reich, Bonmarin, and Peyron[374,373] have more recently made measurements at a few fixed points below room temperature on metal of rather higher purity ($\rho_0 \sim 5 \times 10^{-10}\ \mu\Omega$-cm).

### 2.6.3. Indium (49) and Thallium (81)

The resistivity of In above 77°K has recently been measured by Powell, Woodman, and Tye.[367] Their ice-point reading of 8.0 $\mu\Omega$-cm compares with the previously accepted 8.2 $\mu\Omega$-cm.[313] For Table II we have made use of the resistance ratios tabulated by Swenson[416] between 4 and 273°K. He reports finding a small unexplained kink or change of slope near 210°K. Indium is body-centered tetragonal and measurements at the ice-point on single crystals have been reported by Olsen.[336] In specimens of extremely high purity, a $T^5$ law is followed below 14°K.[42]

Thallium is close-packed hexagonal. The best ice-point value for polycrystalline metal (15 $\mu\Omega$-cm) is that of Grüneisen [M2] and it was used with the data of Onnes and Tuyn[341] for the low-temperature values given in Table II. Another low ice-point measurement is 16.2 $\mu\Omega$-cm, due to Rosenbohm.[385]

## 2.7. THE GROUP IVB METALS (Sn, Pb)

### 2.7.1. Tin (atomic number 50)

The tetragonal metallic form known as "white tin" which is stable at normal and high temperatures is that which concerns us here. For $\rho_{i273}$ we have used Grüneisen's value of 10.1 $\mu\Omega$-cm. [M2] Bridgman[90] has given 13.08 $\mu\Omega$-cm for $\rho_\parallel$ and 9.09 for $\rho_\perp$ from measurements on single crystals. The relative resistance has been determined over a wide range of temperature by Onnes and Tuyn[340] (Table II).

Polycrystalline Sn samples of exceptionally high purity were prepared for the experiments at helium temperatures of Zernov and Sharvin.[455] The residual resistivity of their purest sample was estimated to be only $3.7 \times 10^{-11}$ $\Omega$-cm (i.e., $\rho_0/\rho_{273}$ was $3.7 \times 10^{-6}$!). This sample was prepared by two electrolytic processes with heating *in vacuo* to about 1500°K in between, followed by 166 zone-refining passes. Reich and Quang Kinh[375] had Sn samples of comparable purity. One had a lower resistivity at 4.2°K after 27 zone meltings than did the best of Zernov and Sharvin's, but its $\rho_0$ was estimated to be rather higher ($4.6 \times 10^{-11}$ $\Omega$-cm). Vacuum distillation processes are particularly effective with Sn because of its low melting point, high boiling point, and low vapor pressure.[166] The above authors,[375] as well as others,[42,70] have found $\rho_i$ to be proportional to $T^5$ at the lowest temperatures. Aleksandrov and D'yakov[42] have recently published resistivity data at several representative low temperatures obtained on Sn single crystals almost as pure as those of Zernov and Sharvin.

The element Sn may also assume a semiconducting form in which it has the same lattice as that found in diamond, Si, and Ge. This is in fact its most stable form below 286.3$_5$°K.

### 2.7.2. Lead (atomic number 82)

Lead is a simple fcc metal. Grüneisen[M2] gives $\rho_{i273}$ as 19.3 $\mu\Omega$-cm. Its resistance between about 3 and 90°K has been measured by van den Berg[70] (Table II) and Aleksandrov and D'yakov.[42] Since it is a superconducting metal with a high transition temperature (7.19°K), a magnetic field was applied to quench the superconductivity so that the impurity resistance might more accurately be determined (compare with Nb, Section 2.13). $\rho_i$ is proportional to $T^5$ below 10°K or so.

## 2.8. THE METALS OF GROUP VB (As, Sb, Bi)

### 2.8.1. Arsenic (33) and Antimony (51)

The metals of this column possess crystal structures based on the rhombohedral lattice. Numerous physical and electronic properties indicate that the effective number of free electrons is very small in these metals.

For polycrystalline As, we have utilized the low-temperature results of Meissner and Voigt[M6] in Table II combined with the ice-point resistivity of 26 $\mu\Omega$-cm. [M26] Some experiments on single crystals have also been made—$\rho_{\parallel}$,[302] $\rho_{\perp}$.[M26] Taylor, Bennett, and Heyding[419] give $\rho_{\parallel} = 35.6 \pm 1.8$ and $\rho_{\perp} = 25.5 \pm 0.5 \, \mu\Omega$-cm at 293°K (Table III). Using equation (1.12), this leads to $\bar{\rho}_{293} = 28.9 \pm 0.9 \, \mu\Omega$-cm.

The most complete low-temperature study of Sb is that of White and Woods[444] on polycrystalline specimens (Table II). We also use their absolute figure of 37.6 $\mu\Omega$-cm for $\rho_{i273}$, which is similar to that of Eucken and Gehlhoff[149] (and perhaps Vasenin[429]). Rausch,[371] however, gives a much lower value, 32.0 $\mu\Omega$-cm, obtained using Voigt's formula from single crystal measurements. His results also are given in Tables II and III.

### 2.8.2. Bismuth (atomic number 83)

White and Woods[444] have measured the resistivities of several polycrystalline Bi specimens at low temperatures and good agreement was found between them (Table II). Their averaged values also agreed well with the mean values of Schubnikov and de Haas[390] deduced from experiments on single crystals. White and Woods normalized their results by making use of Grüneisen's mean ice-point value of 107 $\mu\Omega$-cm, which was based on $\rho_{\parallel} = 127$ and $\rho_{\perp} = 99 \, \mu\Omega$-cm.[187,M2]

The electrical resistivity and other transport properties of this metal have been intensively investigated because of their many unusual and anisotropic features resulting from the low number of free electrons (about $10^{-3}$ per atom) and the complex lattice. The oscillatory effects of the de Haas–van Alphen type periodic in $H^{-1}$ which are found in the transport properties of metals at low temperatures are particularly large in Bi, and their discovery in 1930 was made in this metal[391,194] (Section 6.2.2). For general discussions on the resistivity and other transport properties of Bi, reference may be made to Wilson [M11] or Ziman [M12] (see also ref. 165).

### 2.9. GROUP VI B (Po)

Polonium (atomic number 84) is the only metal in this group. Since it is radioactive and not found in nature, little is known about it, but the resistivity of thin films of $^{210}$Po deposited on glass was measured some years ago by Maxwell.[299] The half-life is 138 days; since the Pb content increases by about $\frac{1}{2}\%$ a day for a new sample, Pb is always a major impurity.

Measurements were made on five samples between 293 and 475°K for Po films containing $\frac{1}{2}$ to 2 % Pb, but the effect of the Pb was probably small since the resistance was not noted to be time-dependent. By extrapolating, Maxwell gave a value of $42 \pm 10\,\mu\Omega$-cm at the ice-point for the resistivity of $\alpha$-Po, saying that this figure probably represents a maximum compared to the bulk metal. The crystalline structure of $\alpha$-Po was said to be indistinguishable from that of Pb, while a higher-temperature phase was found to be rhombohedral. The transition temperature for the transformation is $327 \pm 1.5$°K, according to Goode.[179]

## 2.10. THE TRANSITION METALS

These elements differ from one another in the extent to which the sublying $d$-shells are filled. They are treated here in columns of three, rather than in the order of their three long periods, because of the marked affinities shown by elements of the same column. However, La and Lu, both of which have some claim to being treated in the same trio as Sc and Y, are instead considered along with the rare-earth elements. Excepting these metals and radioactive Tc, the electrical resistivities of all the transition elements have been studied at low temperatures by White, Woods, and various collaborators, the results being finally collected together and the data summarized in an important paper by White and Woods.[M10] We make extensive use of their results because with every metal their investigation was thorough and the data were published in a convenient form. Moreover, only in a few cases have other workers had better specimens.

## 2.11. GROUP III A: SCANDIUM (21) AND YTTRIUM (39)

The elements of this column, including La and Lu, have very high resistivities. Of the remaining 21 transition metals, only one, Mn, has a greater resistivity (compare in Table I). The ideal resistivity of Sc at 295°K is $46.8\,\mu\Omega$-cm[106] and that of Y $58.5\,\mu\Omega$-cm.[46,52] As in the rare earths, to which there are close chemical similarities, high purities are difficult to achieve, and the residual resistivities are somewhat high.

Both metals are cph, and in the case of Y the resistivity of single crystals has been measured as a function of temperature.[201] Yttrium is quite anisotropic in its resistivity, and the ratio $\rho_\perp/\rho_\parallel = 2.1$ at room temperature is the highest of all the cph metals. Between 15 and 30°K, the ideal resistivity is proportional to $T^{3.7}$ for Sc[106] and to $T^{3.4}$ for Y.[52]

For La, refer to Section 2.17.1, for Lu, to Section 2.17.15.

## 2.12. GROUP IVA (Ti, Zr, Hf)

### 2.12.1. Titanium (atomic number 22)

White and Woods [M10] have measured the temperature dependence of resistivity of polycrystalline cph Ti specimens down to liquid-helium temperatures. They give $\rho_{273}$ as 41.0 $\mu\Omega$-cm and $\rho_4$ as 2.0 for their best specimen. This compares with respective figures of 42.67 $\pm$ 0.05 and 0.0306 $\mu\Omega$-cm recently published by Wasilewski,[432] who also carried out experiments on single crystals, obtaining at the ice-point $\rho_\perp = 45.35 \pm 0.5$ and $\rho_\parallel = 48.0 \pm 0.7\,\mu\Omega$-cm.

### 2.12.2. Zirconium (40) and Hafnium (72)

These metals are also close-packed hexagonal. They have high intrinsic resistivities similar to that of Ti. The best work on their low-temperature behavior has been done by White and Woods [M10] (Table II). The resistivities of Hf single crystals have been measured at the ice-point by Adenstedt[41] (Table III).

## 2.13. GROUP VA (V, Nb, Ta)

### 2.13.1. Vanadium (atomic number 23)

Vanadium has an interesting unexplained peculiarity in its resistivity behavior in the form of a sudden change in temperature coefficient variously reported by different workers as being located somewhere in the region 190 to 254°K. The fullest investigation and discussion is that of Taylor and Smith.[420] In their pure specimens the anomaly was found at 227°K. The temperature at which it occurred was lowered by the addition of Cr in solid solution, but it nevertheless still visibly persisted in alloys of up to 24% Cr (at which concentration the anomaly was found at 158°K). Related effects have been found in several other physical properties, but X-ray and neutron-diffraction work have provided no supporting evidence. Neither has a study of Young's modulus, which is a property often very sensitive to abnormalities in the electronic structure. The cause may possibly be some uncommon type of impurity effect.

For the temperature dependence of the resistivity we have used in Table II the data of White and Woods.[441, M10] Unfortunately, even their best specimen had a very high residual resistivity ratio

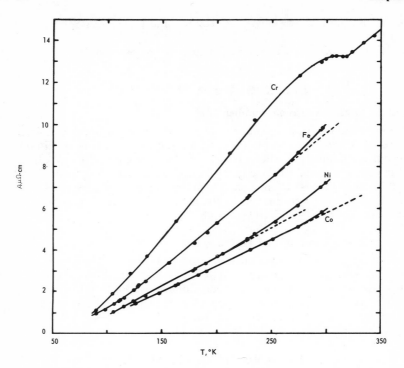

Fig. 5.  Ideal resistivities of Cr, Fe, Co, and Ni from the data
of White and Woods, [M10] indicating the departures of these curves
from normality due to effects of magnetic origin.

$(\rho_0/\rho_{273} = 140 \times 10^{-3})$. The best of Taylor and Smith's had a residual
resistivity ratio over four times smaller.

### 2.13.2.  Niobium (41) and Tantalum (73)

These two metals are body-centered cubic, as is vanadium. They
all have quite high superconducting transition temperatures (Table
IV). The resistivity data given are from White and Woods. [M10,441]
Since the transition temperature of Nb is especially high (9.13°K), it is
difficult to estimate the impurity contribution to the resistivity of this
metal, which is essential for a proper evaluation of the ideal or
intrinsic resistivity. The real problem is that the large magnetic
fields required at 4°K or less to quench the superconductivity introduce
a large magnetoresistance effect.

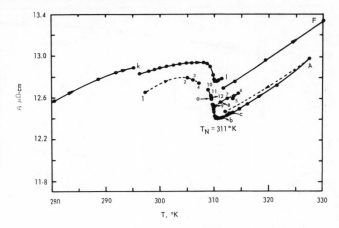

Fig. 6. Electrical resistivity of Cr in the region of the Néel point (Arajs, Colvin, and Marcinkowski[55]).

## 2.14. GROUP VI A (Cr, Mo, W)

### 2.14.1. Chromium (atomic number 24)

Chromium is a bcc metal that is antiferromagnetic below 312°K. The results of measurements on high-purity specimens between 4 and 370°K by Harper, Kemp, Klemens, Tainsh, and White[204, M10] are displayed graphically in Fig. 5 and are summarized in Table II. Anomalous behavior first noticed by Bridgman[90] can be seen to occur in the vicinity of the Néel temperature. This has more recently been further investigated by Arajs, Colvin, and Marcinkowski,[55] using a single crystal specimen of rather lower purity. Their work demonstrates the sensitivity of resistivity measurements in studying magnetic transformations (Fig. 6). The letters and digits in the figure refer to the sequence in which the points were obtained. The details do not concern us here, but it is clear at a glance that hysteresis or time effects are much in evidence. These depend on the nature of the immediately previous thermal history of the specimen. No resistivity anomaly was found in the region 120 to 150°K, where it is believed that a modification of the spin arrangement takes place, although small anomalies supported by neutron-diffraction studies exist in the elastic constants. Overhauser and Arrott[343] have briefly discussed the various suggested antiferromagnetic models of Cr.

The ideal resistivity is proportional to $T^{3.2}$ from low temperatures up to almost 100°K.[55,204]

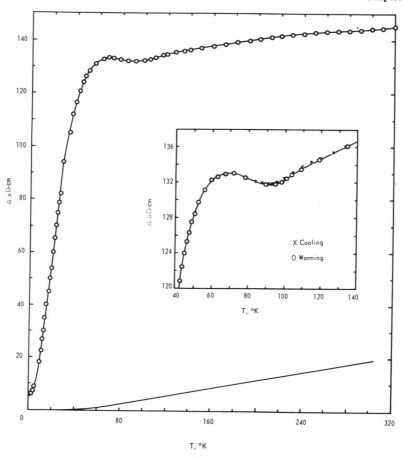

Fig. 7. Electrical resistivity of α-Mn, which is antiferromagnetic below
100°K (Meaden and Pelloux-Gervais[308a]). In order that its large resistivity
may be better appreciated, that of Re, for which $\rho_{295} = 18.6\ \mu\Omega$-cm, has
also been included.

## 2.14.2. Molybdenum (42) and Tungsten (74)

These bcc metals have electrical resistivities that are closely
similar to one another up to 700°K.[427] White and Woods [M10,440] give
the same value of 5.33 $\mu\Omega$-cm for $\rho_{i295}$ to each (Table II). Judging by
residual resistance ratios, Meissner and Voigt [M6] thirty years earlier
had purer samples than did the above authors.

## 2.15. GROUP VII A (Mn, Tc, Re)

### 2.15.1. Manganese (atomic number 25)

The extremely abnormal temperature dependence shown by the resistivity of Mn results from the antiferromagnetism that occurs below 100°K. The behavior may be seen in Fig. 7, which is due to Meaden and Pelloux-Gervais.[308a] The resistivity of this specimen at 295°K was found to be 144.0 $\mu\Omega$-cm ($\pm$ 0.8%), and the residual resistivity estimated for 0°K was 5 $\mu\Omega$-cm. Since Mn is a hard, brittle metal, specimens of a regular shape are difficult to fabricate, and because also the resistivity is sensitive to gaseous impurities, White and Woods[439, M10] gave rather unsatisfactory figures of $\rho_{295} = 155$ and $\rho_0 = 11.3 \mu\Omega$-cm, with error limits of $\pm 20\%$, for the best of their samples (a second sample had $\rho_{295} = 154$ and $\rho_0 = 16.8 \mu\Omega$-cm [$\pm 20\%$]).

With decreasing temperature, the resistivity falls steadily and only slowly at first, but eventually a minimum at about 94°K (131.9 $\mu\Omega$-cm) is reached. Then, for 4 or 5°K, the resistivity remains practically constant before rising again to a weak maximum of 133.0 $\mu\Omega$-cm at 70°K. After this, it drops extremely rapidly, finally becoming proportional to $T^2$ below 17°K. The somewhat high residual resistivity suggests that an appreciable spin-disorder contribution, which is the cause of the large resistivities at higher temperatures, is still present in the helium range (see also Section 3.10.2).

Below 975°K, $\alpha$-Mn has a complex cubic crystal structure with 58 atoms in the unit cell. By rapid quenching to room temperature from the region 975 to 1352°K, it is possible to retain the cubic $\beta$-phase (20 atoms per unit cell) and to study its physical properties, also. This has been done for the resistivity by Brunke,[94] who obtained about 90 $\mu\Omega$-cm for $\rho_{295}$. The fct $\gamma$-phase, normally stable between 1352 and 1416°K as fcc Mn, may be obtained at room temperature by electrolytic deposition. Its resistivity at this temperature is about 40 $\mu\Omega$-cm.[147,356] A fourth phase, bcc $\delta$-Mn, is stable only between 1416°K and the melting point. Resistivity work prior to 1955 has been well summarized by Sully.[M33]

### 2.15.2. Technetium (43) and Rhenium (75)

Technetium is radioactive, with a half-life of $2.1 \times 10^5$ years for the best-known isotope. It has been discovered to be a superconductor of high transition temperature, and the currently accepted value is 8.2°K.[351] This was detected by resistance experiments on a specimen cut from a rolled sheet. Evidently, gram quantities of the metal are now available (at least in the United States), but no other resistance measurements have yet been made.

The best work on Re is that by White and Woods,[440, M10] using a remarkably high-purity specimen on which Hulm and Goodman[221] had earlier made some observations. For this specimen, $\rho_{i273}$ was 16.9 $\mu\Omega$-cm. More recently, a figure of 17.1 $\mu\Omega$-cm has been published for a specimen not quite as pure.[366]

## 2.16. GROUP VIII A METALS (Fe, Ru, Os; Co, Rh, Ir; Ni, Pd, Pt)

### 2.16.1. Group VIIIA (Column 1) (Fe, Ru, Os)

*2.16.1.1. Iron (atomic number 26).* The resistivity of a ferro-magnetic metal is nonlinear over a wide temperature range below the Curie point ($\theta_c$) because of the presence of a temperature-dependent term of magnetic origin that is additional to the usual lattice and impurity resistivities. But above $\theta_c$ this term is constant, and the total resistivity is linear in temperature once more (reference may be made to Chapter 3 for a discussion of these features). In the iron-group metals (Fe, Co, Ni), ferromagnetic effects in the resistivity first become readily apparent at about $\theta_c/4$, but because $\theta_c$ is high for these metals the magnitude of the extra term is still not very great at room temperature. The Curie point of bcc Fe is at 1043°K, and reference to Fig. 5 will show that the departure from linearity appears at around 240°K.[M10] Recent experiments at high temperatures, which provide a full curve almost to the melting point, are those of Arajs and Colvin.[54] The residual resistivity of their specimen was 0.04 $\mu\Omega$-cm, considerably better than that of White and Woods.[M10] Semenenko and Sudovtsov[395] applied a weak magnetic field to their high-purity specimen at low temperatures and found that its resistance fell by about 30%. This demonstrates the effect that scattering at domain walls can have on the electrical resistance of ferromagnetic metals. They show, furthermore, that the normal temperature-dependent resistivity at very low temperatures is composed of terms in $T$, $T^2$, and $T^5$, but that it may alternatively be expressed as $T^{2.28}$ between 14 and 20°K or as $T^{1.45}$ below 4.2°K. White and Woods [M10,241] give $T^{3.3}$ for the region near 20°K and indicate that a $T^2$ law is approached at lower temperatures. This important question will be discussed in some detail in Section 3.11.

*2.16.1.2 Ruthenium (44) and Osmium (76).* The resistivities of polycrystalline specimens of these cph metals have been measured by White and Woods.[443, M10] For Ru, $\rho_{i295}$ is 7.37 $\mu\Omega$-cm. Recently, Powell has obtained $\rho_{\parallel} = 5.73$ and $\rho_{\perp} = 7.29$ for two single crystals at room temperature (293.15°K).[363]

Concerning Os, White and Woods report that $\rho_{i273}$ is 8.35 $\mu\Omega$-cm on a specimen for which $\rho_0$ is 0.087. This differs from the measurements of Powell, Tye, and Woodman,[365] whose value for $\rho_0$ was 0.25 $\mu\Omega$-cm; $\rho_{i273}$ was initially 8.26 $\mu\Omega$-cm but after heating to 1800°K it fell by nearly 5% to 7.88.

### 2.16.2. Group VIIIA (Column 2) (Co, Rh, Ir)

*2.16.2.1. Cobalt (atomic number 27).* Polycrystalline cph Co has for $\rho_{i295}$ a value of 5.8 $\mu\Omega$-cm. [M10,440] It is the best conductor of the iron-group trio (Fe, Co, Ni), whose Debye characteristic temperatures are all very similar. The Curie temperature is very high (1394°K), and the additional magnetic resistivity only becomes obviously apparent above 280°K (Fig. 5). The temperature dependence of the resistivity below 30°K or so is very similar to that of Fe. [M10,397]

*2.16.2.2. Rhodium (45) and Iridium (77).* At ordinary temperatures, Rh and Ir have the lowest resistivities of all the transition elements. The room-temperature ideal resistivity of Rh (4.78 $\mu\Omega$-cm)[438,M10] is indeed hardly different from that of the simplest monovalent metal, Na (4.75). Such a simple comparison, however, made at merely the same temperature, is not strictly fair. It is better to make some allowance for the differing amplitudes of ionic vibration of Na and Rh by comparing instead values of $\rho_i M \theta_D^2$ at the same temperature; Na is then seen to be much the better conductor (Section 3.6.2.).

The ice-point reading for Ir of White and Woods[438, M10] has since been verified exactly by Powell *et al.*,[365] who were using metal of lower residual resistivity.

### 2.16.3. Group VIIIA (Column 3) (Ni, Pd, Pt)

*2.16.3.1. Nickel (atomic number 28).* This metal is ferromagnetic, with a Curie point at 631°K. As with Fe and Co, there is a large magnetic contribution to the total resistivity at high temperatures, but at room temperature it is not very appreciable. In the results of White and Woods [M10] (Fig. 5 and Table II), this extra term first becomes obvious at about 220°K.

At low temperatures the resistivity from which $\rho_0$ has been subtracted is proportional to $T^{3.1}$, but at the lowest temperatures of all, as in Fe and Co, the index of $T$ appears to approach 2. The work of Semenenko and Sudovtsov[395,413] shows that the resistivity at these temperatures may be resolved into several independent terms of similar character to those of Fe.

**2.16.3.2. Palladium (46) and Platinum (78).** These elements complete the 4d and 5d transition series, respectively.

Because it is used in resistance thermometers, the resistance behavior of Pt has been thoroughly investigated. Its choice for this purpose is partly due to the high purity which is fairly readily obtainable and thus the consistency with which the characteristics of the thermometers may be reproduced (Section 8.3.1).

In both Pd and Pt the temperature dependence of the ideal resistivity at the lowest temperatures (4°K) tends toward $T^2$, as in Mn and the iron-group metals.[M10,239,337] At one time it was suggested that Pd is antiferromagnetic below 90°K because of a magnetic susceptibility peak found there,[214,252] but no confirmation has ever been forthcoming from other studies such as on Young's modulus, neutron diffraction,[40] and the Knight shift.[393]

The ice-point resistivity of Pt (9.59 $\mu\Omega$-cm) due to White and Woods [M10,439] is not well confirmed by a more recent determination made by Powell, Tye, and Woodman[365] on metal having an identical residual resistivity ratio (9.84 $\mu\Omega$-cm).

## 2.17. THE LANTHANIDE OR RARE-EARTH GROUP (La, Ce, Pr, Nd, Pm, Sm, Eu, Gd, Tb, Dy, Ho, Er, Tm, Yb, Lu)

In this section we consider together for convenience the fifteen metals from La to Lu inclusive. The term "rare-earth metals" was originally applied in a wide sense, embracing even Sc and Y, which have certain rather similar properties. Nowadays, it has a more specific meaning and is limited to the fourteen metals having 4f-electrons from Ce to Lu only, La not being included. These elements are also commonly called lanthanides. The usual practice is to put La in column 3A and Lu at the end of the lanthanide series. However, a comparison of chemical and physical properties of adjacent and homologous elements will show that Lu could equally well be put in column 3A, in place of La, as the leader of the third transition series.

The group of metals considered in this section forms a progressive series in which the atomic weights and numbers change regularly but only slowly on passing along it, a situation to be distinguished from, say, that of the alkali metals, in which the atomic weight and number gaps are large. This leads to the rare-earth metals, excepting Eu(63) and Yb(70), having many chemical and physical properties (electronegativities and atomic volumes, for instance) that are quite similar to one another or which vary in only a steady slowly changing manner. This is because, in the main, their electron shells differ from each other merely in the extent to which the deep-lying 4f-subshell is filled. Apart from Eu and Yb, which are usually divalent, and Ce(58), which is sometimes tetravalent, the rare earths are principally trivalent metals. La is without any $4f$-electrons, and Yb and Lu have the maximum number (fourteen) permissible by the exclusion principle. The remaining twelve metals have partially filled $4f$-shells, and they are magnetic over certain ranges of low temperatures.

Most, if not all, of the metals in this section are polymorphous, but only in La, Ce, and Pr are there crystallographic phase change effects which are evident at or below room temperature. Apart from Ce, Sm, Eu, and Yb, they have cph structures at room temperature, although in La, Pr, and Nd these assume unusual forms.

### 2.17.1. Lanthanum (atomic number 57)

The structure stable at room temperature is double cph, but above 600°K it is fcc. The latter phase may be retained at room temperature by quenching. Unfortunately, while the resistivity of La has been measured on several occasions, it is clear that most specimens investigated consisted of two-phase mixtures.

James, Legvold, and Spedding[226] apparently began with mostly fcc metal, but successive runs showed that an increasing amount of the cph phase was present. During mere standing at room temperature over a period of 100 days, a partial or whole transformation to cph took place. The room temperature resistivity which was 70 $\mu\Omega$-cm after the first run had increased to 100 after the fourth run performed two months later. A second specimen did not transform as much. The residual resistivities of these specimens were high (8 $\mu\Omega$-cm).

The low-temperature results given in Table II are for La having $\rho_0 \sim 1 \mu\Omega$-cm.[47] Unfortunately, $\rho_{i295}$ is very big (80 $\mu\Omega$-cm), and the authors state that their specimen probably contained both phases. Experiments carried out to high temperatures have also been reported, at the start of which $\rho_{298} = 57 \mu\Omega$-cm was measured.[409] This specimen may initially have been largely in the fcc phase. Clearly, more definitive studies to determine the separate contributions of the two phases to the resistivity still require to be made.

Face-centered cubic La is a superconductor with the high transition temperature of 6.3°K; the cph form has a transition temperature of 4.9°K.

### 2.17.2. Cerium (atomic number 58)

Cerium is subjected to both crystallographic and magnetic phase transformations at low temperatures, the former causing considerable hysteresis and irreproducibility in $\rho$-$T$ curves. At ordinary temperatures Ce is fcc, but on cooling below 263°K it begins to transform at a slow rate to a cph phase.[300]  By 96°K there still remains 20% or so of untransformed fcc metal; this now begins to change into a similar but condensed form with an 8% volume reduction (fcc′).  The cph phase, as well, starts transforming to this new phase at temperatures below 77°K, but the change does not go to completion.  The cph phase still remaining at 12.5°K (and any fcc) finally becomes antiferromagnetic at this temperature.  On heating again, the crystallographic changes proceed in the reverse direction but begin at higher temperatures.  The effect of repeated thermal cycling is to increase the fraction of the cph phase that is present at any temperature.

James, Legvold, and Spedding[226] measured the resistivity of four specimens down to 4°K.  Huge hysteresis effects were found, and at 12.5°K there was a sudden decrease in the resistivity associated

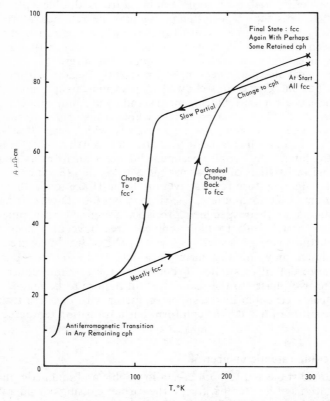

Fig. 8.   Illustration of the way in which the resistivity of Ce is complicated by phase transformations (see text).

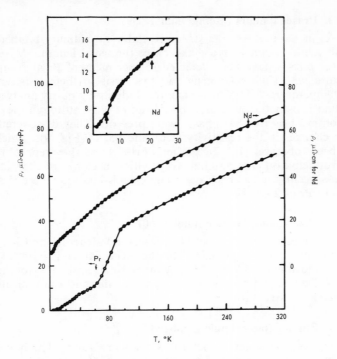

Fig. 9. Electrical resistivities of Pr and Nd.[47]

with the antiferromagnetic transition. At the start, the ice-point resistivity was 81 $\mu\Omega$-cm.

Itskevich[223] determined the temperature dependence of the resistivity of two specimens down to 10°K at normal pressure and also at pressures of up to $10^4$ kg/cm². For one specimen, $\rho_{273}$ was initially 87 $\mu\Omega$-cm and $\rho_0$ was 8 at the first cooling. The antiferromagnetic transition could not be seen in the resistivity measurements perhaps because at 12°K there was insufficient cph phase left in their specimens. Figure 8, which illustrates how the resistivity depends on these various effects, is based on figures given in ref. (223) and (226).

Spedding, Daane, and Herrmann[409] found 75.3 $\mu\Omega$-cm for the resistivity at 298°K prior to their high-temperature experiments. This is considerably lower than the values given above, but we have not used it in Table II since the residual resistivity was never determined (it was probably several microhm-centimeters). Powell and Jolliffe[363a] likewise give a single value of 74 $\mu\Omega$-cm $\pm$ 3% at 291°K.

### 2.17.3. Praseodymium (atomic number 59)

As in La and Nd, the structure stable at ordinary temperatures in this metal is cph with a c-axis twice the usual length. Mixed cph and fcc phases have been detected in specimens of Pr at room temperature, and such specimens had hysteresis in their resistivities at low temperatures.[226] A better sample, judging by purity analyses and residual resistivities, was used by Alstad *et al.*,[47] although they made no comment as to what phases were present. They discovered large slope changes in the resistivity at 61 and 95°K (Fig. 9), which had not been observed in the earlier work,[226] and they reported slight irreproducibility, finding that resistivities became smaller in later runs. Recently it has been definitely established that there is a Néel point in Pr at 25°K.[97]

### 2.17.4. Neodymium (atomic number 60)

Neodymium has the double cph crystal structure and it is antiferromagnetic below 19°K.[319] In the electrical resistivity of both pure[47] and much less pure[226] specimens small anomalies occur near the Néel point and also near 7.5°K, where there is a modification of the magnetic structure.

### 2.17.5. Promethium (atomic number 61)

This is a radioactive metal unknown in nature. The half-life of the best-known isotope is 2.6 years. None of the physical properties have yet been measured.

### 2.17.6. Samarium (atomic number 62)

Samarium has a rhombohedral lattice. Resistivity measurements on polycrystalline metal at low temperatures show two prominent changes of slope[47] (see Fig. 10). One occurs at 14°K, where there is an antiferromagnetic Néel point,[274] and the other at 106°K (origin not known). A recently published measurement for the *total* resistivity at 291°K (94 $\mu\Omega$-cm $\pm$ 3%)[363a] is distinctly lower than that of the specimen used for Table II.[47]

### 2.17.7. Europium (atomic number 63)

With Yb, Eu stands apart from the other lanthanides in being divalent and in having a simple cubic lattice and a significantly lower density. The reason is that the stable half-shell of seven 4f-electrons is filled prematurely by the removal of an electron from the valence band, which in the other lanthanides contains three electrons (see Yb). It possesses an antiferromagnetism of the helical type below 91°K,[56]

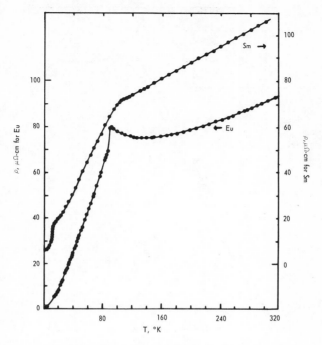

Fig. 10. Electrical resistivities of Sm and
Eu.[47,115]

and there is a sharp peak in the resistivity at this point.[115] A minimum
occurs at 145°K, above which the resistivity rises once again (Fig. 10).
Spedding *et al.*,[410] who made only high-temperature measurements,
report a room temperature value about 10 % lower than Curry *et al.*,[115]
whose values are used in Table II.

## 2.17.8. Gadolinium (atomic number 64)

This is the only element apart from the ferrous metals which is
ferromagnetic at normal temperatures. Its Curie temperature is
293°K, and the resistivity measurements of Colvin and Arajs,[107] among
others, indicate a marked change in the temperature coefficient at this
temperature. Their low-temperature data obtained using a polycrystalline specimen are given in Table II. The high ideal resistivity
that is found (134 $\mu\Omega$-cm at 295°K) ranks behind only Pu and Mn
in magnitude. Its resistivity is fifteen or more times larger than for
the ferrous metals at room temperature. This must be due in part to

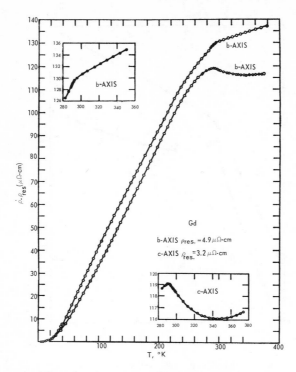

Fig. 11.  The c-axis and basal plane resistivities
of single crystal Gd.[330] Residual resistivities have
been subtracted.

the full contribution made at this temperature by the large magnetic
resistivity term (see Fe). Between 5 and 15°K the variation of the
ideal resistivity is as $T^{3.73}$, which is close to the $T^4$ dependence predicted by Mackintosh.[293]

Figure 11 shows the axial resistivities of a single crystal (cph) as
a function of temperature according to Nigh, Legvold, and Spedding.[330]

### 2.17.9. Terbium (atomic number 65)

Terbium is ferromagnetic below 218°K, and, provided that
external fields are weak, is antiferromagnetic between 218 and
230°K. Otherwise, ferromagnetism persists to the higher temperature.
In the $\rho$-$T$ graphs of Colvin, Legvold, and Spedding,[108] there is a big
change of slope at 229°K and a small anomaly with a slight change of

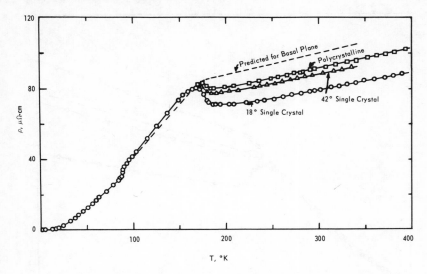

Fig. 12.   The electrical resistivities of single crystals of Dy. A polycrystalline sample was also measured.[202]  Residual resistivities have been
subtracted.

slope at 219°K. These authors' data are given in Table II. In a later
paper, the results of measurements on single crystals (cph) were
published.[209] As is usual for these metals, the c-axis resistivity shows
the greater abnormality. The resistivity variation with temperature
below 40°K has been discussed by Mackintosh.[293]

### 2.17.10.  Dysprosium (atomic number 66)

Dysprosium is a cph metal which is ferromagnetic below 85°K
and antiferromagnetic between 85 and 179°K. The effect of the two
magnetic transitions on the resistivity is clearly seen in the results
obtained on single crystals[202] and on a polycrystalline specimen.[108]
The latter results[108] are summarized in Table II, while the former
are reproduced in Fig. 12. It may be remarked that the only significant axial anisotropy occurs in the paramagnetic region. Below
40°K, the data for polycrystalline Dy fit very well an expression of
the type $\rho = \rho_0 + AT^5 + BT^2 \exp(-20/T)$.[293]

Neutron-diffraction experiments on single crystals reveal that the
antiferromagnetic spin arrangement is spiral in form, the screw
axis being along the hexagonal axis, and that there exists a definite
turn angle of the spins between one layer and the next.[449]

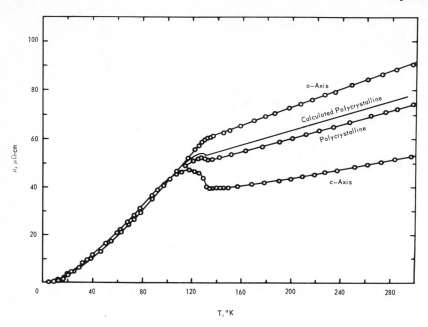

Fig. 13.  The c-axis and basal plane resistivities of single crystal Ho.[412]
Residual resistivities have been subtracted.

### 2.17.11.  Holmium (atomic number 67)

This metal has been shown to be antiferromagnetic between 20 and 133°K and ferromagnetic below 20°K. Anomalous behavior occurs near these temperatures in polycrystalline[108] and single crystal specimens,[412] but it is especially marked in the resistivity parallel to the c-axis, where there exist a minimum at 132°K and a large maximum at 116°K (Fig. 13).

For the tabulated data (Table II) we have utilized mean values deduced from measurements on single crystals[412] rather than direct measurements on a polycrystalline specimen[108] because the latter were lower than the former by some 5%. This difference may have been the result of preferred orientation in the polycrystalline sample since equation (1.12) has proved successful with the other cph lanthanides.[412] Mackintosh[293] has discussed the temperature dependence of the resistivity at low temperatures ($< 40°K$).

### 2.17.12.  Erbium (atomic number 68)

Erbium has a Curie point at 20°K and an antiferromagnetic Néel point at 80°K. Resistivity measurements on single crystals[182]

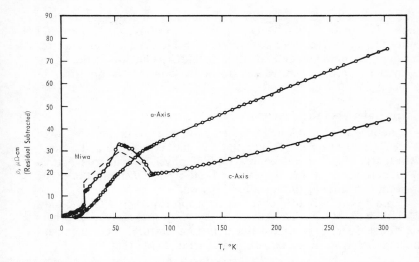

Fig. 14. The $c$-axis and basal plane resistivities of single crystal Er.[182] Residual resistivities have been subtracted. The dashed curve is that obtained theoretically for the $c$-axis resistivity by Miwa.[317]

show the axial anisotropy to be considerable (Fig. 14). Singularities occur in the $c$-axis resistivity, principally at the Curie and Néel points and at 53°K, near which positions specific-heat peaks have also been discovered.[399] This behavior has been fairly well explained by Elliott and Wedgwood,[143] Mackintosh,[292] and Miwa[317] (Section 3.10.2). As in Dy and Ho, the magnetic structure is helical, with the spiral axis along the hexagonal axis. The data given in Table II for a polycrystalline specimen come from the work of Colvin, Legvold, and Spedding.[108] The single crystals had very large residual resistivities.[182]

### 2.17.13. Thulium (atomic number 69)

This element is antiferromagnetic between 60 and 22°K and ferromagnetic below 22°K, according to the magnetic measurements of Davis and Bozorth.[126] The upper transition appears as a small peak on the $\rho$-$T$ curve of Colvin $et\ al.$,[108] but the transition to ferromagnetism is not observable in this polycrystalline specimen.

### 2.17.14. Ytterbium (atomic number 70)

With this metal, the $4f$ electronic shell is filled prematurely, there being only two valence electrons, so that like Eu, Yb is divalent. It is fcc, and its room temperature resistivity (26 $\mu\Omega$-cm) is the lowest of all the rare earths. The resistivity is nonlinear in temperature in a manner similar to the resistivity of Np, in that above 60°K there is a steadily falling temperature coefficient with increase in temperature. Ytterbium is nonmagnetic and no anomalous behavior of the types seen in the preceding rare earths (from Ce onward) is observed in this metal.[115]

### 2.17.15. Lutetium (atomic number 71)

Lutetium has the 4f-shell completely filled and, unlike Yb, three valence electrons as well. It resembles Sc and Y as much as La does, on the basis of a general comparison of physical properties. It is immediately followed in the periodic table by Hf (72) and the other transition elements of the third long period.

From 15 to 35°K the resistivity is proportional to $T^{2.5}$ (the data of Colvin et al.[108] have been discussed by Arajs and Colvin[52]); otherwise, above 50°K it is almost linear in temperature, there being no abnormal behavior since Lu is not magnetic (Table II).[108]

### 2.18. THE ACTINIDE METALS (Ac, Th, Pa, U, Np, Pu, Am, Cm, and the trans-Cm elements)

Taken as a whole, this series of elements is closely similar to the lanthanide series, since free atoms of the actinides differ from one another chiefly in the extent to which the sublying 5f-shell is filled. The energies of the 5f-, 6d-, and 7s-electronic levels are all rather close to one another in these elements, particularly in those near the beginning of the series. In Ac and Th the 5f electronic energy levels are actually unoccupied in both the free neutral atom and in the metal, while Pa metal and perhaps U metal too, are also without 5f-electrons. These four metals have at the same time, but in varying degrees, resemblances to the IIIA to VIA transition elements and to the rare-earth elements. Similarities to the latter are augmented on passing along the actinide series due to the lowering in energy of the 5f-level, until with Am and Cm we find metals that are quite equivalent to Eu and Gd in known chemical and physical properties. The 5f-shell is filled at element number 103 (Lw), which is therefore homologous with Lu (71). Succeeding elements, numbers 104 onward, will be heavy homologs of Hf, Ta, W, etc.

Many of the actinides are polymorphous and in U, Np, and Pu the room-temperature phases have low symmetry.

### 2.18.1. Actinium (89) and Protoactinium (91)

The crystal structures, densities, and melting points of these radioactive elements are now known (Appendix, Table XV), but

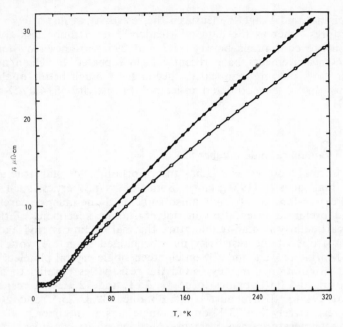

Fig. 15. Electrical resistivity of high-purity U according to Arajs and Colvin[53] (open circles) and Meaden[304] (closed circles). Reference should be made to the text.

not enough metal has yet been obtained for any of the electronic properties to be determined.

### 2.18.2. Thorium (atomic number 90)

This fcc metal has a much lower density than the succeeding elements. As it has a very long half-life (1.4 × 10¹⁰ years), it is found in nature and is reasonably well known.

One of the lowest ice-point resistivities ever reported for this metal (about 13 $\mu\Omega$-cm) is that given by Meissner and Voigt,[M26,M6] who used a single crystal specimen said to contain less than 0.1 % Fe ($\rho_0/\rho_{273} = 16.4 \times 10^{-3}$). But since then all published values, with a single exception, have been considerably bigger, most room-temperature figures being in excess of 18 $\mu\Omega$-cm. Apparently, this is due to the sensitivity of Th to the presence of impurities, notably carbon. The lowest reported room-temperature resistivity is 12.2 $\mu\Omega$-cm, due to Meechan.[311] Despite this low absolute figure the residual resistivity ratio (62 × 10⁻³) is surprisingly high.

Meissner and Voigt [M6] measured the resistivity at just a few low temperatures, whereas the data of Meaden[303] on a much less good specimen are continuous between 1.3 and 295°K. These low-temperature measurements have recently been repeated by Haen and Meaden[198,306] on an unannealed specimen of much better quality having $\rho_0/\rho_{273} = 48 \times 10^{-3}$ and an ice-point resistivity of 14.0 $\mu\Omega$-cm (Table II).

### 2.18.3. Uranium (atomic number 92)

At normal temperatures U has an orthorhombic crystal structure of very high density (19.0 g/cm³). Some of its properties, such as thermal expansion, are strongly anisotropic, and one must be careful to avoid preferred orientation in polycrystalline specimens of this metal, particularly if high-temperature thermal cycling is envisaged. The anisotropy of the resistivity may be judged from the work of Pascal, Morin, and Lacombe[346] on eighteen single crystal platelets of different orientation, for they found the resistivities parallel to the [100], [010], and [001] planes to be 41, 25.1, and 32 $\mu\Omega$-cm, respectively, at 291°K. Berlincourt[72] had obtained 39.4, 25.5, and 26.2 $\mu\Omega$-cm, respectively, at 273°K on one single crystal specimen.

Low-temperature measurements on high-purity samples have been made only in recent years.[72,303,304,53] Solely on the basis of residual resistivity ratios, both Meaden[304] and Arajs and Colvin[53] had specimens of comparable high purity, though the specimens of the latter were best on spectrographic analysis. The results differ quite widely,[304,53] and it is clear that Matthiessen's rule does not hold well (Fig. 15). A similar difference is found among Berlincourt's specimens. Arajs and Colvin say there was some preferred orientation in their swaged specimen,[53] but it was ascertained that there was none in Meaden's, which was machined direct from a large ingot.[304] Both sets of data are given in Table II. The power index of the temperature between 5 and 20°K was found to be 3.1 or 3.2.

A small anomaly appears in the electrical resistivity in the region 40 to 50°K,[303,304,53] and related anomalies are seen in the Hall coefficient[72] and the elastic constants.[153] The origin of these effects remains an open question. Barrett, Mueller, and Hittermann[65] found by X-ray and neutron-diffraction studies that unusual crystal structure changes occur near 43°K and that there is magnetic scattering below this temperature in at least their single crystal samples. A weak antiferromagnetism, perhaps caused by impurities, is thus a possibility. It should be added that U, like Th, is definitely superconducting at low-enough temperatures (U at about 0.7°K and Th at 1.37°K).

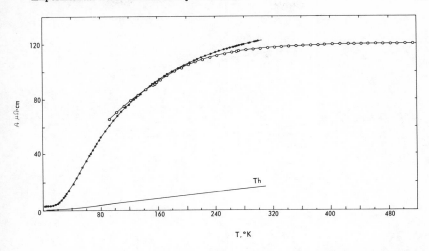

Fig. 16. Electrical resistivity of Np according to Lee and King[261] (open circles) and Meaden[263,304] (closed circles). In order to draw attention to the large resistivity of Np, that of Th, for which $\rho_{295} \simeq 15\,\mu\Omega$-cm, has also been included.

### 2.18.4. Neptunium (atomic number 93)

The density of orthorhombic Np is 20.45 g/cm$^3$, which almost matches that of the Pt group metals, but, unlike them, the melting point is quite low (912°K). The only low-temperature resistivity work is that of Lee and King[261] and Meaden[263,303,304] *on the same specimen*, which was of 99 wt-% purity. The former made measurements between 90 and 520°K, obtaining $\rho_{295} = 116\,\mu\Omega$-cm, and the latter between 0.75 and 300°K, finding $\rho_{295} = 121.9 \pm 0.2\,\mu\Omega$-cm (Fig. 16). The discrepancies in the figures for the absolute resistivities in the range of overlap (90 to 300°K) are probably due in part to the fact that Lee and King made some corrections to their data for the effects of thermal expansion.[261] Also, because there was an interval of several months between the experiments, a little surface oxidation of the specimen undoubtedly occurred, thus perhaps modifying the true form factor slightly. The data used in Table II are those of Meaden as originally given, but if it is considered desirable to normalize the data to that of Lee and King at 295°K, the necessary multiplying factor is 0.9516 (= 116/121.9). Below 32°K, the ideal resistivity is proportional to $T^{3.1}$, which is similar to that of Th and U.

Lee and King found small anomalies in the resistivity at 155 and 273°K, their positions being confirmed by magnetic susceptibility measurements.[261] The anomaly at 155°K appeared from the

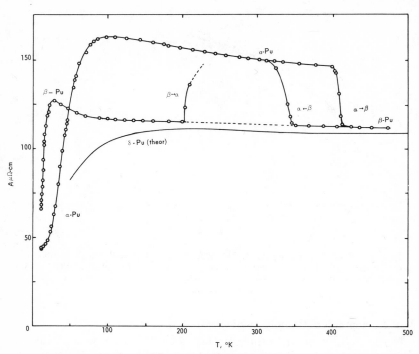

Fig. 17.   The resistivities of α-, β-, and δ-Pu according to King and Lee.[243]

susceptibility investigation to be a ferromagnetic transition. A second specimen did not display these effects in either the resistivity or the susceptibility.[303,305] It is unclear whether the role of impurities was to cause or to conceal magnetic behavior in the respective specimens. Since all rare earths with incomplete 4f-shells are magnetic, it is possible that all actinides (including Np) with incomplete 5f-shells are also magnetic. Unlike the preceding actinides, Np is not a superconductor down to at least 0.41°K.[310]

### 2.18.5. Plutonium (atomic number 94)

Plutonium, which is of immense industrial importance because of its nuclear properties, has every claim to being considered the most remarkable metal of all since it passes through six different crystal structures before its low melting point at 913°K is reached. Moreover, it has negative temperature coefficients of resistance in the high-temperature β-, γ-, and ε-phases,[387] and above 100°K in the monoclinic α-phase, and the greatest absolute resistivity of any metal at

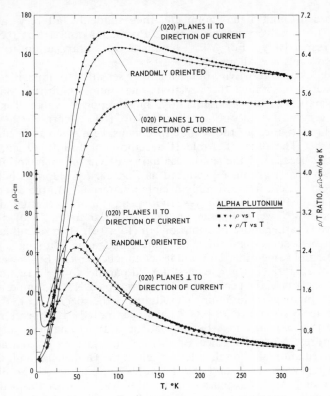

Fig. 18. The resistivities of highly oriented and randomly oriented α-Pu (Elliott, Olsen, and Bronisz[145]). The function $\rho/T$ is also given for these specimens (lower curves, right-hand scale).

and below room temperature. Another peculiarity is that the simple cubic δ-phase, stable from 590 to 726°K, contracts on heating. Unfortunately, Pu is dangerous to handle because of its radioactivity and is metallurgically awkward because of its hardness, brittleness, and multiplicity of phases.

The fcc δ-phase may be studied at ordinary temperatures and below if it is stabilized by the addition of certain other elements such as Al or Ce in solid solution.[191,262,146] Body-centered monoclinic β-Pu, stable from 395 to 475°K, may be studied at low temperatures too after suitable quenching.[243] It is found that the resistivities of α- and β-Pu and alloyed δ-Pu all behave in a similar anomalous manner below room temperature. The resistivities, already high at room temperature, increase still further with decreasing temperature. Eventually, they pass through a maximum and then suddenly fall very rapidly (Fig. 17). In polycrystalline $\alpha$- and $\beta$-Pu the maxima are at 105 and 35°K, respectively. For $\delta$-Pu, obtained by extrapolation to zero solute content, it is about 250°K.[262,303]

The residual resistivity of $\alpha$-Pu is very sensitive to impurities, but at temperatures above the resistivity maximum impurities have a much smaller effect. Consequently, most reported values for $\rho_{295}$ accord very well with one another (148 to 150 $\mu\Omega$-cm),[145,304,263] yet residual resistivities for these same specimens were given as 7, 20, and 49 $\mu\Omega$-cm! The data of Table II are those of Elliott, Olsen, and Bronisz[145] because of the small residual resistivity of their specimen. They also give a graph, reproduced as Fig. 18, for the resistivity of two specimens cut from strongly oriented material. In the direction parallel to the [020] plane, the resistivity peak is more accentuated and is shifted to a lower temperature. Perpendicular to the [020] plane, the curve is rather more like that of Np (Fig. 16). The resemblances between such curves and those of antiferromagnetic Mn (Fig. 7), Eu (Fig. 10), and some other lanthanides cannot be denied. Furthermore, it may well be that for single crystal $\alpha$-Pu parallel to the direction of greatest resistivity, the peak will occur nearer to 65°K, the temperature at which singularities in Young's modulus,[258] the specific heat,[386] and the thermoelectric power[308,304,257] have been noted. It appears quite possible that $\alpha$-, $\beta$-, and $\delta$-Pu may all be antiferromagnetic at low temperatures, especially since Brodsky[90a] has just reported finding pronounced anomalies or changes of sign in the Hall effect of all three phases (in $\alpha$-Pu at 23°K and in $\beta$-Pu at 29°K), but there is no direct evidence such as from neutron diffraction yet. Information about damage and annealing characteristics in Pu at low temperatures, obtained from observations on the effect of self-damage by $\alpha$-irradiation, seems to lend support to the suggestion of antiferromagnetism.[447,244,448] For recent discussions on this complex subject, the reader is referred to refs. 276, 304, 144, 244, and 448.

### 2.18.6. Americium (95) and Curium (96)

These metals have the curious double cph crystal structure previously met with only in La, (Ce), Pr, and Nd. They resemble the rare earths closely, and it is likely that they will be found to be magnetic with high resistivities when sufficient metal eventually becomes available.

### 2.18.7. The Trans-Curium Elements (Bk, Cf, Fm, Es, Md, No, Lw)

Berkelium and californium have relatively long-lived isotopes, but not even microgram quantities will become available for several years.

## Table III. Electrical Resistivities of Noncubic Metals (in $\mu\Omega$-cm)

| | Crystal structure | At 273°K | | | At the temperature indicated | | | | References |
|---|---|---|---|---|---|---|---|---|---|
| | | $\rho_\parallel$ | $\rho_\perp$ | $\rho_\perp/\rho_\parallel$ | Temperature °K | $\rho_\parallel$ | $\rho_\perp$ | $\rho_\parallel/\rho_\perp$ | |
| 4 Be | cph | 3.58 | 3.12 | 0.88 | 293 | 4.30 | | | 185, 186 |
| 12 Mg | cph | 3.47 | 4.17 | 1.20 | 293 | 3.77 | 4.52 | 1.20 | 329, 329 |
| 30 Zn | cph | 5.59 | 5.39 | 0.96 | 293 | 6.05 | 5.83 | 0.96 | 90, 178 |
| 48 Cd | cph | 7.73 | 6.35 | 0.87 | 293 | 8.36 | 6.87 | 0.82 | M2, 178 |
| 80 Hg | rhomb | liquid state | | | 227.6 | 17.8 | 23.5 | } 1.32 | M2 |
| | | | | | 85.6 | 5.6 | 7.4 | | |
| 31 Ga | ortho | 50.3 | (1) 16.05 (2) 7.5 | (1) 0.32 (2) 0.15 | 293 | 55.5 | (1) 17.3 (2) 7.85 | (1) 0.31 (2) 0.14 | 361, 361 |
| 49 In | bc tetr | 7.9 | 8.3 | 1.05 | | | | | 336 |
| 81 Tl | cph | ~18 | ~14 | ~0.8 | | | | | 336 |
| 50 Sn | tetr | 13.08 | 9.09 | 0.695 | 293 | 14.3 | 9.9 | 0.69 | 90, M21 |
| 33 As | rhomb | (~32.5) | (~23.5) | (~0.72) | 293 | 35.6 | 25.5 | 0.72 | 419, 419 |
| 51 Sb | rhomb | 26.3 | 36.0 | 1.37 | 293 | 35.6 | 42.6 | 1.20 | 371, 89 |
| 83 Bi | rhomb | 127 | 99 | 0.78 | 293 | 138 | 109 | 0.79 | 187, 89 |
| 39 Y | cph | 48.0 | 45.35 | 0.94 | 300 | 34.6 | 71.6 | 2.07 | 201 |
| 22 Ti | cph | 32.7 | 32.0 | 0.98 | | | | | 432 |
| 72 Hf | cph | 5.3 | 6.7 | 1.27 | | | | | 41 |
| 44 Ru | cph | | | | 293 | 5.73 | 7.29 | 1.27 | 363, 363 |
| 64 Gd | cph | | | | 300 | 118.0 | 131.0 | 1.11 | 330 |
| 65 Tb | cph | | | | 300 | 91 | 119 | 1.30 | 209 |
| 66 Dy | cph | | | | 300 | 77.4 | 100.3 | 1.30 | 202 |
| 67 Ho | cph | | | | 300 | 54 | 91 | 1.70 | 412 |
| 68 Er | cph | | | | 300 | 43.7 | 75 | 1.72 | 182 |
| 92 U | ortho | 39.4 | (1) 25.5 (2) 26.2 | 0.65 0.665 | 291 | 41 | (1) 25.1 (2) 32 | (1) 0.61 (2) 0.78 | 72, 346 |

The order in which the elements are listed is that of Table II. Residual resistivities have been subtracted wherever possible. In most other cases, except perhaps Hf and U, they may be presumed to be very small (i.e., of the order of magnitude given in Table II).

## Table IV. Transition Temperatures of the Superconducting Elements
### (Compare with the full periodic table—Table I)

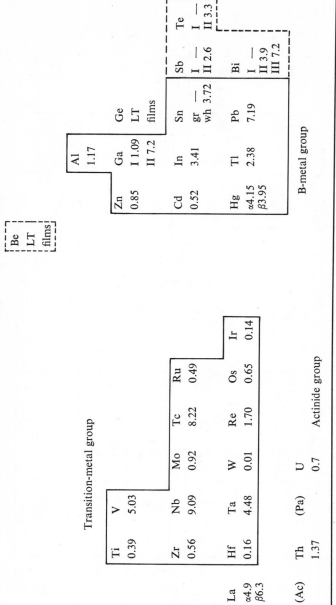

Included in this table are transition temperatures for Te II, Bi II, and Bi III, which are superconducting high-pressure modifications of ordinary Te and Bi (at pressures of 56, 25, and 27 kb, respectively). Ga II and Sb II remain superconducting even when the pressure is removed, and the transition temperatures given are those appropriate for 1 atm pressure. In addition to the bulk superconducting elements of this table, Be and Ge will also become superconducting if deposited as films at low temperatures.

## 2.19. SUPERCONDUCTIVITY IN THE
## PERIODIC SYSTEM

We have summarized in tabular form the transition temperatures of the superconducting elements (Table IV). The values given come largely from the compilation by Matthias, Geballe, and Compton,[296] but some have been revised in the light of more recent information, and there are several additions.

At least thirty elements are now known to be superconductors, and, judging by the examples of purity-sensitive Mo, Ir, and W, it is likely that certain others will be discovered in the future when they are obtained in a pure-enough state and are taken to low-enough temperatures (providing also that extraneous fields are completely annulled). The best possibilities are with Sc, Y, Lu, and Rh, which may have transition temperatures above 0.1°K. For the reasons given in Section 2.18.1, neither Ac nor Pa has ever been tested, but both are probably also superconductors, Pa with a high transition point.

A small number of the superconducting elements have been found to require elaborate techniques of preparation, and when this work has been further extended some fresh discoveries are again likely. For example, Be and Ge, which are not superconductors in the bulk state, become superconducting when condensed as films at 4°K, while Sb, Bi, and Te (the latter, like Ge, being ordinarily a semi-conductor) possess crystal modifications formed under high pressures which are superconducting—and with relatively high transition temperatures too (Table IV). Ge, Si, and P are known to have metallic phases at high pressures, and some of these, with perhaps As, Po, and Se, may prove to have superconducting high-pressure forms also.

From a study of Tables IV and I, superconductivity is seen to be spread very widely across the periodic table, although it will be noticed that the metals of columns IA, IB, and IIA (excluding Be, as described above), which are good conductors at room temperature, and the ferromagnetic and antiferromagnetic elements are not included. Further, since the superconducting metals appear to be arranged in three distinct groups, the basic interactions leading to superconductivity may not necessarily be the same from group to group, and, in point of fact, the well-known isotope effect, which demonstrates that the fundamental interaction is between the conduction electrons and the lattice, is found only in the B-group metals.* In the transition metals, on the other hand, those having five or seven external electrons and thus a resultant spin possess the highest transition

---

* This effect is that for all isotopes of a given metal the transition temperature is inversely proportional to the square root of the atomic mass.

temperatures.[295] Therefore, an interaction of magnetic origin is indicated in these elements.

Besides the thirty metallic elements already mentioned, superconductivity is also found in hundreds of metallic alloys and compounds and even in certain semiconductors,[210,389] including germanium telluride. The highest transition temperature of all found to date is 18.05°K in the compound $Nb_3Sn$.

For further practical and theoretical information on the subject of superconductivity, the reader is referred to the introductory books of Gygax and Olsen, [M18] Lynton, [M25] Mendelssohn, [M27] and Rosenberg [M30] and to ref. 296 cited above.

# The Theory of the Electrical Resistance of Metals

### 3.1. INTRODUCTION

From a study of the experimental results of the previous chapter, the following are the main features that emerge regarding the electrical resistance of the metallic elements:

1. Metals have low resistivities lying in the range 1.5 to 150 $\mu\Omega$-cm at room temperature, whereas semiconductors have resistivities that are $10^6$ to $10^{12}$ times larger than these and insulators $10^6$ to $10^{12}$ times larger still.

2. To a first approximation the resistivity is linear in temperature for most metals above $0.5\theta$.

3. Below $0.25\theta$ the ideal or thermal component of the resistivity decreases faster than linearly—roughly as $T^3$ in many metals and as $T^5$ in several others, particularly the monovalent ones.

4. Some dependence of the magnitude of the resistivity on position in the periodic table is evident from Table I, both as regards valency and atomic number.

5a. The total resistivity is composed of thermal and impurity contributions; in magnetic metals there is a term of magnetic origin as well.

5b. The separation of the total resistivity into the above independent components, commonly known as Matthiessen's rule, may be said to be generally valid [Equation (1.5)].

6. In some supposedly pure metals, notably Cu, Ag, Au, and Mg, a minimum occurs in the resistance close to the 5 to 15°K temperature region.

7. Nearly half the metals and a good many alloys and compounds become superconducting at low-enough temperatures.

Other important facts not specifically mentioned so far include the following:

8. Metals are also good conductors of heat, and there is a definite relation between the electrical ($\sigma$) and thermal ($\kappa$) conductivities, called the *Wiedemann–Franz law*, namely, $\kappa/\sigma$ is constant[445] (discovered in 1853). Later, an important extension to $\kappa/\sigma T =$ constant was made by Lorenz,[278] and this constant is now known as the *Lorenz number*.

9. The resistance of most metals decreases with increasing pressure.

All these characteristics, including even the sixth to a limited extent, can now be discussed and understood fairly adequately in a qualitative way, although very little can yet be said in quantitative terms. The mathematical difficulties remain quite formidable, and present theories, originated by Sommerfeld and Bloch in 1928, are restricted quantitatively to the monovalent metals. Even here, theory is weak when the heavier alkalis and the noble metals are considered, especially at low temperatures where the temperature variation of the resistivity is very complicated in detail.

We begin our discussion of metallic resistance with the early free electron theories of Drude and Lorentz, as these contain certain seeds of truth used in the quantum theories of Sommerfeld, Bloch, and others that follow. Selected aspects of the modern theory of metals are then outlined where they have a direct relevance to an understanding of the present problem of electrical resistance. We then deal with the ideal resistance itself and the work of Bardeen, who was the first to consider the contribution made by *Umklapp* processes. Further developments by Ziman, Bailyn, and others bring us to the present day. The theoretical difficulties encountered at low temperatures are also discussed, and the semi-empirical Grüneisen–Bloch relation, which gives a serviceable description of the resistance behavior for a good many metals over a wide range of temperature, is described. Next we deal with the effect that impurity scattering has on the resistance, indicate to what extent Matthiessen's rule is valid, and then consider the resistance-minimum phenomenon. After that, we discuss to what extent the more complicated resistances of the divalent, transition, and other multivalent metals can be explained in terms of our present ideas, finishing with the rare-earth and iron-group metals, in which magnetic effects abound. The chapter finally concludes with a brief mention of what are, in the main, occurrences outside our province—nonlinear resistivities at high temperatures and melting-point phenomena.

The treatment throughout is kept simple and straightforward.

A previous acquaintance with basic solid state physics is assumed, however. Recent books dealing with such topics are those of Ziman,[M12] Rosenberg,[M30] Olsen,[M8] and of course Kittel[M22] and Dekker.[M15]

## 3.2. EARLY THEORIES

The earliest significant steps were made by Drude[133] and Lorentz[277] at the turn of the century, shortly after Thomson's discovery of the electron. Electrons detached from the atoms were considered responsible for the transport of the electric current under an applied electric field, and collisions with the lattice were held to be the cause of resistance to this current. In order that the problem might be made at all tractable, the electrons were supposed to be quite free, not interacting with each other, and to behave as a perfect gas. Thus the relevant methods of the kinetic theory of gases, including Maxwell–Boltzmann statistics, could be applied.

In this approach, assuming no external field, the $n$ electrons in unit volume move about randomly between the fixed ions of the metallic lattice with a mean velocity $\mathbf{v}$ which is dependent on the temperature. We assume that the application of a field $\mathbf{E}$ encourages the electrons, of charge $-e$, to move with a mean drift velocity $-\mathbf{v}_d$ in the direction of $\mathbf{E}$. This drift velocity is very much smaller than the thermal velocities. An equilibrium state in which a steady flow of charge occurs, instead of continued acceleration, is possible because of collisions that the electrons undergo with the lattice. Thus we may write for the current density

$$\mathbf{J} = -ne\mathbf{v}_d \tag{3.1}$$

The energy gained by an electron *from the field* is further assumed to be wholly given up at a collision so that the drift velocity momentarily becomes zero and the motion of the electron immediately after can be taken to be entirely random. A quantity $\tau$ is now introduced such that the probability of an electron undergoing a collision in time $dt$ is $dt/\tau$. Then, since just after collisions velocities are random, the rate of change of $\mathbf{v}_d$ due to collisions with the lattice alone is

$$\left[\frac{d}{dt}(\mathbf{v}_d)\right]_{\text{coll}} \equiv (\dot{\mathbf{v}}_d)_{\text{coll}} = -\mathbf{v}_d(1/\tau) \tag{3.2}$$

and during the interval between two successive collisions the equation of motion of an electron of mass $m$ due to the field may be written

$$(\dot{\mathbf{v}}_d)_{\text{ext fields}} = -e\mathbf{E}/m \tag{3.3}$$

In the steady state

$$(\dot{\mathbf{v}}_d)_{\text{ext fields}} + (\dot{\mathbf{v}}_d)_{\text{coll}} = 0$$

so we finally obtain by using equations (3.2) and (3.3)

$$\mathbf{v}_d = -\frac{e\mathbf{E}\tau}{m} \tag{3.4}$$

and

$$\mathbf{J} = \left(\frac{ne^2\tau}{m}\right)\mathbf{E} \tag{3.5}$$

This is Ohm's law given previously as equation (1.1), but with the conductivity $\sigma$ now expressed by

$$\sigma = \frac{ne^2\tau}{m} \tag{3.6}$$

In like manner it may be shown (Wilson [M11]) that the thermal conductivity of a good conductor is given by

$$\kappa = \frac{2\tau v^2 n C_v}{3} \tag{3.7}$$

where $C_v$ is the specific heat at constant volume per free electron and $v$ is the mean thermal velocity of the electrons.

Division of equation (3.6) by (3.7) gives the result

$$\frac{\kappa}{\sigma} = \frac{2mv^2 C_v}{3e^2} \tag{3.8}$$

which is equivalent to

$$\frac{\kappa}{\sigma} = 3\left(\frac{k}{e}\right)^2 T \tag{3.9}$$

since in a classical gas the average energy of a particle is $\frac{1}{2}mv^2 = \frac{3}{2}kT$, and $C_v = \frac{3}{2}k$ ($k$ is Boltzmann's constant and $T$ the absolute temperature). Equation (3.9) will be recognized as the Wiedemann–Franz law given under item 8 in Section 3.1. The constant of proportionality is seen to be $3(k/e)^2$ which is numerically equal to $2.23 \times 10^{-8}$ W-$\Omega$/deg$^2$.

We thus find that this simple free electron theory has accounted for the important Wiedemann–Franz law and has provided a value for the Lorenz constant that is only some 10% below the average obtained for a good many metals at or near room temperature.

Moreover, for the simpler monovalent elements, equation (3.6) gives the electrical conductivity at room temperature to within an order of magnitude, if $n$ is taken to be roughly the same as the number of atoms per unit volume and if $\tau = l/v$, where $l$, the mean free path, is assumed to be about equal to the interatomic distance. Unfortunately, the mean square velocity $v^2$ is proportional to $T$, so, with $\tau = l/v$, equation (3.6) also indicates that the resistivity $\rho(\equiv 1/\sigma)$ will vary as $T^{1/2}$ and not as $T$, which is obtained experimentally. Also, regarding the thermal conductivity, equation (3.7) leads to $\kappa \propto \sqrt{T}$, whereas $\kappa$ is usually almost temperature-independent at room temperature.

In addition, this theory has two other inherent weaknesses. First, there is a discrepancy of one hundred times between the calculated and observed values of the paramagnetic susceptibility of the conduction electrons. Second, according to the theory a contribution of $\frac{3}{2}k$ to the specific heat would be expected from each electron, giving a total of $\frac{3}{2}nk$ per unit volume. That is, if $n$ is of the order of the number of atoms, metals should have specific heats very distinctly higher than insulators, because the electronic part would be important and large at ordinary temperatures. However, this is not the case, and the small electronic term found in practice suggests that few of the conduction electrons are contributing to the total specific heat.

These difficulties were only resolved some twenty years later, following the introduction and development of quantum mechanics and the application of Fermi–Dirac statistics, instead of Maxwell–Boltzmann statistics, to the electron gas assembly. The success of the Drude–Lorentz theory was due to the correctness of the free electron concept, the valid neglect of electron–electron interactions (see discussion given by Jones [M3]), and the fact that $\tau$ and $n$ happily do not enter into the final statement of the Wiedemann–Franz law, equation (3.9).

## 3.3. SOMMERFELD'S THEORY

The next advance toward present theories of conductivity came in 1928 when Sommerfeld[402] applied the methods of the recently developed Fermi quantum statistics to the problem. The key had been provided by Pauli's exclusion principle, according to which only one electron may occupy any one quantum state. Consequently, at absolute zero all the free electrons fill those energy states which are the lowest ones available; below a certain energy $E_{max}$ (the Fermi energy) all states are occupied and above it all are vacant (Fig. 19a). On warming to a temperature $T$, some of the electrons acquire an additional energy $kT$, but the number involved is small because only those electrons that have empty energy states within their reach may

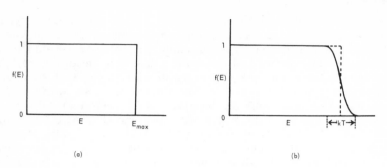

Fig. 19. The occupied energy states according to Fermi statistics at (a) absolute zero and (b) a temperature $T$.

possibly change state. Since the available extra energy $kT$, up to normal temperatures at least, is very much less than the Fermi energy (which is several electron volts), such electrons are those already near the top of the Fermi distribution, namely, those within about $kT$ of $E_{max}$. Thus the effect of a temperature $T$ is to excite merely a small fraction, of the order of $kT/E_{max}$, of the total number of free electrons (Fig. 19b). At room temperature this fraction is less than $10^{-2}$ for most metals, so that only this tiny percentage of the total number of free electrons are in fact conduction electrons. Obviously, the electronic contribution to the total specific heat is also correspondingly smaller, and is seen to be quite negligible compared to the lattice specific heat at all except the very lowest temperatures (for ultimately, as $T \to 0°K$, the lattice term decreases as $T^3$, while the electronic term decreases only as $T$).

On the question of electrical conductivity, Sommerfeld assumed, following Drude and Lorentz, that the conduction electrons are influenced neither by the ionic field of the lattice nor by interactions with one another. Electrons therefore move around freely between collisions with the lattice, and under an applied electric field the conductivity is still given by equation (3.6). However, whereas in the preceding theories $l = \tau v$ was of the order of the interatomic distance, here it is considerably longer. Indeed, $l$ often exceeds a hundred interatomic distances at room temperature if $n$ is taken as one free electron per atom. The reason is that in Fermi statistics $v$ turns out to be much greater than that given by the classical theorem of equipartition of energy, where the mean kinetic energy is simply $\frac{3}{2}kT$. Such long mean free paths could not be understood in classical terms, since it could not be visualized how an electron could very well move more than a few atomic spacings before being scattered by a lattice ion.

The paradox is no more, though, as soon as we recall that in quantum mechanics we can discuss the behavior of electrons in terms of wave-like properties. For, since we are quite familiar with the almost unperturbed passage of X-rays through metal crystals, it is not so difficult to imagine electrons as being propagated in a similar way—that is, the constructive interference of the scattered wavelets continually maintains the wave front. At very low temperatures, paths of the order of 1 mm occur in certain pure metals. This is equivalent to some 10 million interatomic distances! In fact, quantum mechanics and the Bloch theory, which we shall now discuss, demonstrate that in a *perfect* metal at absolute zero mean free paths are infinite and electrical resistance is zero.

## 3.4. THE BLOCH THEORY

The essential new feature introduced by Bloch[81] was that the electrons should be considered as moving in an electrostatic field which is periodic with the period of the lattice. The waves associated with the electrons are then no longer ordinary plane waves, as in Sommerfeld's theory, because they are modulated by a function which has the period of the lattice.

Now it is convenient and usual to describe the behavior of electrons in metals in terms of their wave-number aspects as seen in three-dimensional wave-number space (**k**-space). This is just the same as the reciprocal lattice space used in X-ray crystallography, where each electronic state is represented by a point whose coordinates are the components ($k_x$, $k_y$, $k_z$) of the wave vector **k**.

To obtain the wave functions that describe the electronic wave states in a metal, it is simply necessary to solve the Schrödinger wave equation for the case of a periodic potential. Bloch showed that the appropriate solutions were of the form

$$\psi_{\mathbf{k}} = u_{\mathbf{k}}(\mathbf{r}) \cdot e^{i\mathbf{k}\cdot\mathbf{r}} \qquad (3.10)$$

where $u_{\mathbf{k}}(\mathbf{r})$ is a function periodic in the lattice spacing. Thus the Bloch functions $\psi_{\mathbf{k}}$ represent plane waves modulated with the lattice periodicity and having a wavelength of $2\pi/k$ traveling in the direction of **k**.

If the lattice potential is truly periodic, with no imperfections whatever, the electron waves will be propagated through the lattice without loss of energy, i.e., there will be zero resistance to the motion of the conduction electrons. But, in practice, the lattice potential is not perfect and resistance arises from two primary sources.

1. The major source is the vibrations of the lattice ions themselves, as a consequence of the thermal energy they gain on increase in temperature. That this should be the origin of the large temperature-dependent part of the resistivity in metals had already been proposed fifteen years earlier (in 1913) by Wien.[446] This part of the resistivity is known variously as the *thermal*, the *ideal*, the *intrinsic*, the *lattice*, or the *phonon* resistivity. The word *phonon* may be defined as a single quantum of the quantized energies of the lattice vibrations. For an analogy one may equally think of the photons of the electromagnetic field.
2. The other source is the presence of chemical or physical imperfections, which provides a generally small and temperature-independent term in the total resistivity (refer also to Sections 1.4 and 3.8). The imperfections may be foreign atoms in solid solution, or they may result from localized lattice damage or strains which have caused atoms of the metal itself to be displaced, giving vacancies and interstitials or extended lattice faults. Even mixed isotopes will locally disrupt the lattice potential,[354] and if the specimen is not a single crystal so will intercrystallite boundaries.

Other causes of electrical resistivity, such as boundary-size effects at low temperatures and localized spin scattering, will be dealt with at later stages (Sections 6.3, 3.9, and 3.10.2).

The perfect crystal, which will have no electrical resistance at absolute zero, is thus seen to require the following properties: it must be a quite faultless and unconstrained monoisotopic single crystal having no impurity atoms, no vacancies, or no defects of any kind and be of infinite extent (to avoid external boundary effects), and, if magnetic, possess no internal magnetic-domain boundaries. Fortunately, the phenomenon of superconductivity is a means of short-circuiting such perfection in very many metals (in nineteen of them above $1°K$, Section 2.19)—and it may be that most nonferromagnetic metals will yet prove to be superconductors at low-enough temperatures and under suitable conditions.[297]

## 3.5. ELECTRON MOTION IN A PERIODIC FIELD

Before we discuss the actual effects that departures from perfect lattice periodicity have on the resistance, we shall consider how the energy and $k$-spectra of the conduction electrons are influenced by a periodic potential.

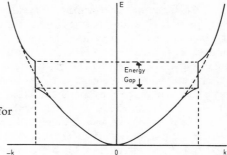

Fig. 20. *E* versus *k* relationship for a one- dimensional crystal.

We begin by returning to our X-ray analogy in order to qualify the statement that X-rays may be propagated through perfect crystals without attenuation. The qualification is that there are certain critical wavelengths and directions in the crystal for which X-ray propagation is not possible, because when the Bragg relation, $2d \sin \phi = n\lambda$, is satisfied total reflection occurs. In this equation $d$ is the distance between parallel layers of the lattice, $\phi$ the angle of incidence, $n$ an integer, and $\lambda$ the wavelength. ($d$ is by no means necessarily equal to $a$, the lattice constant. In cubic metal crystals, for instance, $d$ is always less than $a$.)

The situation is no different for the passage of electron waves. For a given direction there are particular values of the electron wave number $k$, given by the Bragg relation, which are not permitted and propagation of these particular waves cannot occur. Although each forbidden gap measured in wave numbers is infinitely thin, the corresponding gap arising in the energy is certainly finite, as can be understood from Fig. 20. This is due to the anomalous variation of electron energies that occurs near each critical $k$ value. Since the wavelength of the wave specified by **k** is $\lambda = 2\pi/k$, then by using the Bragg relation we see that the gaps recur when

$$k = \frac{2\pi}{\lambda} = n \frac{\pi}{d} \qquad \text{where } n = 1, 2, 3, \dots$$

These energy gaps form boundaries between zones concentric about the origin in three-dimensional **k** space, within each of which the energy is a continuous function of the wave vectors not excluded by the Bragg relation. The zones are called *Brillouin zones* and assume forms characteristic of the symmetry of the lattice. As such, they concern the manner of propagation not only of electron waves but also of X-ray, phonon, and other waves through the crystal lattice.

In short, the zones correspond to *bands* of allowed energies separated by gaps of forbidden energies. This is not to say that bands in actual crystals are always separated by gaps, since there is a variety of circumstances under which band overlap may occur. For example, if the energy $E$ at a given distance from the center of a zone is direction-dependent (constant-energy surfaces nonspherical), as it always is for large $\mathbf{k}$, then there may be distant parts of the zone having higher energy states than the lowest ones of the second zone. This is the case in the *divalent metals*, which have two conduction electrons per atom. As the total number of electronic energy states in the first zone is such that two electrons per atom can be accommodated, the valence electrons of divalent metals could just be fully held by the first zone. But because electrons (at absolute zero) always seek to enter the states of lowest energy available to them (Section 3.3), in divalent metals some electrons enter states in the higher zone to achieve this end, since they are able to do so on account of band overlap. Thus the *Fermi surface*, which represents those electrons of maximum energy, lies partly in one zone and partly in the other. It is evident that a feature of all metals must be the possession of at least one partially full Brillouin zone, because a requirement for good electronic conductivity is the existence of vacant energy states adjacent to filled ones. It is because the conduction electrons are those near the Fermi surface that a knowledge of the location and shape of the latter is of such importance when discussing the conductivity of a metal.

In the *monovalent elements* there is one valence electron per atom, which is only half the number needed to fill the first Brillouin zone. Simple calculation or geometrical construction then shows that in the bcc alkali metals the Fermi surface, if considered spherical, may be contained entirely within the first zone without touching it anywhere. This model would apply for a metal having free or almost free electrons, and the experimental evidence suggests that this is the state of affairs actually pertaining in Na and, to a lesser extent, in K. The shape of the Fermi surface is much less simple in the other monovalent metals, because the electrons can no longer be considered nearly free. Even a spherical Fermi surface in bcc metals extends to 90 % of the distance from the origin to the nearest regions of the zone boundaries. So in less perfect metals the effect of a periodic lattice field is to distort the Fermi surface from a sphere at those parts nearest zone boundaries. As an example, we illustrate in Fig. 21 Pippard's model of the Fermi surface of fcc Cu.[352] The other noble metals are also rather similar to this in having Fermi surfaces that contact the zone boundaries.

Metals of higher valence have band structures of considerable complexity, with Fermi surfaces crossing several zones. Several

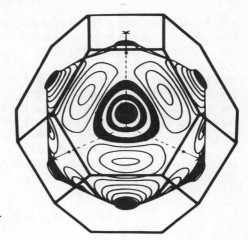

Fig. 21. The Fermi surface of Cu according to Pippard.[352]

elements of high valence are semiconductors or insulators, because all their lowest zones are completely filled and the energy gap to the next unfilled zone is too great for all but perhaps a few highly excited electrons to cross. Thus high temperatures and high fields favor conduction in such substances, which are known as *intrinsic semiconductors*. Impurities, whose energy levels lie within the energy gap, also aid conduction, since the gap width is effectively narrowed, permitting a more ready movement of electrons between the bands involved. These substances are called *impurity semiconductors*. By contrast, the effect of impurities and high temperatures in metals is just the opposite, since the flow of electrons is impeded and the conductivity lowered.

## 3.6. RESISTANCE DUE TO THERMAL SCATTERING

When an electric field is applied to a metal which has the free electron distribution shown in Fig. 22, the whole Fermi distribution

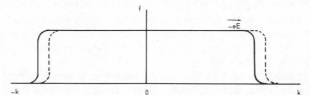

Fig. 22. Movement of the Fermi distribution under an applied field $E$.

gets displaced in the direction of the field, as indicated in the diagram. Initially the conduction electrons accelerate, but an equilibrium state giving a steady current is quickly reached because of interactions with lattice vibrations (or more strictly with phonons) and with lattice imperfections. Since the effect of the latter on the resistance is independent of the temperature, we shall defer its consideration until Section 3.8. In order to determine the temperature variation of the resistance, it is necessary to consider only the scattering of electrons by phonons.

The analysis usually begins with the Boltzmann transport equation, which expresses the steady-state condition of the electron distribution. It may be written

$$\dot{\mathbf{k}}\nabla_{\mathbf{k}}f + \dot{\mathbf{r}}\nabla_{\mathbf{r}}f = \left(\frac{\partial f}{\partial t}\right)_{\text{coll}} \tag{3.11}$$

where $(\partial f/\partial t)_{\text{coll}}$ is the rate at which the distribution function is changed by the collision processes; the distribution function is represented by $f$ when disturbed and $f_0$ when undisturbed; $\mathbf{k}$ and $\mathbf{r}$ are wave and position vectors of the electrons.

The simplification is next made that, provided collisions are elastic, it is justifiable to introduce a relaxation time $\tau$. This is the case for the ideal resistance at high temperatures. It is also the case for the impurity resistance, and may therefore be applied at very low temperatures in ordinary metals (where $\rho_i \to 0$) and at all temperatures in very impure metals (where $\rho_0 > \rho_i$). We say that a relaxation time exists when, after removing the external fields, $f$ relaxes exponentially to $f_0$ because of the collision processes alone. Thus

$$\left(\frac{\partial f}{\partial t}\right)_{\text{coll}} = -\frac{f - f_0}{\tau} \tag{3.12}$$

When conditions are such that a relaxation time can be utilized, it may, after appropriate computation by a quantum mechanical method, be substituted into an equation similar to equation (3.6), thereby giving the electrical conductivity. Because $\tau$ and the probability per unit time of an electron collision are inversely related, the problem reduces to a calculation of the total transition probability per unit time taken over the whole metal.

It should be said at this stage that the Lorenz number can be derived quite easily by means of the Boltzmann equation without making any special assumptions regarding the nature of the relaxation time, since the same variables enter into the formal equations for both $\kappa$ and $\sigma$.[M11] The result obtained for the Lorenz number $L$ is found to be

$$L = \frac{\kappa}{\sigma T} = \frac{\pi^2}{3}\left(\frac{k}{e}\right)^2 \tag{3.13}$$

$$= 2.445 \times 10^{-8} \text{ W-}\Omega\text{/deg}$$

For many metals the experimentally determined Lorenz number comes fairly close to this figure when calculated for the region of room temperature or for the region below $4°K$. These are just the temperature regions in which $\tau$ may be considered identical for both electrical and thermal transport. The Wiedemann–Franz law does not, however, hold at intermediate temperatures, and the Lorenz number as given by experiment is often some 70% lower at $\theta_D/10$ than the value given by equation (3.13). At these intermediate temperatures, electron–phonon interactions involve changes in electron energy which are large compared to $kT$, and yet the effect on the momentum is relatively small; this means that the thermal conductivity is reduced much more than the electrical conductivity, and the Wiedemann–Franz law breaks down.

The various attempts that have been made to calculate the total transition probability differ among themselves with respect to the assumptions that first had to be made concerning the coupling between the conduction electrons and the lattice. But all analyses do have in common the feature that, if they are to be quantitative, it must be assumed that the energy of an electron in state **k** is dependent on **k** only—or, in other words, that the Fermi surface is spherical, a condition nearly satisfied in only the monovalent metals.

In obtaining a solution at high temperatures $(T > \theta_D)$ it is immaterial whether a Debye or Einstein model is used to describe the lattice vibrational spectrum. Mott and Jones[M7] and Jones[M3] have shown that an Einstein model works well enough, but normally a Debye spectrum is assumed, since it must in any case be employed at low temperatures. At each collision, a quantum of vibrational energy is exchanged, which at low temperatures is not small compared to $kT$, so there is the added difficulty that no relaxation time may be specified. On the other hand, at high temperatures the relaxation time approximation holds good, as mentioned before, because the change in electron energy at a collision is very much smaller than $kT$ and collisions are effectively elastic. Under these circumstances, even a classical approach leads to the transition probability being proportional to the mean square amplitude of the lattice vibrations $\overline{x^2}$, as first hypothesized by Wien.[446] Application of the theorem of equipartition of energy to the vibrating ions of mass $M$ and frequency $\nu$ then gives

$$4\pi^2\nu^2 M\overline{x^2} = kT$$

Therefore, if $\theta$ is a characteristic temperature defined by $h\nu = k\theta$, we have

$$\frac{1}{\tau} \sim \overline{x^2} = \frac{h^2}{4\pi^2 k}\frac{T}{M\theta^2}$$

or

$$\rho_i \propto \frac{T}{M\theta^2} \qquad (3.14)$$

### 3.6.1. Electron–Phonon Processes

The Debye model treats the vibrations of the ions caused by their thermal motion collectively by analyzing them into traveling plane waves. The vibrations themselves are quantized in the energy values they are allowed to assume, and we designate the quanta or phonons by wave vectors $\mathbf{q}$. Each $\mathbf{q}$ has three independent modes of vibration corresponding to transverse and longitudinal waves.

Interactions between electrons and phonons may be of two kinds, known as *normal processes* and *Umklapp processes*. By a *normal interaction* of an electron with a phonon we mean that an electron in state $\mathbf{k}$ interacts with a phonon in state $\mathbf{q}$ with the result that the phonon is annihilated and the electron gets scattered into a vacant energy state $\mathbf{k}'$. Thus

$$\mathbf{k} + \mathbf{q} \gtrless \mathbf{k}' \qquad (3.15)$$

Note that this event could equally well happen in the reverse direction.

In such a process the angle of deviation of the electron depends on the magnitude of the wave vector $\mathbf{q}$. The phonon energy is always much smaller than the Fermi energy of the electrons at ordinary and low temperatures, so the emission or absorption of a phonon changes the electron's energy only slightly. As a consequence, the electron which begins its transition close to or on the Fermi surface can only be scattered to another part of the Fermi surface. Figure 23 illustrates the process, a phonon of wave vector $\mathbf{q}$ being absorbed according to equation (3.15). The limitations just mentioned show that regardless of the temperature there must be an upper limit to the angle through which electrons can be scattered (79°), because,

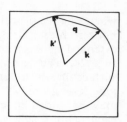

Fig. 23. Normal process in a metal having a
spherical Fermi surface.

since the Brillouin zone is also relevant to phonon waves, the magnitude of $q$ cannot exceed the distance between the zone center and the zone boundary. At low temperatures $q$ is inevitably small because of the temperature, so scattering by such "normal" processes is always through small angles. It is for this reason that the low-temperature region, where the resistance is nonlinear with temperature, is sometimes called the small-angle scattering region.

The second class of interaction processes, the *Umklapp* or *flip-over processes*,[349] can cause scattering through large angles at all but the very lowest temperatures. In such an interaction the electron, on being scattered by a phonon, also suffers a Bragg reflection at the Brillouin zone boundary, and it is implicit in the mechanism that the scattering angle lies between 79 and 180°.

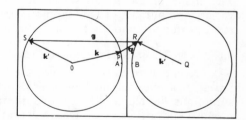

Fig. 24. Umklapp process in a
metal having a spherical Fermi
surface.

In order to understand this, it must be recalled that a basic feature of zone theory is that the addition of a reciprocal lattice vector of any magnitude to a given wave vector produces another vector that is indistinguishable from the first. The selection rule, equation (3.15), must therefore be revised to include such a possibility. We now have the new equation

$$\mathbf{k} + \mathbf{q} + \mathbf{g} = \mathbf{k}' \qquad (3.16)$$

where the reciprocal lattice vector **g** is zero for a normal process and nonzero for an Umklapp process. This is best explained by using the extended zone scheme drawn in **k**-space, part of which is shown in Fig. 24. The left-hand side shows a hypothetical spherical Fermi surface on whose surface the possible vectors **k** end. As vectors of the type **k** + **g** are also permissible, surfaces representing such vectors may be added indefinitely according to the extended zone scheme, each being displaced from the next by the vector **g**. One adjacent possibility is given in the diagram. An electron represented by **k** undergoes an Umklapp process by interacting with a phonon **q**, which results in a state **k′** represented by $QR$. This vector is displaced by **g** from the original Fermi surface, to which it must be returned by subtraction of **g** in order to satisfy the principle of conservation of energy. The final state is indicated by $OS$. The intermission of the large vector **g** has resulted in a scattering angle greater than could have been possible in any normal process. The greatest value that **q** can ever assume is $\frac{1}{2}$**g**, and the smallest (for the Fermi surface of Fig. 24) is the distance $AB$. For this minimum value, the electron momentum is totally reversed in direction.

Umklapp processes would be expected to die out gradually as the temperature is lowered, since the maximum values actually taken by **q** decrease in magnitude. If the Fermi surface does not contact the zone boundary, they must eventually disappear altogether. Nevertheless even in Na, which is the metal coming nearest to having a spherical Fermi surface, Bailyn[60] has demonstrated that Umklapp processes are dominant down to at least 8°K and important down to 1°K. The shape of the Fermi surface obviously influences the possible variety and number of Umklapp processes and from this cause alone must profoundly modify the lattice resistivity.

### 3.6.2. The Theoretical Situation Today

Present theories of resistance are based on the quantum mechanical principles initiated by Bloch.[81] Unavoidable simplifying assumptions limited his theory quantitatively to somewhat idealized monovalent metals with Debye vibrational spectra and spherical Fermi surfaces—and to high temperatures ($T > \theta_D$) at that. Alternative solutions and developments by Houston,[217] Brillouin,[M14] Sommerfeld and Bethe,[403] and Mott and Jones [M7] appeared in the ensuing years, and those of Bardeen[64] (1937), who was the first to take proper account of Umklapp processes, were particularly noteworthy. His approach, as further refined by Ziman,[456, M12] Bailyn,[60] and others, is the most satisfactory general theory available today.

Reference should be made to Ziman's book, Chapters 9 and 5, for an account of the long and involved calculation. The complicated

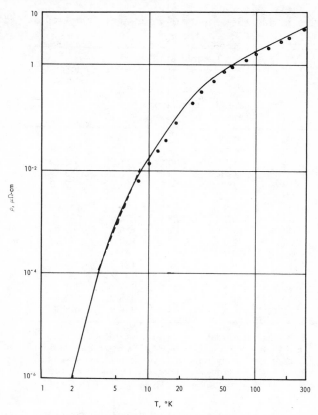

Fig. 25. The electrical resistivity of K. ————
Hasegawa's calculation.[206]  –o–o–o– Dugdale and
Gugan's experimental results.[139]  – – – – – – Mac-
Donald, White, and Woods' experimental results.[291]

final result (equation 9.5.22, p. 364, *loc. cit.*) contains functions that
have to be calculated numerically; but, with further approximations,
it may be shown to reduce to the $T$ and $T^5$ laws at high and low
temperatures, respectively, that are expected of the more idealized
metals to which it then applies.   Quantitative evaluation for the
eight monovalent elements at room temperature leads to figures for
the ideal resistivity that generally agree to within a factor of two
with the experimental values.   Agreement at low temperatures is
very poor, however.

No account of Umklapp processes had been taken by Bloch in
his theory, whereas Bardeen's calculation suggested they made up 60%

## Table V. Ideal Resistivity of Potassium Compared to Theory*

| T(°K) | Theoretical values | | | $\rho$ (experimental) |
|---|---|---|---|---|
| | $\rho_N$ (due to normal processes) | $\rho_U$ (due to Umklapp processes) | $\rho_N + \rho_U$ | |
| 8 | 0.14 | 0.62 | 0.76 | 0.64 |
| 10 | 0.33 | 1.38 | 1.71 | 1.38 |
| 14 | 1.16 | 4.02 | 5.18 | 3.89 |
| 16 | 1.86 | 5.89 | 7.75 | 5.79 |
| 18 | 2.72 | 8.05 | 10.77 | 8.10 |
| 20 | 3.74 | 10.44 | 14.18 | 10.74 |
| 25 | 6.8 | 17.1 | 23.9 | 19.0 |
| 30 | 10.3 | 24.3 | 34.6 | 28.3 |
| 40 | 17.7 | 39.0 | 56.7 | 49.0 |
| 60 | 32.3 | 67.7 | 100.0 | 92.1 |
| 80 | 46.3 | 95.2 | 141.5 | 132.9 |
| 100 | 59.9 | 122.0 | 181.9 | 171.5 |
| 140 | 86.5 | 174.7 | 261.2 | 247.1 |
| 180 | 112.5 | 226.8 | 339.3 | 318.5 |
| 240 | 151.4 | 304.3 | 455.7 | 426.4 |
| 273.15 | 172.6 | 346.9 | 519.5 | 486.5 |

* Theoretical data by Hasegawa.[206] Experimental data by Dugdale and Gugan.[139] The experimental data differ from those given in Table II because they have been adjusted to constant-volume conditions to which theory always refers. The units are $10^{-8}$ $\Omega$-cm.

of the total resistivity. Ziman's computation increased the percentage to rather more than 70, while the work of Bailyn[60] indicates that it is as much as 80% of the total. Bailyn used a lattice vibrational spectrum more detailed than a Debye spectrum in his analysis, observing the important role played by very low frequencies at low temperatures in raising the resistivity in this region. Reasonable agreement with experiment was found for Na and K at room temperature, but agreement was much less good for the other alkalis and not at all good at low temperatures. Later, Collins and Ziman[105] made allowances for departures of the Fermi surface from spherical form, but they still used a Debye model for the phonon spectrum.

The most recent advances are those of Hasegawa[206] and of Bross and Holz,[93] who have made numerical computations of the resistivities of Li, Na, and K using more likely spectra for the lattice vibrations and making some allowance for the distorted Fermi surface of Li. For K, Hasegawa's calculated values of the resistivity as a function of temperature are compared to the experimental values of Dugdale and Gugan[139] in Fig. 25 and in Table V. The agreement is seen to be quite close over the entire temperature range from 3 to 273°K, the greatest deviation being 25% at 25°K. In the table, contributions to the resistivity from normal and Umklapp processes are given separately so that their relative proportions may be judged. The effect of Umklapp processes is greater than that of normal processes down to 3°K, below which it dies away very quickly. For Na, Hasegawa's calculated results match the experimental ones very closely at high temperatures and even down to 120°K; but below 80°K the discrepancy increases rapidly, and at 10°K the calculated resistivity is 3.7 times larger than that observed. Agreement in the more difficult case of Li is less good, although the calculated results never exceed experimental ones by more than a factor of three. The distorted Fermi surface leads to a huge Umklapp resistivity, which, when more precisely calculated, will be of the order of ten times the normal component at all but low temperatures. The discrepancies in the low-temperature regions of Na and Li are no doubt also linked to the martensitic phase transformations which may be expected to modify the phonon spectra. Bross and Holz's calculations of the resistivities of the above three metals (K, Na, Li) also give reasonable agreement with experiment.[93] Recently, Darby and March[117] have done a computation for Na using actual measured phonon-dispersion relations for the metal.[451]

Returning again to the more general problem of the resistivity at normal and high temperatures, we remark that Ziman's final equation for the resistivity in the high-temperature limit contains the factor $T/M\theta^2$, as also do the equations of other theoreticians, Bloch[81] and Mott and Jones,[M7] for instance. This appearance of $M\theta^2$ in the denominator is perfectly natural, since, as shown earlier, the dependence of the resistivity on the square of the amplitude of the lattice vibrations leads to $\rho_i \propto T/M\theta^2$, using very simple considerations. In comparing the factor $\rho_i M\theta^2$ at a given (high) temperature for different metals what one is doing is comparing resistivities under conditions of equal lattice vibration. Such comparisons are more realistic than merely comparing ideal resistivities alone. Study of Fig. 26, where this has been done, reveals more truly the periodic variation of resistivity among the elements.* As expected, however, the lowest values of $\rho_i M\theta^2$ are still with the monovalent elements, and the transition and rare-earth metals have extremely large values. Notice particularly that on this basis the best conductors, taken as a

---

* For consistency, $\theta$ has been taken as $\theta_D$ at 0°K throughout; high-temperature $\theta_D$ (or $\theta_R$) values would be more satisfactory, but experimental data are less complete (Table VIII).

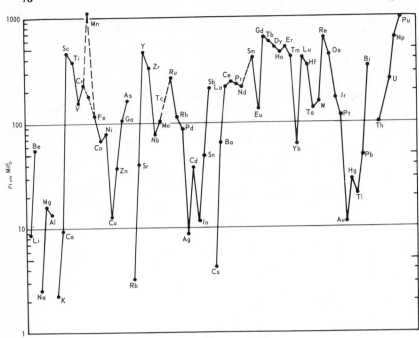

Increasing Atomic Number

**Fig. 26.** Variation of the quantity $\rho_i/M\theta_D^2$ through the metallic elements. The value $\rho_i$ has been taken at 295°K from Tables I and II, $\theta_D$ from Table VIII (explanation of the choice of $\theta$ given in Section 4.2), and $M$ (the atomic weight) from Table XV in the Appendix. Two values are indicated for Mn; the lower one was obtained by subtracting a spin-disorder term of 115 $\mu\Omega$-cm from $\rho_{i295}$.

group, now appear to be the alkali rather than the noble metals. The explanation of the lower real resistivity of the noble metals is their greater atomic mass on the one hand (compared to Li, Na, and K), which means smaller amplitudes to the lattice vibrations, giving therefore a smaller scattering effect, and their hardness on the other hand, with its implication of higher characteristic temperatures (because hard metals have high lattice vibrational frequencies and therefore a small amplitude for a given energy). In Section 2.16.2.2 it was pointed out that Na and the transition metal Rh have very similar absolute resistivities at room temperature. It is now seen that the resistivity for equal lattice vibrations is 45 times greater in Rh than in Na.

Other parameters related to $\rho_i M\theta^2$ are also to be found in the literature, e.g., with a multiplying factor $V^{1/3}$ ($V$ is the atomic volume) [M3, M11, M10] or with a dividing factor $Q$ (the radius of the Debye sphere). [M12] $Q$ is inversely proportional to the cube root of the volume of the unit cell and is equal to $3.898/a$, where $a$ is the lattice constant. According to Ziman, the revised parameter $\rho_i M \theta^2 / Q$ is mainly dependent on the Fermi surface area that is not in actual contact with zone boundaries relative to the spherical area that would have been possible had there been no such contact.

## 3.7. THERMAL SCATTERING AT LOW TEMPERATURES

The theoretical situation in the simpler alkali metals at normal and fairly low temperatures has already been discussed. Attention has been drawn to the special problems that arise in these metals at the lower temperatures; but in more complicated metals, such problems, both at high and at low temperatures, are still more severe. In the small-angle scattering region ($T \ll \theta$), the real difficulty is that the resistivity is particularly sensitive to exact details of the scattering mechanism and use cannot be made of a relaxation time for the solution of the Boltzmann transport equation. However, at the lowest temperatures of all, the situation does improve again somewhat: a fairly uniform pattern of behavior is seen to emerge, and it is found that in several metals of widely differing crystal structure and valence there exists a $T^5$ term in the ideal electrical resistivity. Examples from among many include the bcc and fcc monovalent metals, divalent Cd and Zn (cph), trivalent In (tetr.), tetravalent Sn (tetr.) and Pb (fcc), and the transition metals Ti (cph) and Mo (bcc). This temperature dependence can be shown to result quite naturally from an elementary approach based on the Debye spectrum, in which the low-temperature phonon variation is as $T^3$. At each collision, a deviation through a small angle of order $T/\theta_D$ can be expected; but the effectiveness of the scattering on the resistivity depends on the square of the angle, if small, i.e., on $T^2/\theta_D^2$. Thus the total transition probability for an electron–phonon interaction varies as $T^2 \times T^3$, giving a resistivity proportional to $T^5$ at low temperatures. [M22, M12, M30]

It is the intermediary range of continuously varying temperature dependence between the $T^5$ and $T$ regions that gives most trouble when an attempt at a theoretical analysis is made. In K, for instance, the ideal resistivity results can be described as being proportional to $T^5$ between 4 and 8°K, to approximately $T^3$ between 10 and 20°K, and finally to $T$ above 35°K (using ref. 291 and 139). Although Hasegawa's calculations were quantitatively least perfect in the 10 to

30°K range, he did obtain roughly these same temperature dependences.

Not all metals are as straightforward as K, however, differing immensely in their band structures, Fermi surfaces, and phonon spectra. Many do not follow a $T^5$ law at low temperatures, although in most cases the phonon component in $T^5$ is merely being smothered by a grosser resistive mechanism such as electron–electron scattering or because the metal is of insufficiently high purity. The variety of possibilities is discussed in Section 3.11. Undoubtedly, at least all the simpler metals will eventually be described closely by theory, but each will have to be evaluated individually. It is too much to expect that one single formula of relatively simple form will be found to describe the temperature variation of the resistance of all metals from low to high temperatures and also to give correct numerical agreement. Nevertheless, there does already exist one widely used relation that moderately well accounts for the temperature variation of a large number of metals over quite a wide range of temperature. This equation, discovered by Bloch as the result of a necessarily approximate approach, reduces to $\rho_i \propto T^5$ in the low-temperature limit. Since it also becomes linear in temperature at high temperatures, Grüneisen[183] more boldly suggested that it might be applicable to intermediate temperatures, too. Known now as the Grüneisen–Bloch relation, it may be written in the form

$$\rho_i = \frac{C}{M\theta_R}\left(\frac{T}{\theta_R}\right)^5 \int_0^{\theta_R/T} \frac{z^5 dz}{(e^z - 1)(1 - e^{-z})} \tag{3.17}$$

where $M$ is the atomic weight and $C$ is a constant. $\theta_R$ is a temperature characteristic of the metal's lattice resistivity in the same way as is the Debye characteristic temperature $\theta_D$ characteristic of a solid's lattice specific heat. With the given limits, the integral itself reduces to $\frac{1}{4}(\theta_R/T)^4$ at high temperatures and to a constant (124.4) at low temperatures.

When $C$ and $\theta_R$ have been suitably chosen, the above expression is found to represent the experimental temperature variation of the resistivity of a wide selection of metals rather well, mono- and multivalent metals alike. This may be judged to some extent from Fig. 27, which is due to Meissner. [M26] The important consequence that follows immediately is that because of its comparative simplicity the Grüneisen–Bloch equation provides a most valuable tool for analyzing and discussing experimental data. Its success is surprising insofar as the theory on which it is based might be thought to limit its use to no more than idealized monovalent metals with Debye phonon spectra and spherical Fermi surfaces. What is more, Umklapp

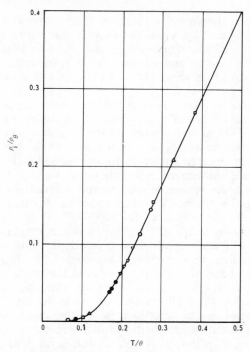

Fig. 27. The reduced resistivity $\rho_{iT}/\rho_{i\theta}$ as a function of reduced temperature $T/\theta$ for several metals compared to the Grüneisen–Bloch relation (Meissner[M26]). The $\theta$ values used were 202°K for Na ($\square$), 333 for Cu($\bigcirc$), 175 for Au($\triangle$), 395 for Al($\triangledown$), and 472 for Ni($\bullet$).

processes were totally neglected. Clearly, some of the assumptions taken concerning the freedom of the conduction electrons and the lattice vibrational spectra are not quite so sweeping after all, although it has been remarked that because $\theta$ occurs in the formula at a high power and because it is essentially an adjustable parameter, all that one is doing is curve-fitting. This discussion of the Grüneisen–Bloch expression is carried further in the next chapter, where some of its uses and its limitations are dealt with.

## 3.8. RESISTANCE DUE TO IMPURITY SCATTERING

The residual resistance of metals has previously been referred to in Sections 1.4 and 3.4. It arises from the scattering of conduction electrons by impurities in solid solution or by other imperfections present in the lattice. This scattering is, to a fair approximation at least, independent of the temperature, and the rule that the total resistivity $\rho_T$ is given by the addition of the impurity and ideal resistivities has already been introduced (Matthiessen's rule, Section 1.4).

A time of relaxation always exists for impurity scattering since the collisions involved are effectively elastic, negligible energy being transferred at any interaction. When a time of relaxation can also be stated for the lattice scattering, as at medium and high temperatures, Matthiessen's rule may be shown to follow immediately. [M3, M4, M11] But according to Sondheimer[405] some departures are to be expected in the low-temperature region, where the approximation of a relaxation time for electron–phonon collisions is not valid. Also, departures are expected[407,251] and indeed found[254,45,246,119] in multivalent metals, which may be described by a two-band model; it is simple to demonstrate that if each conduction band depends in a different way on the scattering, then, although Matthiessen's rule may apply separately to each band, deviations occur when the total conductivity is evaluated. The experimental studies made of the performance of Matthiessen's rule in dilute alloy systems often indicate more complicated behavior than can be accounted for by the above theory. For one thing, the nature of the departures found depends on the type of impurity atoms or other defects present as well as on their quantities; this is particularly evident when transition-metal or rare-earth impurity atoms are present. However, with nonmagnetic solutes in dilute Mg-rich alloys, the situation is more straightforward, and Das and Gerritsen[119] have been able to analyze their data tolerably well.

Deviations from Matthiessen's rule found experimentally may generally be expressed by treating the impurity resistivity as a temperature-dependent quantity. If we call $\rho_0$ the impurity resistivity measured at 4°K, then it is unusual to find deviations so large that even at room temperature the impurity resistivity has increased by as much as $0.25\rho_0$. Thus the complete assumption of Matthiessen's rule never involves great errors, and certainly with most pure metals it may be employed quite freely.

## 3.9. THE RESISTANCE-MINIMUM PHENOMENON

Many years ago, Meissner and Voigt [M5, M6] discovered that some of the supposedly pure metals they were studying had negative temperature coefficients of resistance in the helium range. Later, the temperature region between 1 and 20°K was very carefully investigated by de Haas and van den Berg,[196,69] who established that in certain metals of varying purity shallow minima appear in resistance–temperature curves at about 10°K and that below the minimum the resistivity rises to a few percent above its smallest value. Further intensive investigation since 1950 has definitely revealed that the minimum is due to an impurity effect caused by trace amounts of certain transition metals in solid solution and that in special classes of dilute alloys its presence and the form it assumes can now be controlled and analyzed.

The phenomenon is particularly apparent in dilute alloys of the noble metals when small quantities of transition elements are used as solutes. There either appears a minimum only in the resistivity, Fe in Cu[348] and Cr or Co in Cu,[245] for instance; or a minimum and also a maximum at an even lower temperature. Examples of the latter

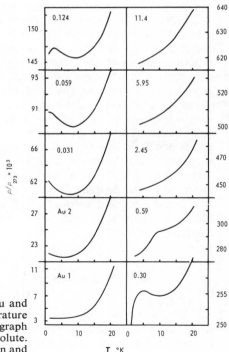

Fig. 28. Reduced resistivities of Au and Au-Mn alloys as a function of temperature below 20°K. The numbers on each graph give the atomic percentage of Mn solute. This series of graphs, due to Gerritsen and Linde,[171] demonstrates the resistance-minimum phenomenon very well.

are Mn or Cr in Au[171] and Mn in Cu[171] or Ag[170]. To illustrate the effect of a progressive change in solute concentration, we reproduce as Fig. 28 Gerritsen and Linde's results for dilute alloys of Mn in Au. An interesting recent discovery results from an extension of the work to embrace noble metal alloys having second and third long period transition metals as solutes.[248,383] It is that resistance anomalies appear only when the solute bears five or six $d$-electrons. Divalent metals as solvents occasionally display resistance minima, too (see Fig. 3 for Mg), and related anomalous behavior is to be found in most magnetic and electrical properties of almost all alloys that possess resistance-minimum phenomena. For example, there are changes in the thermoelectric power,[289] the magnetoresistance,[169] electron spin resonance, and the magnetic susceptibility.[344,104]

No full theoretical explanation has been prepared as yet to explain all the various problems posed by the above interrelated effects, although it is now evident that in the neighborhood of the resistance minimum the anomalous scattering of the conduction electrons is fundamentally caused by exchange coupling between the $s$-conduction electrons and localized $d$-spins of the magnetic impurity ions.[87,128] Kondo's recent analysis[253] of the scattering probability of the conduction electrons on the basis of an $s$-$d$ interaction model explains quite well the resistivity behavior of those alloys showing only a plain resistivity minimum. A resistivity term, including $c \log T$ as a factor, where $c$ is the concentration of the impurity atoms, is found to be additional to the normal $\rho_0 + aT^5$ expected at these temperatures ($a$ is a constant). This extra term is negative, provided that the $s$-$d$ exchange interaction is negative, and it accounts for the experimental resistivity results on many of these dilute magnetic alloys very well. Furthermore, the temperature at which the minimum occurs is proportional to $c^{1/5}$ and the depth of the minimum to $c$, as observed experimentally.[348,247]

For a complete account of all aspects of this subject, reference should be made both to the review by van den Berg[71] and to Kondo's paper.[253]

## 3.10. RESISTANCE OF THE TRANSITION METALS

We have repeatedly stressed the difficulties that are encountered when attempting to describe the resistances of metals other than monovalent ones because of the complexity of their Fermi surfaces, which overlap two or more Brillouin zones, and for other reasons. The introduction of a two-zone theory has, however, permitted deduction of certain qualitative features of the divalent metals and several other multivalent metals such as Bi—that is to say, at least at high temperatures, where it is possible to specify a relaxation time. [M3, M11] But the transition metals which generally have high resistivities occupy a very special and important realm of their own because they are characterized by numerous unusual properties, particularly magnetic properties, that are not found in other elements. We shall therefore discuss them at some length. Some of what immediately follows applies to the rare-earth metals and the actinide metals, too, but they are also dealt with specifically later on in Section 3.10.2.

The common feature possessed by all the transition metals is a partially filled, sublying electron shell, which in the first, second, and third long period transition elements is the $3d$, $4d$, and $5d$ shells, respectively. It is also typical of these elements that they have high resistivities and high electronic specific heats compared to the corresponding monovalent and divalent metals, and in addition are strongly paramagnetic, while some are even ferromagnetic or antiferromagnetic over limited temperature ranges. The way in which these properties result from the partially empty $d$-shells has been explained fairly satisfactorily in general qualitative, and sometimes pictorial, terms, so that the broad behavior of these metals is now more or less understood (see for example the texts by Kittel, [M22] Dekker, [M15] Hume-Rothery, [M20] Ziman, [M12] and Wilson, [M11] among others). In the case of the high electrical resistivities, the accepted explanation which is in terms of interband scattering is due to Mott.[324]

### 3.10.1. Interband Scattering Model

Mott's supposition is that the valence electrons are shared between a wide, low density of states $s$-band and a narrow, high density of states $d$-band. This high density of states arises because the spatial extension of the $d$-electron wave functions is much less than that for the $s$-electrons, with consequently less overlap from atom to atom. Hence the $d$-band is narrower, yet it has to accommodate ten electrons compared to the $s$-band's two. Because of this, the $d$-band electrons contribute very little to the conductivity, their effective mass being so great. All the same, the $d$-band plays an important part in the resistivity, since the conduction ($s$) electrons can be scattered not only into energy states in the $s$-band but into vacant states in the $d$-band. Because the density of the latter is so high, these $s$-$d$ transitions will add greatly to the scattering probability and thus to the resistivity. Mott,[324] Ziman, [M12] or Jones [M3] should be consulted for mathematical details.

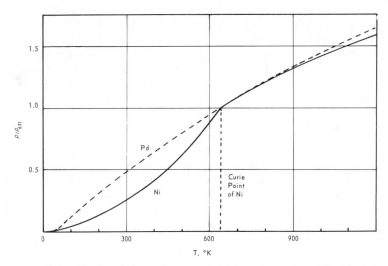

Fig. 29. Comparison of the resistivities of paramagnetic Pd and ferromagnetic Ni.[109,355] Each has been normalized to unity at 631°K, the Curie point of Ni.

This type of band model describes the resistivity of several transition elements, such as Pd, Ni, and Co, quite well. We contrast in Fig. 29 the resistivities of Pd, a normal transition metal, and Ni, which is ferromagnetic.[109,355] All ferromagnetic metals behave similarly in having an irregularity at the Curie point below which the resistivity falls more quickly than linearly. In such metals the existence of a spontaneous magnetization, involving as it does the *d*-electrons, has the effect of reducing the *s-d* scattering and thus the resistivity in this region; the resulting shape of the resistivity curve is characteristic of the cooperative process that magnetization is.

### 3.10.2. Localized Spin Model

In recent years there has been developed a rival concept to the above collective band model to explain the resistivities of ferro- and antiferromagnetic metals. This new approach, based on so-called spin-disorder scattering, has proved successful where the other has not, in the magnetic metals Fe, Mn, and the rare earths.[326,103]

Spin-disorder effects result from exchange interactions taking place between conduction electrons and certain unpaired ("magnetic") electrons localized on particular atoms, the energy of an interaction depending on the relative orientations of the spins of the electrons involved. Conduction electrons progressing through such a disordered exchange field receive scattering from it additional to the conventional impurity and lattice scattering, and the extra contribution to the resistance can be very large. This spin-disorder component is essentially constant above the Curie or the Néel point, when the spins are totally disordered, and zero at low temperatures, when (or rather if) all the localized spins are aligned parallel. Some of the earliest papers on this subject are those of Kasuya,[234] Yosida,[454] de Gennes and Friedel,[168] and Weiss and Marotta.[433]

A particular success of the localized spin model has been in connection with rare-earth metals and alloys, which owe their characteristic magnetic properties to a partially empty 4$f$-shell. In these substances the scattering originates from an $s$-$f$ exchange interaction between $s$-conduction electrons and spins localized on $f$-electrons. In fact, the twelve metals Ce to Tm inclusive all have certain temperature regions over which they are antiferromagnetic or ferromagnetic, while those having more than half-filled 4$f$-shells (together with Eu) are especially noted for their screw-type spin orderings. The effect of such a helical, sinusoidal, or other periodic spin arrangement is to add planes of energy discontinuity to the existing Brillouin zone structure, and in cph metals these new planes are perpendicular to the $c$-axis, since the periodic spin system lies parallel to it. Hence, the component of the Fermi surface vector along the $c$-axis changes considerably, whereas that in the basal plane is hardly affected. The magnetic and electrical properties measured parallel and perpendicular to the long axis are therefore temperature-dependent in quite different ways. The anomalous behavior of the $c$-axis resistivity of Er and neighboring rare earths has been explained qualitatively with such a model by Mackintosh[292] and Elliott and Wedgwood,[143] and Miwa[317] has also given a semiquantitative discussion of the singular resistivity of Er (see Fig. 14). It is instructive to consider the interplay of the various contributory effects to the resistivity of Er, so we quote the following description given by Mackintosh.[292] At the lowest temperatures,

"the magnetic moments form a ferromagnetic spiral and the decrease of conductivity with increasing temperature is due to increasing scattering of the conduction electrons by phonons and spin waves. At 20°K (the Curie point) the moment components along the $c$-axis form a sinusoidal arrangement, while those in the hexagonal plane remain in a spiral. The abrupt decrease in conductivity (at 20°K) can be explained by the appearance of new magnetic planes of energy discontinuity, together perhaps with a change in the spin-disorder scattering. From 20 to 53°K the ordering in the plane disappears, causing a change in electronic structure which, together with the rapid change of magnetic disorder scattering, leads to a decrease of conductivity with temperature. From 53 to 80°K the rapid reduction in the amount of sinusoidal ordering along the *c*-axis causes a reduction in the energy gaps which outweighs the increase in magnetic disorder scattering and causes the conductivity *to increase.* Above 80°K (the Néel point) the decrease in conductivity with temperature is due just to increased lattice scattering."

A model based on magnetic Brillouin zone effects has been used by Bellau and Coles[68] to give a reasonable qualitative explanation of their own experimental results on the transition metal α-Mn and alloys.

### 3.11. THE TRANSITION AND RARE-EARTH METALS AT LOW TEMPERATURES

It has already been remarked that the lattice resistivity of a metal in the low-temperature limit should decrease as $T^5$, owing to the quantum nature of the events which are occurring, in the same way that the low-temperature dependence of the lattice specific heat is as $T^3$ (Section 3.7). The knowledge that such a $T^5$ law is obeyed in many nontransition metals of greatly differing crystal structure and valence is relatively recent, for it is very largely due to much-improved specimen purities and increased accuracy of measurement.* As usual, however, the transition metals display more complicated behavior than do nontransition metals, and temperature exponents ranging from 2.0 to 5.3 have been found for the various elements [M10] (also those of the actinides appear to range between 2.0 and 3.2). The latest experimental and theoretical work makes it increasingly evident that in these metals at low temperatures there are often two or more separate scattering mechanisms operating simultaneously and that the effect of impurities is to smear out and disguise the true temperature dependence that would otherwise have obtained. In this section we now discuss the various possible mechanisms that can give rise to temperature variations other than $T^5$.

One of the earliest proposals to account for the resistivity variation of the transition metals was made by Wilson.[450] He followed

* Sodium is exceptional in that below the region in which $\rho_i \propto T^5$ (8 to 15°K) the index of $T$ increases still further to 6 (Woods,[452] see also Bailyn[60]).

Mott in assuming that the high resistivities of these metals were dominated by scattering of the conduction electrons into vacant states of the $d$-band, and he obtained for the contribution to the ideal resistivity from this cause a resistivity given by

$$\rho_i(sd) = K\left(\frac{T}{\theta}\right)^3 \int_{\theta_E/T}^{\theta/T} \frac{x^3 dx}{(e^x - 1)(1 - e^{-x})} \qquad (3.18)$$

where $K$ is a constant and $x = \theta/T$. This gives at once $\rho_i(sd) \propto T$ at high temperatures, and $\rho_i(sd) \propto \exp(-\theta_E/kT)$ at low temperatures, supposing that $s$-$d$ transitions die out below a characteristic temperature $\theta_E$. The latter is never found in practice, so if instead no lower limit for $s$-$d$ transitions is presumed, $\rho_i(sd)$ then becomes proportional to $T^3$ at low temperatures. Thus, temperature indices between 3 and 5 might be expected for transition metals, depending on the particular shapes and locations of the Fermi surfaces of the $s$- and $d$-bands. Wilson's approach is open to certain criticisms, and it is probably unnecessary to invoke a model of this type now that the role played by electron–electron interactions in transition metals is better understood and appreciated.[59,259,50]

In simple metals the effect of electron–electron scattering on the resistivity may justifiably be totally neglected because of momentum conservation in individual collisions,[M3,49] but this is less certain in transition metals, because momentum is not conserved in interactions involving $s$-conduction electrons and $d$-band electrons. The predicted additional resistivity from this cause varies as $T^2$, and the resistivities of several transition elements do appear to tend toward such a variation at the lowest temperatures. As examples, we cite the cases of Pt,[195] and Fe, Co, Ni, Rh, Pd, W, and Pt.[337,315, M10] White and Woods[M10] also gave the exponent of an $\alpha$-Mn specimen that had a high residual resistivity as 2.0. Most likely, better purity and improved accuracy of measurement to lower temperatures will indicate that several scattering terms are present in this antiferromagnetic metal, as has already been demonstrated in the ferromagnetic iron-group metals. A careful study by Russian workers on Fe between 4.2 and $0.38°K$[395,396] and on Co and Ni between 4.2 and $1.3°K$[395,397,413] has disclosed that the resistivity of these metals may be represented by the equation

$$\rho = \rho_0 + AT + BT^2 \qquad (3.19)$$

with $A$ and $B$ constants. These authors attribute a part of the $T^2$ term to electron–electron scattering, but a part also, along with the linear term, to scattering of conduction electrons by spin waves (Turov[425]). It is significant that the linear term is absent in nonferromagnetic Pt[395] and Yb.[431] It should also be said that all the polynomial expressions found experimentally can also be represented by a single variable. Thus the low-temperature resistivity of Fe may also be written as $\rho = \rho_0 + CT^{1.45}$ instead of as equation (3.19). Originally, Turov's spin-wave treatment[424] gave only a $T^2$ contribution; the later theories of Kasuya[235] and Mannari[294] also lead to $T^2$ only. Other theoretical analyses are due to Goodings[180] and Liu.[272] The latter obtains at low temperatures $\rho = \rho_0 + aT^{3/2} + bT^2$.

The temperature dependence of those cph rare-earth metals in which considerable magnetic anisotropy exists has been discussed by Mackintosh for the low-temperature region[293] using Niira's spin-wave spectrum for such metals.[331] Assuming that the magnetic

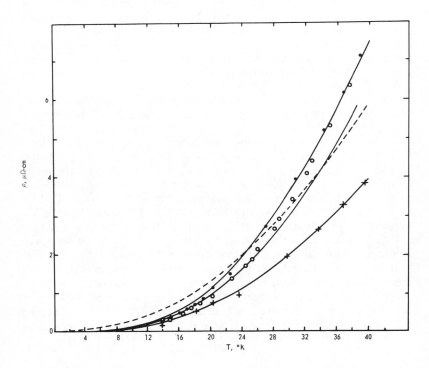

Fig. 30. The temperature dependence of Dy(-●-), Tb(-○-), and Lu(+) below 40°K. The continuous curves through the points for Dy and Tb are plots of equation (3.21) (made to agree with experiment at 25°K). The dashed curve is obtained if a $T^2$ law is used for the magnetic resistivity, and is fitted to the Dy data at 25°K (Mackintosh[293]).

contribution to the resistivity in a simple ferromagnet is $cT^2$, Mackintosh showed that in an anisotropic one it should be of the form

$$\rho_M = cT^2 \exp(-\Delta/kT) \qquad (3.20)$$

where $k$ is Boltzmann's constant and $\Delta$ is an energy gap representing the minimum energy to excite a spin wave. Electron–electron interactions were neglected, and the temperature-dependent part of the resistivity for Dy and Tb was then written as

$$\rho = aT^5 + cT^2 \exp(-20/T) \qquad (3.21)$$

$\Delta/k = 20°$K being consistent with the known anisotropy of Dy. The lattice contribution, $aT^5$, was crudely estimated by comparing the experimentally determined resistivities of Dy and Tb with nonmagnetic Lu,[108] an otherwise rather similar metal, and $c$ was selected to give numerical agreement at 25°K. The semiquantitative theoretical curves which were obtained are compared to the experimental results in Fig. 30. General agreement is seen to be quite good, particularly for Dy, and the magnetic-scattering term of equation (3.21) is evidently far more satisfactory than a pure $T^2$ term would be (as indicated by the dashed curve).*

Altogether different is Gd, in which the magnetic anisotropy energy is negligible in the basal plane and small for the $c$-axis. A linear spin-wave dispersion law should be applicable (Niira), and with $\Delta = 0$ a magnetic resistivity proportional to $T^4$ should be expected. In fact, the total temperature-dependent resistivity below 15°K is found to vary as $T^{3.73}$ [107]

The various theories considered in this section have rather considerable deficiencies at present, although it should be added that the theories relating to the magnetic elements are still in their youth and that much will depend also on the findings of experimental workers. For instance, better accuracy on purer metals in the low-temperature regions will greatly facilitate the separation of the various temperature-dependent scattering terms involved. It is to be noted that the data can often be broken down in more than one way—either as one single temperature-dependent variable or as a polynomial expression in $T$.

### 3.12. NONLINEAR EFFECTS AT NORMAL AND HIGH TEMPERATURES

At high-enough temperatures (usually above 1000°K), a strict proportionality of the resistivity with temperature no longer holds

---

* More recently, Arajs and Colvin[54a] have said that equation (3.21) does not appear to be applicable to their results on Tb between 5 and 20°K.

for a large number of metals (this is quite apart from magnetic and phase change effects). The resistivity may either begin to increase faster than linearly, as in the noble metals and in Mo and W, or less quickly than linearly, as in many of the nonmagnetic transition metals, lanthanides, and actinides. A brief discussion is given here because in several metals such nonlinear effects of this second type are evident even at room temperature. Extreme examples are afforded by Yb and Np (Fig. 16), while the most discussed have been Pt and Pd (Fig. 29).

On the basis of the two-band $s$-$d$ scattering model, Mott[324] has provided a possible explanation for the behavior of Pt and Pd. Reference may be made to Jones [M3] for a recent account. In these metals the electrons are regarded as occupying overlapping $s$- and $d$-bands, the $d$-band having a high density of states $N_d(E)$ and the $s$-band a low density of states. Since the $d$-band is nearly full, $N_d$ at the Fermi energy $E = \zeta$ is falling rapidly with rising energy; hence $(dN_d/dE)_\zeta$ is large, too. Such a variation would affect the probability with which $s$-$d$ scattering processes take place and thus also the electrical resistivity. These circumstances amend the normal linear $\rho$-$T$ relation as follows: [M7, M3]

$$\frac{\rho}{T} \propto 1 - \frac{\pi^2 k^2 T^2}{6} \left[ 3\left(\frac{1}{N_d}\frac{dN_d}{dE}\right)^2 - \frac{1}{N_d}\frac{d^2N_d}{dE^2} \right]_{E=\zeta} \quad (3.22)$$

From this formula it is seen that the departure of the resistivity from linearity with temperature is determined by the magnitudes and signs of $N_d$ and its derivatives with respect to energy, evaluated at the Fermi energy. In particular, large deviations that will decrease the resistivity are to be expected when $N_d$ and $dN_d/dE$ at $E = \zeta$, as well as $T$, are all large. This is probably the case in Pt and Pd at ordinary and high temperatures, and also in Yb, U, and Np.[304]

If the Fermi energy comes near a minimum in the density of states curve, $(dN_d/dE)_\zeta$ will be small and $(d^2N_d/dE^2)_\zeta$ positive, so that according to equation (3.22) the resistivity will rise faster than linearly. This could be the situation in Mo and W at high temperatures, but definitely not in the noble metals. For the latter, the explanation may be that thermal expansion results in a decreasing $\theta$ which modifies $\rho/T$ through equation (3.14). Allowance for this leads to the revised equation

$$\frac{\rho}{T} \propto 1 + 2\alpha\gamma T \quad (3.23)$$

where $\alpha$ is the thermal expansion coefficient and $\gamma$ is Grüneisen's

## Table VI. Comparison of Resistivities in the
## Solid and Liquid States of Several Metals at
## Their Melting Points

| $T_m(°K)$ | $\rho_S(\mu\Omega\text{-cm})$ | $\rho_L(\mu\Omega\text{-cm})$ | $(\rho_L/\rho_S)_{T_m}$ | Reference |
|---|---|---|---|---|
| Li  453 | 15.48 | 25.31 | 1.64 | 101 |
| Na 371 | 6.60 | 9.57 | 1.45 | 86 |
| K   336.8 | 8.32 | 12.97 | 1.56 | 88 |
| Rb 312 | 13.7 | 22.0 | 1.60 | 88 |
| Cs  302 | 21.7 | 36.0 | 1.66 | 88 |
| Hg 234.3 | 21.9* | 90.96 | 4.15 | 392, 224 |
| Ga 303 | 15.4* | 25.8 | 1.67 | 361 |

* For anisotropic solid Hg and Ga, mean resistivities are given.

constant. [M7, M3] The numerical agreement of this equation with the experimental results of the noble metals is good.

## 3.13. EFFECTS AT THE MELTING POINT
## AND IN THE LIQUID STATE

We shall discuss very briefly the changes occurring near the melting points of the low-melting-point metals, Hg, Ga, and the alkalis. The data presented in Table VI are taken largely from the review by Cusack.[116] In all of these metals the electrical resistivity increases abruptly on passing through the melting point and continues to rise in the liquid phase, in some in proportion to the temperature (see also Figs. 2 and 4). The sudden change is connected with the greater disorder of the liquid state and the removal of any definite crystal structure.

An early, simple, and fairly successful theory of liquid metals was that of Mott.[321] He ignored the disordered positions and diffusive movements of the vibrating ions, and assumed that, at least near the melting point, the liquid ions still maintain a more or less regular pattern. With an Einstein model, a resistivity in the liquid state proportional to $T/M\theta_L^2$ is obtained, and the resistivities of the liquid and the solid, $\rho_L$ and $\rho_S$, at the melting temperature $T_m$ are given by $(\rho_L/\rho_S)_{T_m} = \theta_S^2/\theta_L^2$, where $\theta_S$ and $\theta_L$ are Einstein characteristic temperatures for the solid and liquid phases, respectively.

Finally, after some further manipulation, the more practical equation given below was obtained:

$$\left(\frac{\rho_L}{\rho_S}\right)_{T_m} = \exp\left(\frac{80L_F}{T_m}\right) \tag{3.24}$$

where $L_F$ is the latent heat of fusion in kilojoules per mole. Calculated values of $\rho_L/\rho_S$ according to this formula compare moderately well with experiment for a wide range of metals (principal exceptions are Ga, Hg, Sb, and Bi), although a small adjustment must be made for the alkalis. Later and more microscopic theories take into account the effect of the disordered structure on electron scattering.[172,192,458,85] Ziman[458] treats the alkali metals on the basis of a free electron model, assuming that each ion interacts with conduction electrons through a localized "pseudopotential." A sequel to his paper deals with polyvalent metals.[85] Quantitative calculations by Sundström[413a] support this pseudopotential approach.

*Chapter 4*

# Methods of Evaluating $\theta_R$

## 4.1. INTRODUCTION

It has been mentioned in Section 3.7 that the Grüneisen–Bloch relation (equation 3.17) can often usefully aid an analysis of experimental resistivity–temperature data of not only the simpler monovalent metals but of many polyvalent and transition metals as well. This is in spite of the fact that the underlying theory makes use of a Debye vibrational spectrum for the lattice, assumes perfectly free conduction electrons, and ignores the role played by Umklapp processes. All the same, the Grüneisen–Bloch relation is not so precise as is superficially apparent, for the reason that, since the resistances of most metals are linear in temperature above $\theta_R/4$ (the temperature range which interests most people), it is only below this temperature that the relation receives a test that is at all exacting. A close scrutiny in fact reveals that the Grüneisen–Bloch equation never holds over the entire small-angle scattering region (between $\theta/4$ and $\theta/20$, say), even including the alkali metals Na and K, as shown by Dugdale and Gugan.[139] Other equations have been proposed that also lead to $\rho_i \propto T^5$ at low temperatures and to $\rho_i \propto T$ at high temperatures, but the superiority of the Grüneisen–Bloch equation resides in its relatively simple form, which facilitates comparison of its predictions in individual cases with experiment. Moreover, by inverting the computation, one may intercompare the behavior of metals by treating the experimental results as deviations from the Grüneisen–Bloch equation, which then takes on the role of providing the "standard form." This is done by employing $\theta_R$, the characteristic temperature defined in Section 3.7, as a variable parameter and computing the value that it must possess at any temperature in order that the Grüneisen–Bloch equation may agree with experiment. Only if $\theta_R$ turns out to be constant will the equation give perfect

95

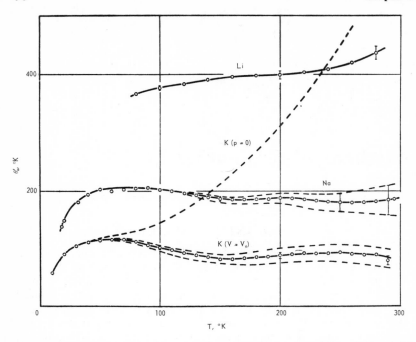

Fig. 31.  $\theta_R$ values for bcc Li, Na, and K according to Dugdale and Gugan.[139] Ideal resistivities corrected to constant-density conditions were employed.

account of the experimental results.  The extent to which it achieves this for Li, Na, and K may be judged by studying Fig. 31.[139]

## 4.2. PROPERTIES OF THE GRÜNEISEN–BLOCH EQUATION

In this section we shall discuss some of the properties of the Grüneisen–Bloch equation and include more about the significance of $\theta_R$ as a characteristic temperature.

We begin by writing $\kappa = C/4M$ and

$$G\left(\frac{\theta_R}{T}\right) = 4\left(\frac{T}{\theta_R}\right)^4 \int_0^{\theta_R/T} \frac{z^5\,dz}{(e^z-1)(1-e^{-z})} \tag{4.1}$$

Then, by substitution in equation (3.17), we obtain

$$\rho_{iT} = \frac{\kappa T}{\theta_R^2} G\left(\frac{\theta_R}{T}\right) \tag{4.2}$$

## Table VII. The Grüneisen Function $G(\theta/T)$, Defined by Equation (4.1), Tabulated in Terms of $\theta/T$

| $\theta/T$ | $G(\theta/T)$ | $\theta/T$ | $G(\theta/T)$ | $\theta/T$ | $G(\theta/T)$ | $\theta/T$ | $G(\theta/T)$ |
|---|---|---|---|---|---|---|---|
| 0 | 1.0000 | 4.5 | 0.3867 | 9.0 | 0.06740 | 14.0 | 0.01289 |
| 0.1 | 0.9994 | 4.6 | 0.3729 | 9.1 | 0.06490 | 14.2 | 0.012185 |
| 0.2 | 0.9978 | 4.7 | 0.3595 | 9.2 | 0.06250 | 14.4 | 0.011528 |
| 0.3 | 0.9950 | 4.8 | 0.3466 | 9.3 | 0.06021 | 14.6 | 0.010915 |
| 0.4 | 0.9912 | 4.9 | 0.3340 | 9.4 | 0.05800 | 14.8 | 0.010344 |
| 0.5 | 0.9862 | 5.0 | 0.3217 | 9.5 | 0.05589 | 15.0 | $0.0_29805$ |
| 0.6 | 0.9803 | 5.1 | 0.3098 | 9.6 | 0.05386 | 15.2 | $0.0_29302$ |
| 0.7 | 0.9733 | 5.2 | 0.2983 | 9.7 | 0.05192 | 15.4 | $0.0_28831$ |
| 0.8 | 0.9653 | 5.3 | 0.2871 | 9.8 | 0.05005 | 15.6 | $0.0_28389$ |
| 0.9 | 0.9563 | 5.4 | 0.2763 | 9.9 | 0.04826 | 15.8 | $0.0_27974$ |
| 1.0 | 0.9465 | 5.5 | 0.2658 | 10.0 | 0.04655 | 16.0 | $0.0_27584$ |
| 1.1 | 0.9357 | 5.6 | 0.2557 | 10.1 | 0.04490 | 16.2 | $0.0_27218$ |
| 1.2 | 0.9241 | 5.7 | 0.2460 | 10.2 | 0.04332 | 16.4 | $0.0_26873$ |
| 1.3 | 0.9118 | 5.8 | 0.2366 | 10.3 | 0.04181 | 16.6 | $0.0_26549$ |
| 1.4 | 0.8986 | 5.9 | 0.2275 | 10.4 | 0.04035 | 16.8 | $0.0_26243$ |
| 1.5 | 0.8848 | 6.0 | 0.2187 | 10.5 | 0.03896 | 17.0 | $0.0_25955$ |
| 1.6 | 0.8704 | 6.1 | 0.2103 | 10.6 | 0.03762 | 17.2 | $0.0_25683$ |
| 1.7 | 0.8554 | 6.2 | 0.2021 | 10.7 | 0.03633 | 17.4 | $0.0_25427$ |
| 1.8 | 0.8398 | 6.3 | $0.1942_5$ | 10.8 | 0.03509 | 17.6 | $0.0_25185$ |
| 1.9 | 0.8238 | 6.4 | 0.1867 | 10.9 | 0.03390 | 17.8 | $0.0_24956$ |
| 2.0 | 0.8073 | 6.5 | 0.1795 | 11.0 | 0.03276 | 18.0 | $0.0_24740$ |
| 2.1 | 0.7905 | 6.6 | 0.1725 | 11.1 | 0.03167 | 19.0 | $0.0_23819$ |
| 2.2 | 0.7733 | 6.7 | 0.1658 | 11.2 | 0.03061 | 20.0 | $0.0_23111$ |
| 2.3 | 0.7559 | 6.8 | 0.1593 | 11.3 | 0.02960 | 22 | $0.0_22125$ |
| 2.4 | 0.7383 | 6.9 | 0.1531 | 11.4 | 0.02863 | 24 | $0.0_21500$ |
| 2.5 | 0.7205 | 7.0 | $0.1471_5$ | 11.5 | 0.02769 | 26 | $0.0_21089$ |
| 2.6 | 0.7026 | 7.1 | 0.1414 | 11.6 | 0.02680 | 28 | $0.0_38097$ |
| 2.7 | 0.6846 | 7.2 | 0.1359 | 11.7 | 0.02593 | 30 | $0.0_36145$ |
| 2.8 | 0.6666 | 7.3 | 0.1306 | 11.8 | 0.02510 | 32 | $0.0_34747$ |
| 2.9 | 0.6486 | 7.4 | $0.1255_5$ | 11.9 | 0.02430 | 34 | $0.0_33724$ |
| 3.0 | 0.6307 | 7.5 | $0.1206_7$ | 12.0 | 0.02353 | 36 | $0.0_32963$ |
| 3.1 | 0.6128 | 7.6 | 0.11599 | 12.1 | 0.02279 | 38 | $0.0_32387$ |
| 3.2 | 0.5950 | 7.7 | 0.11150 | 12.2 | 0.02208 | 40 | $0.0_31944$ |
| 3.3 | 0.5775 | 7.8 | 0.10719 | 12.3 | 0.02139 | 44 | $0.0_31328$ |
| 3.4 | 0.5600 | 7.9 | 0.10306 | 12.4 | 0.02073 | 48 | $0.0_49375$ |
| 3.5 | 0.5428 | 8.0 | 0.09909 | 12.5 | 0.02009 | 50 | $0.0_47964$ |
| 3.6 | 0.5259 | 8.1 | 0.09529 | 12.6 | 0.01948 | 52 | $0.0_46806$ |
| 3.7 | 0.5091 | 8.2 | 0.09165 | 12.7 | 0.01889 | 56 | $0.0_45061$ |
| 3.8 | 0.4927 | 8.3 | 0.08816 | 12.8 | 0.01832 | 60 | $0.0_43841$ |
| 3.9 | 0.4766 | 8.4 | 0.08480 | 12.9 | 0.01777 | 64 | $0.0_42967$ |
| 4.0 | 0.4608 | 8.5 | 0.08159 | 13.0 | 0.01725 | 68 | $0.0_42328$ |
| 4.1 | 0.4453 | 8.6 | 0.07851 | 13.2 | 0.01624 | 70 | $0.0_42073$ |
| 4.2 | 0.4301 | 8.7 | 0.07555 | 13.4 | 0.01531 | 72 | $0.0_41852$ |
| 4.3 | 0.4153 | 8.8 | 0.07272 | 13.6 | 0.01445 | 76 | $0.0_41492$ |
| 4.4 | 0.4008 | 8.9 | 0.07000 | 13.8 | 0.01364 | 80 | $0.0_41215$ |

as the form in which the Grüneisen–Bloch relation will be used in this chapter. This has been done in order to keep our notation in line with that of Grüneisen[183] and Kelly and MacDonald.[238] The parameter $\kappa$ is generally taken to be a constant (but see next section) which typifies the electron–phonon interaction in the metal. The function defined by equation (4.1) has been tabulated by Grüneisen, and because of its indispensability it is reproduced again here as Table VII.

At high temperatures, as $T \to \infty$, $G(\theta_R/T) \to 1$ and

$$\rho_{iT} \to \frac{\kappa T}{\theta_R^2} \tag{4.3}$$

But at low temperatures $(T < 0.1\theta_R)$, $G(\theta_R/T) \to 497.6(T/\theta_R)^4$ so that

$$\rho_{iT} \to \frac{497.6\kappa}{\theta_R^6}T^5 \tag{4.4}$$

Therefore, by division we find as the ratio of the resistivity $\rho_{il}$, at a low temperature $T_l$ where the $T^5$ law holds, to the resistivity $\rho_{ih}$, at a high temperature $T_h$, the result

$$\frac{\rho_{il}}{\rho_{ih}} = \frac{497.6}{\theta_R^4} \cdot \frac{T_l^5}{T_h} \tag{4.5}$$

assuming that $\kappa$ and $\theta_R$ do not change from one temperature region to the other. This formula may be made the basis of a simple means of calculating an average $\theta_R$ for a metal. It will be discussed in Section 4.4.

At a temperature $T = \theta_R$, equation (4.2) becomes

$$\rho_{i\theta} = \frac{\kappa}{\theta_R}G(1) = 0.9465\frac{\kappa}{\theta_R} \tag{4.6}$$

Thus, from equations (4.2) and (4.6) we obtain

$$\frac{\rho_{iT}}{\rho_{i\theta}} = 1.056\frac{T}{\theta_R}G\left(\frac{\theta_R}{T}\right) \tag{4.7}$$

This reduced resistivity equation gives a single curve which should apply for all metals that can be represented by a constant $\theta_R$. It is shown plotted both in Fig. 27, due to Meissner, [M26] and in Fig. 32, due to White. [M9] Experimental data for several metals have been included in these figures to illustrate the degree to which equation (4.7) is followed by real metals. White has tabulated the function in terms of $\theta_R/T$, and by means of large-scale graphs drawn

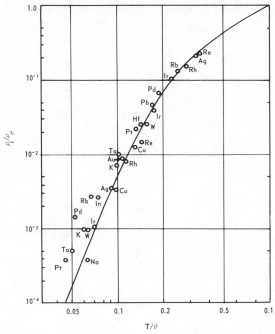

Fig. 32. Comparison of the reduced resistivities of several metals at low reduced temperatures with equation (4.7) (White[M9]).

using his table, $\theta_R$ values can be deduced from practical data. Other methods by which characteristic temperatures may be estimated using resistance data will be given in subsequent sections, but first we should discuss how fully we may expect $\theta_R$ values to agree with those derived from other physical properties, particularly the specific heat.

In practice, it is found that the result of applying the Debye theory to specific-heat measurements gives $\theta_D$ values rather similar in magnitude (and to a lesser extent in temperature dependence) to $\theta_R$ values. The $\theta_D$ value most commonly encountered in the literature is the one calculated from low-temperature experiments, because its specification in the $T^3$ region of the specific heat is accurate and unambiguous. For this reason, we list in the second column of Table VIII $\theta_D$ values derived from low-temperature specific-heat data, while in the third column we give $\theta_D$ values estimated from measurements made at high temperatures in the range $\theta_D/2$ to $\theta_D$. At

## Table VIII. General Comparison of $\theta_D$ and $\theta_R$ Values

|  | $\theta_D$ at 0°K | $\theta_D$ for range $\theta_D/2$ to $\theta_D$ | $\theta_R$ for range $\theta_R/3$ to $\theta_R$ | References for $\theta_R$ |
|---|---|---|---|---|
| 3 Li | 370 | 430 | 440* | 139 |
| 4 Be | 1390 | 1000 | 1240 | 377 |
| 11 Na (bcc) | 152 | 160 | 195* | 139 |
| 12 Mg | 395 | 325 | 340 | 207† |
| 13 Al | 428 | 385 | 395 | 183 |
| 19 K | 89 | 100 | 110* | 139 |
| 20 Ca | 230 | 225 | ~145 | 288 |
| 21 Sc | 470 | | 275 | 106 |
| 22 Ti | 430 | 355 | 342 | M6 |
| 23 V | 395 | 390 | | |
| 24 Cr | 585 | 450 | 485 | M2 |
| 25 α-Mn | 385 | 400? | | |
| β-Mn | | | 330 | M2 |
| 26 α-Fe | 465 | 400 | | |
| γ-Fe | | 320 | | |
| 27 Co | 445 | 380 | 401 | M6 |
| 28 Ni | 440 | 390 | | |
| 29 Cu | 344 | 320 | 320 | 237 |
| 30 Zn | 310 | 245 | 175 | 129 |
| 31 Ga | 325 | 240 | 215 | 373 |
| | | | 205 | † |
| 33 As | 275 | | (290) | M6 |
| 37 Rb | 56 | 63 | 55 | 142 |
| | | | 65 | M4 |
| 38 Sr | 147 | | 170 | M26 |
| | | | 100 | 288 |
| 39 Y | 300 | 213 | 215 | 106 |
| 40 Zr | 292 | 250 | | |
| 41 Nb | 240 | ~240 | | |
| 42 Mo | 455 | 380 | | |
| 43 Tc | | | | |
| 44 Ru | 600 | ~450 | 426 | M6 |
| 45 Rh | 480 | 350 | 370 | 183 |
| 46 Pd | 280 | 300 | 270 | M26 |
| 47 Ag | 226 | 220 | 200 | 237 |
| 48 Cd | 215 | 165 | 130 | † |
| 49 In | 111 | ~120 | | |
| 50 Sn | 195 | 165 | (183) | 376 |
| 51 Sb | 207 | 170? | | |
| 55 Cs | 39 | 46 | 37 | 142 |
| | | | 45 | M4 |
| 56 Ba | 110 | | 100 | 288 |
| | | | 133 | M5 |

## Table VIII. *Cont'd*

| | $\theta_D$ at 0°K | $\theta_D$ for range $\theta_D/2$ to $\theta_D$ | $\theta_R$ for range $\theta_R/3$ to $\theta_R$ | References for $\theta_R$ |
|---|---|---|---|---|
| 57 La | 142 | 132 | | |
| 58 Ce | 147‡ | | | |
| 59 Pr | 152‡ | | | |
| 60 Nd | 157‡ | | | |
| 61 Pm | 162‡ | | | |
| 62 Sm | 166‡ | | | |
| 63 Eu | | | | |
| 64 Gd | 176‡ | | | |
| 65 Tb | 181‡ | | | |
| 66 Dy | 186‡ | | | |
| 67 Ho | 191‡ | | | |
| 68 Er | 195‡ | | | |
| 69 Tm | 200‡ | | | |
| 70 Yb | 118‡ | | | |
| 71 Lu | 210‡ | | | |
| 72 Hf | 252 | 210 | | |
| 73 Ta | 240 | 230 | 228 | M6 |
| 74 W | 400 | 315 | 333 | 183 |
| 75 Re | 430 | 290 | 294 | 221 |
| 76 Os | 500 | ∼350 | 340 | † |
| 77 Ir | 420 | 285 | 305 | † |
| 78 Pt | 240 | 225 | 240 | M26 |
| 79 Au | 162 | 185 | 200 | 237 |
| 80 Hg | 72 | 95 | | |
| 81 Tl | 79 | 100 | 140 | M6 |
| 82 Pb | 107 | 88 | ∼100 | 70 |
| 83 Bi | 119 | 120 | | |
| 84 Po | | | (380?) | † |
| 90 Th | 170 | 150 | 141 | 198 |
| 91 Pa | | | | |
| 92 U | 200 | 162 | ∼100 | 304 |
| 93 Np | | | (137) | 304 |
| 94 α-Pu | | 175 | | |

\* Resistivity results corrected to constant density were used.

† Calculated by the author, using data from Table II.

‡ Values suggested by Lounasmaa.[280]

intermediate temperatures ($\theta_D/10$ to $\theta_D/2$, say), $\theta_D$ figures are often anomalously small in magnitude, but they do tend toward constant figures again at higher temperatures. In contrast to the specific-heat situation, one cannot estimate $\theta_R$ values uniquely as $T \rightarrow 0°K$ [as from equation (4.4), for example] because it is not yet possible to enumerate the interaction parameter $\kappa$ with the requisite precision.

It is on this account that $\kappa$, whether it is truly constant or not, must always be eliminated by some means or other in order to determine $\theta_R$. In other words, all methods of calculating $\theta_R$ are intrinsically methods of comparison. Generally speaking, the Grüneisen–Bloch relation is obeyed well at high temperatures so that $\theta_R$ values are more or less constant in the range $\theta_R/3$ to $\theta_R$ (and higher). We therefore give in the fourth column of Table VIII $\theta_R$ values referred to this temperature region. A comparison of these lists of $\theta$ values now shows that the $\theta_R$ given agree more closely with high-temperature $\theta_D$ than with low-temperature ones, as one would perhaps expect. The $\theta_R$ figures are about equally divided between those smaller and those larger than the high-temperature $\theta_D$.

Blackman has discussed the approximate accord shown by $\theta_D$ and $\theta_R$ data.[76] He correctly points out that for the idealized metals with quasi-free electrons to which the theory applies one would imagine that electrons could only be scattered by longitudinal lattice vibrations. He further shows that the characteristic temperature $\theta_L$ appropriate for such vibrations is larger than $\theta_D$, perhaps even by as much as 50 to 100%. A strict theoretical analysis has not yet been given, but at any rate it would be expected from this that $\theta_R \sim \theta_L > \theta_D$. Since instead $\theta_R \sim \theta_D$, we take this as indicating that $\theta_R$ is smaller than expected because of a contribution to the electron scattering by transverse lattice waves as well; this is especially likely in Umklapp processes. As explained earlier (Section 3.6.1), the role of Umklapp processes becomes increasingly important at intermediate and lower temperatures because much larger angle scattering is possible by them than by normal processes. This raises the resistivity above that predicted by the Grüneisen–Bloch function and is one reason why $\theta_R$ usually decreases at low temperatures, even in the simplest metals. In many transition metals, electron–electron scattering is also appreciable below $\theta_R/10$, thus raising the resistivity above the Grüneisen–Bloch calculations for the ideal resistivity and leading to an apparent fall in $\theta_R$.

## 4.3. THE PRINCIPAL METHODS OF CALCULATING $\theta_R$ VALUES

We shall consider in this section the four principal methods discussed by Kelly and MacDonald[238] for obtaining, by means of the Grüneisen–Bloch equation, $\theta_R$ as a function of temperature from measured resistance data. The various methods differ inherently in their degree of reliability and in their relative ease of calculation, both these factors being dependent on the nature of the assumptions made about the constancy or otherwise of $\kappa$ and $\theta_R$.

In the first method, $\kappa$ and $\theta_R$ are initially taken as constants. Then, by comparing the resistances or resistivities $\rho_{iT_1}$, $\rho_{iT_0}$ at two temperatures $T_1$, $T_0$, respectively, $\kappa/\theta_R^2$ is eliminated on applying equation (4.2). The procedure simply involves finding the value of $\theta_R$ that satisfies the equation

$$G\!\left(\frac{\theta_R}{T_1}\right) = \frac{\rho_{iT_1}}{\rho_{iT_0}}\cdot\frac{T_0}{T_1}G\!\left(\frac{\theta_R}{T_0}\right) \tag{4.8}$$

by means of successive approximation. For convenience, $T_0$ may be taken as room temperature.

But if we have previous knowledge that over a certain region of temperature the characteristic temperature ($\theta_0$ at $T_0$, say) is practically constant, then equation (4.2) may be used to give instead

$$\left(\frac{T_1}{\theta_1}\right)^2 G\!\left(\frac{\theta_1}{T_1}\right) = T_1\rho_{iT_1}\!\left[\frac{T_0}{\theta_0^2\rho_{iT_0}}G\!\left(\frac{\theta_0}{T_0}\right)\right] \tag{4.9}$$

From this equation the unknown characteristic temperature $\theta_1$ at $T_1$ may be arrived at without any difficulty, since the factor in square brackets is decided at the outset and the right-hand side is easily evaluated afresh at each resistivity point ($\rho_{iT_1}$, $T_1$). To aid the reader in obtaining a rapid solution, we provide in Table IX values of $(T/\theta_R)^2 G(\theta_R/T)$ as a function of $\theta_R/T$.

This method of analysis is more straightforward than the first one and is at the same time more accurate, since from the start it treats $\theta_R$ as a variable parameter. As in the first method, constancy of $\kappa$ is assumed, and a minor drawback is that the effect of a suitable choice of reference temperature can occasionally be critical. The following, more elaborate methods which overcome these objections involve a knowledge of the quantity $(d\rho/dT)/(\rho/T) \equiv (d\log\rho)/(d\log T)$.

We take logarithms of the Grüneisen–Bloch equation (4.2) and differentiate with respect to $\log T$:

$$\frac{d\log\rho_i}{d\log T} = 1 + \frac{d\log G}{d\log T} - 2\frac{d\log\theta_R}{d\log T}$$

$$= 1 + \left[\frac{d\log G}{d\log(\theta_R/T)}\left(\frac{d\log\theta_R}{d\log T}-1\right)\right] - 2\frac{d\log\theta_R}{d\log T}$$

Therefore,

$$\frac{d\log\rho_i}{d\log T} = 1 + \left|\frac{d\log G}{d\log(\theta_R/T)}\right| - \frac{d\log\theta_R}{d\log T}\left[2 + \left|\frac{d\log G}{d\log(\theta_R/T)}\right|\right]$$

$$\tag{4.10}$$

### Table IX. The Function $G'(\theta/T) \equiv G(\theta/T)/(\theta/T)^2$ in Terms of $\theta/T$

| $\theta/T$ | $G'(\theta/T)$ | $\theta/T$ | $G'(\theta/T)$ | $\theta/T$ | $G'(\theta/T)$ |
|---|---|---|---|---|---|
| 0 | $\infty$ | 3.1 | 0.06378 | 7.4 | $0.0_22293$ |
| 0.1 | 99.94 | 3.2 | 0.05811 | 7.6 | $0.0_22008$ |
| 0.2 | 24.94 | 3.3 | 0.05304 | 7.8 | $0.0_21762$ |
| 0.3 | 11.06 | 3.4 | 0.04845 | 8.0 | $0.0_21548$ |
| 0.4 | 6.195 | 3.5 | 0.04430 | 8.2 | $0.0_21362$ |
| 0.5 | 3.946 | 3.6 | 0.04058 | 8.4 | $0.0_21201$ |
| 0.6 | 2.723 | 3.7 | 0.03718 | 8.6 | $0.0_21062$ |
| 0.7 | 1.986 | 3.8 | 0.03412 | 8.8 | $0.0_39391$ |
| 0.8 | 1.508 | 3.9 | 0.03133 | 9.0 | $0.0_38322$ |
| 0.9 | 1.180 | 4.0 | 0.02880 | 9.2 | $0.0_37384$ |
| 1.0 | 0.9465 | 4.1 | 0.02650 | 9.4 | $0.0_36563$ |
| 1.1 | 0.7732 | 4.2 | 0.02439 | 9.6 | $0.0_35843$ |
| 1.2 | 0.6418 | 4.3 | 0.02246 | 9.8 | $0.0_35258$ |
| 1.3 | 0.5395 | 4.4 | 0.02070 | 10.0 | $0.0_34655$ |
| 1.4 | 0.4584 | 4.5 | 0.01909 | 10.5 | $0.0_33534$ |
| 1.5 | 0.3932 | 4.6 | 0.01762 | 11.0 | $0.0_32708$ |
| 1.6 | 0.3400 | 4.7 | 0.01628 | 11.5 | $0.0_32093$ |
| 1.7 | 0.2960 | 4.8 | 0.01505 | 12.0 | $0.0_31634$ |
| 1.8 | 0.2592 | 4.9 | 0.01391 | 12.5 | $0.0_31285$ |
| 1.9 | 0.2282 | 5.0 | 0.01287 | 13 | $0.0_31021$ |
| 2.0 | 0.2018 | 5.2 | 0.01104 | 14 | $0.0_46577$ |
| 2.1 | 0.1793 | 5.4 | $0.0_29475$ | 15 | $0.0_44357$ |
| 2.2 | 0.1598 | 5.6 | $0.0_28155$ | 16 | $0.0_42963$ |
| 2.3 | 0.1429 | 5.8 | $0.0_27034$ | 17 | $0.0_42061$ |
| 2.4 | 0.1282 | 6.0 | $0.0_26075$ | 18 | $0.0_41463$ |
| 2.5 | 0.1153 | 6.2 | $0.0_25258$ | 20 | $0.0_57777$ |
| 2.6 | 0.1040 | 6.4 | $0.0_24558$ | 22 | $0.0_54390$ |
| 2.7 | 0.09391 | 6.6 | $0.0_23960$ | 24 | $0.0_52604$ |
| 2.8 | 0.08502 | 6.8 | $0.0_23445$ | 26 | $0.0_51611$ |
| 2.9 | 0.07713 | 7.0 | $0.0_23003$ | 28 | $0.0_51033$ |
| 3.0 | 0.07008 | 7.2 | $0.0_22662$ | | |

When $\theta_R$ is constant, this simplifies to

$$\frac{d \log \rho_i}{d \log T} = 1 + \left| \frac{d \log G}{d \log(\theta_R/T)} \right| \qquad (4.11)$$

The function on the right-hand side of this last equation is tabulated in terms of $\theta_R/T$ in Table X. The lower part of the range as far as $\theta_R/T = 1.6$ has been evaluated by making use of the simple polynomial expansion of $G(\theta_R/T)$ in terms of $\theta_R/T$ given by Grüneisen.[183] The remainder of the table up to $\theta_R/T = 15.0$ we have solved using a graphic method.[303] Henry and Schroeder[211] have calculated the above function at intervals of 0.04 between $\theta_R/T = 0.04$ and 1.80.

## Table X. Values of $1 + |(d \log G)/[d \log (\theta_R/T)]|$ as a Function of $\theta_R/T$

| $\theta_R/T$ | $1 + \left|\dfrac{d \log G}{d \log(\theta_R/T)}\right|$ | $\theta_R/T$ | $1 + \left|\dfrac{d \log G}{d \log(\theta_R/T)}\right|$ | $\theta_R/T$ | $1 + \left|\dfrac{d \log G}{d \log(\theta_R/T)}\right|$ |
|---|---|---|---|---|---|
| 0.1 | 1.00111 | 2.6 | 1.654 | 6.2 | 3.446 |
| 0.2 | 1.00444 | 2.7 | 1.700 | 6.4 | 3.538 |
| 0.3 | 1.00998 | 2.8 | 1.747 | 6.6 | 3.627 |
| 0.4 | 1.01772 | 2.9 | 1.795 | 6.8 | 3.707 |
| 0.5 | 1.02764 | 3.0 | 1.844 | 7.0 | 3.784 |
| 0.6 | 1.03972 | 3.1 | 1.893 | 7.2 | 3.860 |
| 0.7 | 1.05393 | 3.2 | 1.943 | 7.4 | 3.932 |
| 0.8 | 1.07024 | 3.3 | 1.993 | 7.6 | 4.002 |
| 0.9 | 1.08861 | 3.4 | 2.044 | 7.8 | 4.069 |
| 1.0 | 1.1090 | 3.5 | 2.095 | 8.0 | 4.13 |
| 1.1 | 1.1314 | 3.6 | 2.146 | 8.2 | 4.19 |
| 1.2 | 1.1556 | 3.7 | 2.197 | 8.4 | 4.25 |
| 1.3 | 1.1818 | 3.8 | 2.249 | 8.6 | 4.31 |
| 1.4 | 1.2098 | 3.9 | 2.301 | 8.8 | 4.36 |
| 1.5 | 1.2396 | 4.0 | 2.354 | 9.0 | 4.41 |
| 1.6 | 1.2710 | 4.2 | 2.461 | 9.2 | 4.46 |
| 1.7 | 1.303 | 4.4 | 2.568 | 9.4 | 4.50$_5$ |
| 1.8 | 1.336 | 4.6 | 2.673 | 9.6 | 4.55 |
| 1.9 | 1.370 | 4.8 | 2.774 | 9.8 | 4.59 |
| 2.0 | 1.405 | 5.0 | 2.873 | 10.0 | 4.63 |
| 2.1 | 1.442 | 5.2 | 2.970 | 11.0 | 4.75 |
| 2.2 | 1.481 | 5.4 | 3.066 | 12.0 | 4.83 |
| 2.3 | 1.522 | 5.6 | 3.162 | 13.0 | 4.88$_5$ |
| 2.4 | 1.565 | 5.8 | 3.257 | 14.0 | 4.93 |
| 2.5 | 1.609 | 6.0 | 3.352 | 15.0 | 4.96$_5$ |

With this table, $\theta_R/T$ can be deduced directly at any temperature by means of equation (4.11), since $(d \log \rho_i)/(d \log T)$ is given by the experimental observations. This is the third method of Kelly and MacDonald. It is not exact because the derivation of equation (4.11) itself assumes a constant $\theta_R$. Its purpose is to obtain a preliminary, though rough, $\theta_R$–$T$ graph before passing on to use the more precise equation (4.10); the procedure with equation (4.10) is to begin in a region in which $\theta_R$ has already been discovered to be virtually constant. Then the correction term in this equation is small, and accurate $\theta_R$ values may be calculated quickly by successive approximation. The success of these two methods depends on good, closely spaced experimental results in order that $(d\rho/dT)/(\rho/T)$ may be enumerated with sufficient precision.

The relative merits of all four methods may be compared by referring to Fig. 33, in which $\theta_R$–$T$ curves derived from the same set of

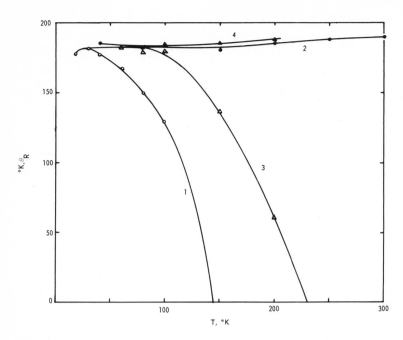

Fig. 33. $\theta_R$ for Na evaluated by four different methods. Experimental data of MacDonald, which were corrected for thermal expansion, were used (Kelly[237]).

experimental data are given. In this example by Kelly,[237] based on MacDonald's experimental results, the first and third methods do not work out well. The huge temperature coefficients of $\theta_R$ arise chiefly because the basic formulas assume constant $\theta_R$ values. Naturally, then, the methods prove to be correct at only the lower temperatures where $\theta_R$ really is almost constant. The computations made by employing methods 2 and 4 both began in these regions. That they both result in rather similar temperature dependences implies that $\kappa$, the electron–phonon interaction parameter, is in fact constant over the temperature range considered. In such a case, method 2 is to be recommended on account of its greater ease of manipulation.

In analyzing the data for Fig. 33, Kelly also took into consideration another factor that is particularly important in the highly compressible alkali metals. He corrected for the dependence of the electrical resistivity on thermal expansion. This was also done by Dugdale and

Gugan for the alkali metals of Fig. 31, whose $\theta_R$ values were computed according to the fourth method above. We have indicated before that experimental observations are normally taken under conditions of constant pressure, while theory always relates to the resistivity at constant volume. The density corrections necessary because of temperature changes can only be accurately applied if the pressure coefficient of resistivity is known. Fortunately, such corrections are small for most metals and are usually neglected. They are, however, very large for some of the alkalis, notably K, and the corrections to be made have been considered by Kelly[237] (also for the noble metals), Dugdale and Gugan,[139] and Meixner.[314]

## 4.4. RULE-OF-THUMB METHOD FOR $\theta_R$

This is a simple and rough and ready method that gives only a single $\theta_R$ value for a metal but which can be worked out almost instantly and sometimes even by mental arithmetic. More often than not, the accuracy is to within 10%.

We make use of equation (4.5) and always take $T_l = 20$ and $T_h = 295°K$. We then obtain

$$\theta_R = 48.20 \left( \frac{\rho_{i295}}{\rho_{i20}} \right)^{1/4} \tag{4.12}$$

as a practical and easily remembered formula. Resistances at just three temperatures need to be known or measured in order that it may be solved, namely, the resistances at room temperature and at the hydrogen and helium points. The result achieved is a single value that represents $\theta_R$ for the metal over a wide temperature range below room temperature. The formula must be used with care, and the conditions under which it is valid recognized from the beginning.

First, equation (4.5) itself cannot be expected to be correct (or almost correct) unless $\rho_{il}$ is taken in a region where $\rho_{il} \propto T^n$ with $n = 4.5$ to $5.5$. $T_l = 20°K$ was chosen not only because it s the hydrogen point and because $\rho_{i20}$ is sufficiently large in magnitude to be measured with adequate precision but also because in a number of metals this temperature is located in the $T^5$ region ($T_l < \theta/5$ to $\theta/10$). Obviously, the formula leads to $\theta_R$ values which are too small in the cases of transition metals, rare earths, and very impure metals, where other temperature-dependent scattering mechanisms partially or wholly conceal the $T^5$ lattice scattering term to which equations (4.5) and (4.12) relate. We now append a list of $\theta_R$ values calculated by equation (4.12) for nontransition metals using data abstracted from Table II. The reader can judge for himself the extent of the agreement between these albeit rough $\theta_R$ figures and the high-temperature $\theta_D$ and $\theta_R$ values of Table VIII. The list is: Li 241*; Na 189,* Mg 229, Al 396; K 130,* Cu 327, Zn 157(177†), Ga 173, As 152; Rb 107,* Sr 125, Ag 219, Cd 132, In 131, Sn 156, Sb 152; Cs 99,* Ba 130, Au 176, Hg 106, Tl 120, Pb 119, and Bi 102°K. It should be recalled that these $\theta_R$ values are appropriate for the range up to 295°K, which is not always the same as the range between $T \sim \theta/2$ and $\theta$. If we therefore make comparisons with the appropriate $\theta_R$ wherever possible, otherwise with $\theta_D$, we find differences greater than 10% only in Li, Mg, K, Ga(?), As, Rb, and Cs. In these metals there is either no $T^5$ region at all or else it appears only at temperatures well below 20°K. The latter would certainly be the case in Rb and Cs, which have very low $\theta_D$. The use of a $T_l$ lower than 20°K would obviously produce more satisfactory results all round, but accurate data for $\rho_i$ at 10°K or so are much scarcer in the literature and more difficult to obtain in practice than are data at the hydrogen point. But if we recalculate $\theta_R$ values for K, Rb, and Cs using $T_l = 8$°K, for which accurate figures are available,[139,142] we obtain for the respective $\theta_R$ values for these metals 82, 57, and 47°K. These figures compare quite well with mean $\theta_R$ and $\theta_D$ for the temperature range below room temperature.

Of the transition elements, satisfactory agreement is found for Ti 328, Mo 372,‡ Ru 395,‡ Rh 346, Hf 200, Re 279, Os 335,‡ and Ir 272. These are transition metals for which White and Woods [M10] give temperature exponents at low temperatures that lie in the range 4.6 to 5.3. For other transition metals, equation (4.12) gives $\theta_R$ values that are between 10 and 35% smaller than the $\theta_R$ and $\theta_D$ figures of Table VIII for the reasons explained above. With data from Table II, quite reasonable $\theta_R$ values are obtained for the actinide metals, namely, Th 144, U 128 and 121, and Np 135 (see Table VIII).

Semenenko and Sudovtsov[395] have analyzed their 14 to 20°K resistivity data on Fe, Ni, and Pt into separate $T^2$ and $T^5$ terms. If we make use of their figures for $\rho_{i20}$ (based on the $T^5$ term) and $\rho_{i273}$ and then employ the formula $\theta_R = 49.14 \ (\rho_{i273}/\rho_{i20})^{1/4}$, we discover that for Fe $\theta_R = 460$, for Ni it is 440, and for Pt it is 217°K. These are all perfectly acceptable values compared to the $\theta_D$ results. Obviously, this approximate method is best used when a $(\rho_i, T_{il})$ point is available from a region where the $T^5$ law is valid; in those cases where other scattering terms are present in the $T_{il}$ region, the lattice term should be separated if possible and used alone in equation (4.12). Such a

---

* Readings corrected to constant density were used.[139,142]
† With data from ref. 42.
‡ $T_l$ was taken as 25°K since ref. M10 had no data for 20°K. The formula then becomes $\theta_R = 63.70 \ (\rho_{i295}/\rho_{i25})^{1/4}$.

procedure requires experimental measurements of very high precision if an accurate plot of $\rho_i T^{-2}$ against $T^3$ is to be obtained, but while such studies are important for theoretical purposes, they are not in keeping with the spirit of the rough and ready $\theta_R$ rule.

Summarizing, we are able to say that equation (4.2), or any of its related equations, provides a rapid means of estimating a representative $\theta_R$ value for a metal (with the admitted limitations discussed above) in a convenient and practical manner requiring a minimum of experimental data, since in principle only the relative ideal resistances at 20°K and room temperature are required.

*Chapter 5*

# Alloyed, Deformed, and Irradiated Metals

The consequences of alloying, deforming, quenching, and irradiating metals are considered in this chapter, albeit rather briefly. The result of alloying is to introduce foreign impurity atoms into the metallic lattice, whereas the other treatments introduce lattice defects of various types. In all cases the transport properties are modified to a greater or a lesser degree, depending on the severity of the experimental process, and a study of the lattice perturbations or damage by means of electrical resistivity measurements is often very rewarding. The experimental and theoretical matter embraced by this general subject is quite broad and could easily be expanded into a book itself. We shall be content to summarize the more important effects and to give references where appropriate for further reading.

## 5.1. THE ELECTRICAL RESISTANCE OF ALLOYS

Alloys generally are marked by having very high resistivities that at first sight appear to be out of all proportion to the relative amounts of the constituent elements. For example, only 0.2 at.-% of either As or Fe as solutes in Au will raise the residual resistivity by 1.6 $\mu\Omega$-cm, thus doubling the ice-point resistivity of the pure metal.[268] Consequently, alloys, apart from dilute ones, are distinguishable from metals by the lesser importance of the temperature-dependent component of the resistivity ($\rho_i$), since as a rule the constant impurity term ($\rho_0$) is much the greater one. Any defect contribution which may also be present in the residual resistivity (Section 5.5) will not be considered in this and subsequent sections on alloys (Sections 5.2 to 5.4).

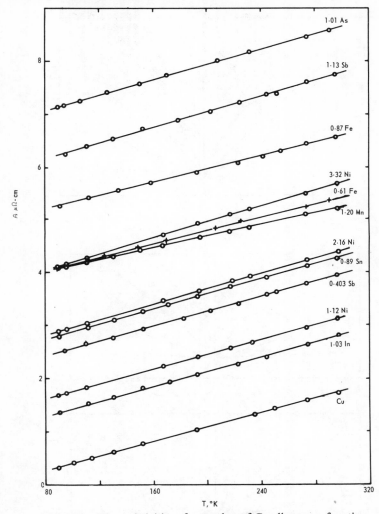

Fig. 34.   The resistivities of a number of Cu alloys as a function
of temperature.[267]  These  curves  illustrate  Matthiessen's rule.
The numbers refer to the atomic percentages of the solute used.

The behavior of most solid-solution, nonmagnetic alloys falls
into comparatively simple patterns and can be explained by simple
laws. The subject will be considered in two parts, the one dealing with
dilute alloys and the other with nondilute disordered and ordered
alloys.

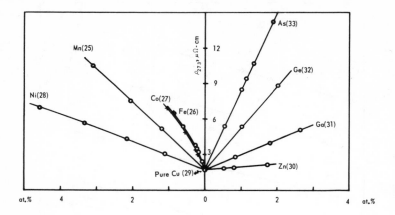

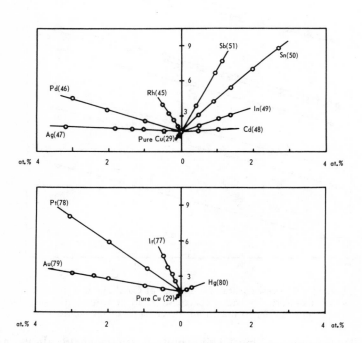

Fig. 35.  Nordheim's rule for low concentrations exempli-
fied by using the data of Linde.[267,268]  The resistivity
measurements were made at 273°K on binary alloys of
Cu ($Z = 29$) and are given as a function of the concentration of the second component.

## 5.2. DILUTE ALLOYS

Certain aspects of the behavior of dilute alloys have been treated elsewhere in connection with Matthiessen's rule and the resistance-minimum phenomenon (Sections 1.4, 3.8, and 3.9). Disregarding a few obvious (principally magnetic) exceptions, Matthiessen's rule holds well for alloys of low concentration, and only begins to fail when the concentration is (a) of a quantity that makes $\rho_0$ more than a small fraction of $\rho_i$, or (b) of a quality that causes severe local disruptions of the lattice potential. The latter would result if there were considerable size or valence differences between solute and solvent atoms. Figure 34 shows alloys for which Matthiessen's rule is holding well, since all the curves are practically parallel.

For systems of homogeneous random solid solutions,* the impurity resistivity, caused by a concentration $x$ of solute atoms in the solvent metal, may be described by Nordheim's concentration rule[333] in the form

$$\rho_0 \propto x(1 - x) \qquad (5.1)$$

from which it is seen that for small $x$ the impurity resistivity is proportional to $x$. The truth of this statement for Cu-rich binary alloys at constant temperature is demonstrated in Fig. 35, which is due to Linde.[268] The extent to which Nordheim's rule applies for a given pair of metals depends on how similar the metals involved are, but at least for homologous elements that are totally soluble in one another [as in the fcc Cu-Au system, Fig. 37(a)] equation (5.1) holds throughout the entire range. From the form of equation (5.1), one might guess that the increase in resistivity due to dissolving a given quantity of one metal in a second would be identical to dissolving the same amount of the second in the first (Mott[320]). This is found to be roughly true, provided that the metals have similar crystal structures, valences, and atomic volumes.

The increase in the impurity resistivity that occurs with widening valence differences between atoms of the solute and atoms of the solvent was established by Norbury[332] in 1921. The effect was later thoroughly investigated by Linde[267] for alloy systems based on the noble metals, as a result of which he concluded that for a given quantity of solute the impurity resistivity is proportional to the square of the valence difference ($\Delta Z$) between the solute and the solvent. Thus

$$\rho_0 = A + B(\Delta Z)^2 \qquad (5.2)$$

$A$ and $B$ are constants for solutes coming from any one period of

---

* The reason for these adjectives is made clear in the next section.

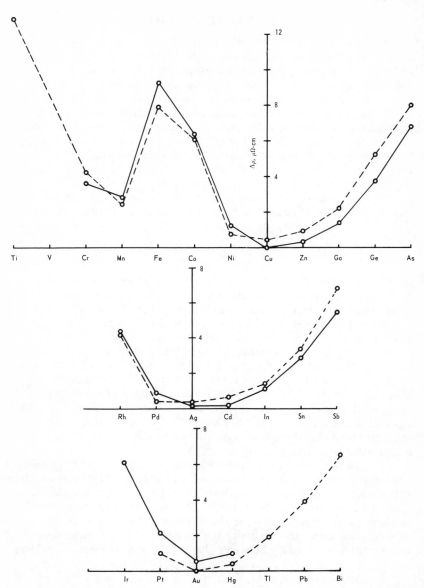

Fig. 36.   Impurity resistivities of Cu (————) and Au (– – – –) alloys caused by
1 at.-% of the solutes indicated.[267,268] The Norbury–Linde rule is illustrated by
the parabolic forms of the alloy resistivities on the right-hand sides of the figures.

the periodic table. In particular, $A$ is zero if the solutes lie in the same period as the solvent.

From the parabolic form of the right-hand parts of the curves of Fig. 36 it may be deduced that the Norbury–Linde rule works satisfactorily in these alloys, but evidently it does not hold for the transition-metal solutes. This is partly because it is no easy task to decide just how many free electrons the transition metals provide. Despite this difficulty, a fair theoretical description of the general form of the left-hand curves has now been given by Friedel.[160]

A simple way of regarding the effect of the perturbation produced by a solute atom of valence different from that of the host metal is to carry over from nuclear physics Rutherford's principle by which particles are scattered by nuclei. Then, since the excess charge of an impurity center over that of surrounding solvent atoms is $(\Delta Z)e$, a scattering cross section proportional to $(\Delta Z)^2$ can be expected. Many years ago, Mott[323] gave a mathematical treatment of this problem that led to quantitative results a few times too large, but the more recent exact approach by de Faget de Casteljau and Friedel[151] agrees closely with experiment.

The Norbury–Linde rule has also been tested for other alloys, besides those based on the noble metals, of which we mention Al-rich ones. Robinson and Dorn[382] found the rule to be tenable so long as the valence of Al in the solid state was assumed to be 2.5.

## 5.3. NONDILUTE ALLOYS

As in the previous section, we shall consider only homogeneous alloys in which the constituent metals are in mutual solid solution. Cases of complete miscibility for all compositions, as in the Cu–Au system [Fig. 37(a)], are exceptions rather than the rule, and most systems are restricted in their ranges of solid solubility. When an alloy consists not of a solid solution but of a mixture of individual crystallites each composed wholly of one component or the other, the resulting total resistivity is lower than if the two components were mutually soluble. This is because each crystallite is almost free from impurities, and the total resistivity is a function of the resistivities of the separate crystallites. Thus, for any concentration, the resistivity is a weighted mean based on the relative proportions of the two constituents. By contrast, the mixed atoms of a disordered solid solution are distributed at random over all the lattice points of the entire sample, the periodic potential of the pure metal is badly disrupted, and the consequent alloy resistivity has the characteristic hump-backed concentration dependence of Fig. 37(a). It will be noted that

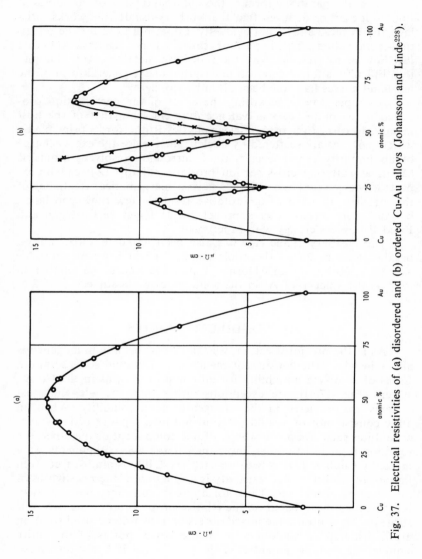

Fig. 37.  Electrical resistivities of (a) disordered and (b) ordered Cu-Au alloys (Johansson and Linde[228]).

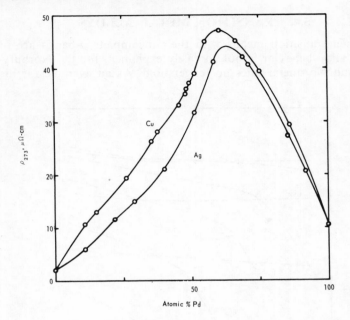

Fig. 38. Electrical resistivities of Cu-Pd and Ag-Pd alloys (Svensson[414]).

the resistivity for the 50 at.-% concentration is some seven times greater than that of either component metal taken singly, because although the two metals are alike with respect to valence and crystal structure, they have very dissimilar atomic volumes. The influence of atomic volume on the scattering may, however, be rendered very much less effective if the atoms are ordered from their purely random arrangement onto interpenetrating superlattices. This can be achieved by suitable annealing techniques,[228] and the result for Cu-Au alloys is shown in Fig. 37(b). The deep minima at the 25 and 50 at.-% Au concentrations correspond to the chemical compounds $Cu_3Au$ and $CuAu$, at which points the resistivity is not more than twice that of either Cu or Au alone. Owing to such differences in resistivity between ordered and disordered lattice structures (of which this is perhaps a rather extreme example), it follows that an immediate test of the spatial state of order of a given alloy may be carried out very simply by resistivity measurements.

## 5.4. TRANSITION METAL ALLOYS

When transition metals with their incomplete *d*-bands are involved, alloy behavior is not so easily explained, for the Norbury–Linde and Nordheim rules no longer hold. As an example for dis-

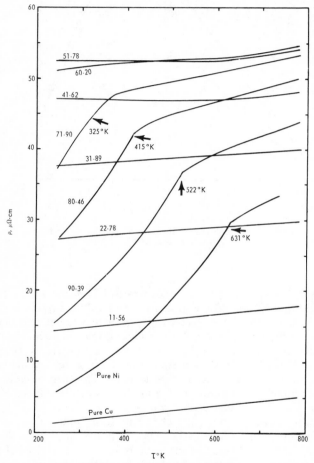

Fig. 39. Electrical resistivities of Cu-Ni alloys (Svensson[415]). The numbers relate to the atomic percentages of Ni present in the alloys. The temperatures indicated are those of Curie points. Those alloys containing about 40 to 45 at.-% Ni which have very low temperature coefficients are known as the *constantans*.

cussion, we present in Fig. 38 the resistance–concentration curves for Cu-Pd and Ag-Pd alloys,[414] in which the maximum resistivities occur for the compositions having 60 at.-% Pd. The Au-Pd and Cu-Ni systems have similar, though less angular, asymmetrical curves. Mott[322, M7] has given an explanation of the behavior of these alloys based on his $s$-$d$ scattering model. The $d$-shell in the noble metals is completely occupied and there is a single valence electron outside, whereas Pd and Ni have an electron missing from their $d$-shells—a factor that results in high resistivities for these metals because of $s$-$d$ scattering contributions. Adding Cu, say, as solute to Ni progressively fills the $d$-band holes, and this is complete when about 60 at.-% Cu has been added. After this point, Cu-Ni alloys are no longer magnetic, and the disappearance of the Curie point is to be seen in the resistivity–temperature graphs of Svensson (Fig. 39). Notice also in this figure the high and nearly temperature-independent resistivities for the compositions containing 40 to 45 at.-% Ni. These alloys are the constantans. In Table XI we give the resistivities of two constantans at low temperatures together with the resistivities of other

## Table XI.  Resistivities of Some Important Alloys (in microhm-centimeters)

| Alloy (plus special treatment, if any) | Composition | 295°K | 80°K | 20°K | 4°K | References |
|---|---|---|---|---|---|---|
| Manganin ...    ...    ... | Cu 84, Mn 12, Ni 4 | 48 | 45.5 | 43.5 | 43 | 163 |
| Karma ...    ...    ... | Ni 76, Cr 20, Fe, Al | 133 | 132 | 132 | 132 | 163 |
| Evanohm ...    ...    ... | Ni 75, Cr 20, Al 2.5, Cu 2.5 | 134 | 133 | 133 | 133 | 163 |
| Constantan (advance)    ... | Cu 57; Ni 43 | 49 | 48 | 46.5 | 45.5 | 163 |
| Constantan ...    ...    ... | Cu 60, Ni 40 | 52.5 | 45 | 44 | 44 | 73 |
| German silver    ...    ... | Cu 47, Zn 41, Ni 9, Pb 2 | 30.5 | 27.5 | 26.5 | 26.5 | 73 |
| Stainless steel (Ti stabilized) | Fe 71.4, Ni 7.9, Cr 18.9, Si 0.7, Ti 1, C ~ 0.1 | 72 | 52 | 48.5 | 47.5 | 73 |
| Stainless steel (Type 347-Nb stabilized) | | 74.5 | 53.5 | | 53 | 148 |
| Stainless steel (Type 303) | | 73.5 | 52 | | 51 | 148 |
| Cupro-nickel (annealed or cold-worked) | Cu 90, Ni 10 | 14.7 | 13 | 12.5 | | 148 |
| Cupro-nickel    ...    ... | Cu 80, Ni 20 | 26 | 24 | 23 | 23 | 220 |
| Monel (annealed or hard-drawn)    ...    ... | Ni 60-70, Cu 25-35, Fe 1-3, Mn, Si, C | 50 | 32 | | 30 | 148 |
| Inconel (annealed) ...    ... | Ni 72, Cr, Fe | 103 | 100 | | 102 | 148 |
| Inconel (hard-drawn)    ... | | 94 | 90.5 | 90.5 | | 148 |
| Brass (annealed)    ...    ... | Cu 70, Zn 30 | 6.6 | 4.1 | | 3.6 | 240 |
| Brass (as drawn)    ...    ... | | 7.2 | 4.9 | | 4.3 | 240 |
| Brass (annealed)    ...    ... | Cu 90, Zn 10 | 3.8 | 2.3 | | 1.9 | 240 |
| Au–2.1 at.-% Co ...    ... | Au with 2.1 Co | ~13-14 | 12.2 | 12.0 | 12.1 | 358 |
| Normal silver    ...    ... | Ag with 0.37 Au | 1.77 | 0.45 | 0.16 | 0.16 | 190* |

* These authors give 1.63 μΩ-cm at 273°K. The tabulated values were calculated using data for Ag from Table II and assuming Matthiessen's rule.

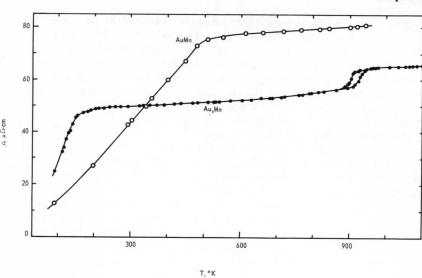

Fig. 40. Electrical resistivities of Au₃Mn and AuMn as a function of temperature, showing the effect of both atomic and magnetic ordering on the resistivities
(Giansoldati and Linde[173]).

commercial alloys of importance in cryogenic work. It will be observed
that the special Ni-Cr alloys which go under the trade names of
Evanohm and Karma are even more satisfactory than constantan and
manganin for constant resistance applications at low temperatures.

As an example of a binary alloy system possessing regions of
atomic and magnetic order, we mention Giansoldati and Linde's work
on the resistivity of Au₃Mn and AuMn[173] (Fig. 40). When Au₃Mn is
cooled through 900°K, the disordered fcc structure transforms to
another, but ordered, structure with an accompanying drop in
resistivity. Below this temperature, the resistivity decreases slowly
and monotonically until the Néel point at 145°K is reached, at which
temperature antiferromagnetic ordering begins and the huge spin-
disorder contribution falls away rapidly, just as in pure Mn.

The variety of interesting alloy systems having one or more
transition-metal components is most extensive, and further information on them may be gleaned from the reviews of Mott[325] and Coles,[103]
among others. For fuller overall discussion of points touched upon
in this and previous sections, we refer the reader to Ziman, [M12]
Gerritsen, [M1] and Mott and Jones. [M7]

## 5.5. DEFECT RESISTANCE DUE TO DEFORMATION, QUENCHING, AND IRRADIATION

Having discussed the effect of impurities, we now consider the other major contribution to the residual resistance of a metal. This is the resistance which arises from the presence of imperfections in the crystal lattice due to vacancies and interstitials (point defects) and dislocations. The principal ways in which imperfections originate in a specimen may be grouped as follows: (1) more-or-less severe deformation of the specimen by such means as stretching, bending, or rolling; (2) continued thermal cycling through regions of phase change; (3) quenching of the specimen from a high to a very low temperature; and (4) irradiation of the specimen with high-energy particles (neutrons, deuterons, and electrons are chiefly used).

The lattice defects introduced by any of these procedures may be conveniently studied by methods making use of electrical resistance measurements, since the resistivity is generally raised by such treatments. The actual natures of the defects formed are dependent upon the treatment used, but clues as to their identities may be deduced from careful annealing experiments performed at increasingly higher temperatures. It is found that the recovery processes of the metal resulting from the movement and gradual disappearance of the defects usually take place in well-defined steps over definite intervals of temperature. Each of these may be presumed to correspond to the annealing-out of a particular type of defect, and often the kinetics of the annealing process allow calculation of an activation energy for the defect motion. Eventually, at a high-enough temperature, called the *recrystallization temperature*, all the initial excess resistivity disappears. Interpretation of recovery curves is much aided when results subsequent to several initially different damage processes are available, but a deep and proper analysis is rarely possible, owing to the complexity of the various mechanisms that simultaneously prevail and because a theoretical description is not yet far-enough advanced.

In order to obtain the most complete information, the damage is best introduced at helium or hydrogen temperatures, since the lowest annealing regions are to be found at less than 50°K. The result of the isochronal annealing of Cu following 1-MeV electron irradiation at helium temperatures illustrates the so-called Stage I recovery processes of this metal (Fig. 41).[110] For each point, the specimen was warmed to the indicated temperature and held there for a definite time interval before being returned to 4°K for the remeasurement of $\rho_0$. At least five substages may be identified, the first three corresponding to the recombination of close interstitial–vacancy pairs and the next two

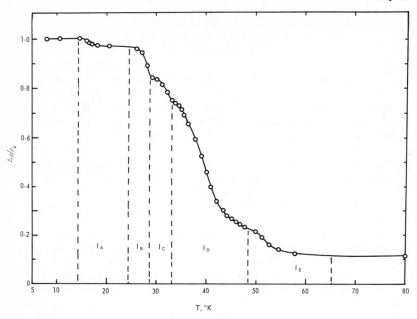

**Fig. 41.** Isochronal annealing curve of Cu, showing the various substages that occur during Stage I recovery of the metal (Corbett, Smith, and Walker[110]).

to the migration over greater distances of interstitials to vacancies, to impurities, and to other interstitials. At still higher temperatures, other recovery processes occur, due to the release of interstitials from impurity and other traps and the migration of vacancies, until, for temperatures higher than 473°K, recrystallization takes place.

The shape of recovery curves such as these is dependent on the severity and type of the damage processes applied, since heavy-particle irradiation, quenching, and deformation give rise to vacancies, interstitials, and dislocations in quite different proportions from those which are produced by 1-MeV electron irradiation. Dislocations, for instance, occur only after relatively intense damage, as by actual deformation of the metal, and they are correspondingly more difficult to anneal out. For, while vacancies and interstitials can migrate fairly readily at low temperatures (to each other or to dislocations, say), dislocations, being very extensive faults, are more sluggish and are liable to get stuck on crossing one another, so they require higher temperatures for their removal.

It is possible to determine both theoretically and experimentally the actual resistivity provided by definite concentrations of defects. Thus, for 1 % vacancies a resistivity of about 1.5 $\mu\Omega$-cm is indicated for the simpler metals (that is, about $1.5 \times 10^{-21}$ $\mu\Omega$-cm per vacancy), and the resistivity due to interstitials is probably about the same.[79] For a single dislocation line, resistivities between 2 and $20 \times 10^{-13}$ $\mu\Omega$-cm are found for a wide range of metals, and a theoretical approach based on scattering from local distortion of the lattice in the neighborhood of the dislocation accounts well for these values.[66] This kind of scattering is quite distinct from that caused by lattice dilatation[222,411,205] and stacking faults,[90b,218] which give theoretical figures one or two orders of magnitude too low.

For general theoretical and experimental accounts of the influence of defects on the resistivity of metals, reference may be made to the following books and articles: refs. M12, 91, 92, 95, 112, and 394.

## 5.6. RESISTANCE DUE TO SELF-IRRADIATION DAMAGE

To close this chapter, we draw attention to the fact that naturally radioactive metals may be studied for their susceptibility to damage and for the processes that govern their recovery from such damage by utilizing their *own* radioactivity as the source of defects. Plutonium has come in for particular attention on this account, but the method can be used for any radioactive metal, especially those with even shorter half-lives than that of Pu.

The principal isotope of normal research Pu is $^{239}$Pu, which has a half-life of 24,360 years and decays to $^{235}$U with recoil energy 87 keV by releasing 5.14 MeV $\alpha$-particles. These and decay products from other isotopes are simultaneously the source of phonons, impurities, and multiple lattice defects in the crystal. Since at room temperature the resistivity does not appear to be time-dependent, we assume that at this temperature defects disappear spontaneously— and also that accumulating impurity centers as such do not increase the resistivity significantly either at this or at lower temperatures. But on mere holding at low temperatures (below 40°K), the resistivity is found to increase at a remarkable rate and in a manner not at all in accordance with Matthiessen's rule. Evidently, at these low temperatures the damage from the self-irradiation is destroying the mechanism that produces the acute temperature dependence of the metal which is shown in Fig. 18. Isochronal annealing experiments have also been carried out, and they show that there exist two main regions of recovery centered on 80 and 160°K. A proper analysis of the results obtained is difficult at the present time, but will be further aided when recovery processes after other forms of damaging (for instance, by quenching subsequent to prolonged thermal cycling) have been studied. The present state of this subject may be determined from the papers of King, Lee, Mendelssohn, and Wigley,[244] Wigley,[448] Elliott and Olsen,[144] and Lord.[276]

*Chapter 6*

# Pressure, Magnetic-Field, and Size Effects

We shall consider in this chapter some further miscellaneous effects that can also influence the magnitude of the electrical resistivity and which contribute greatly in their various ways to our understanding of the electronic structure and behavior of metals.

## 6.1. THE INFLUENCE OF PRESSURE AND TENSION

### 6.1.1. The Influence of Pressure

The subjection of metals to high pressures at constant temperature profoundly modifies the electrical resistance, and some of the resultant changes, such as phase and electronic transitions, are similar to those produced by changing the temperature at constant pressure or volume. Unfortunately, the theory of the effect of pressure on the electrical resistance is much less well understood than is the theory of the effect of temperature at constant volume. Thanks largely to Bridgman, whose single-minded devotion to the practical field spanned some 50 years in all, experimental results at any rate have never been wanting. [M13,260] Furthermore, recent advances in techniques have now extended the pressure range of investigation up to 600 kb (about $6 \times 10^5$ atm)* for temperatures as low as 4°K, [61] or to 100 kb for temperatures of up to 3000°K or so. [200,273] Although generalizations are not at all easy to make, we shall begin by giving a rapid survey of the experimental findings.

Considering first the pressure dependence of the resistivity at room temperature only, we may at least say that for the majority of

* 1 b = 0.98692 atm; 1 kg/cm$^2$ = 0.96784 atm.

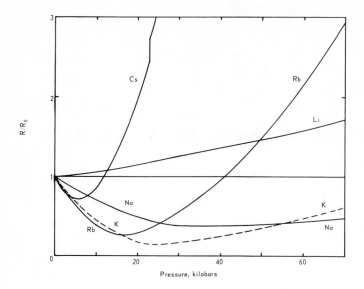

Fig. 42. Change of resistance of the alkali metals at room temperature with change of pressure (Bridgman's data, amended by Bundy and Strong[96]).

metals the resistivity initially decreases with increasing pressure and that it does so with upward curvature. In some, the resistivity eventually passes through a minimum (Na, K) and at still higher pressures perhaps a maximum also (Rb at 420 kb) (see Figs. 42 and 43). Others, however, increase in resistivity directly from zero pressure (Li, Bi), but occasionally they too possess a high-pressure maximum (Ca 370, Sr 36, and Sb 25 kb) (Figs. 44 and 45). Some of these maxima, plus also certain steplike anomalies in resistivity, are due to crystallographic phase transitions or to changes in electronic configuration, as in Cs (42 kb), Ce (7 kb), and Yb (40 kb), but the broader, less abrupt maxima more likely result from variations in the relative contributions arising from such factors as Umklapp processes and detailed changes in the Fermi surface and the lattice vibrational spectrum. The last factor may be regarded as the "purest" of the various influences affecting the resistivity, because in the idealized metals governed by the Grüneisen–Bloch relation [equation (4.2) with $\kappa = $ constant] it would be operating alone and would lead to a fall in resistivity with mounting pressure. This may be seen quite simply by noting that high pressures will reduce the amplitudes of the lattice vibrations and thus also the resistivity, since $\rho \propto \overline{x^2}$, the mean square

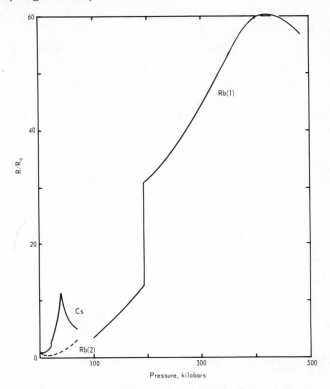

Fig. 43. Change of resistance of Rb and Cs at room temperature with change of pressure. Rb (1) : Balchan and Drickamer[61]; Rb (2) and Cs : Bridgman.[96] Observe the great difference in scales between Figs. 42 and 43.

amplitude of vibration (Section 3.6). Alternatively, we see that the resulting greater frequencies of vibration raise $\theta$ and therefore lower the resistivity through equations of the type (3.14), (4.2), (4.3), and (4.4). In fact, from equations (4.3) and (4.4), we may obtain immediately at high temperatures

$$\frac{d \log \rho_i}{dp} = -2\frac{d \log \theta}{dp} \qquad (6.1)$$

and at low temperatures

$$\frac{d \log \rho_i}{dp} = -6\frac{d \log \theta}{dp} \qquad (6.2)$$

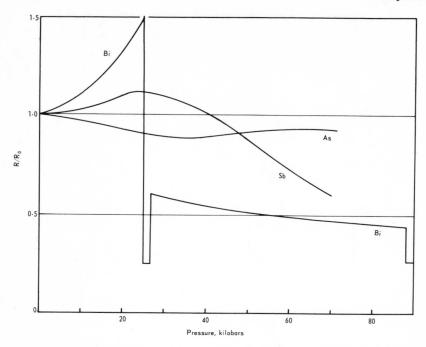

Fig. 44. Reduced resistances of the pentavalent metals (As, Sb, and Bi) at room temperature as a function of pressure (Bridgman's data, amended by Bundy and Strong[96]).

on the continued assumption of constant $\kappa$. That is, the pressure coefficient of resistivity $(1/\rho_i)(d\rho_i/dp) \equiv d \log \rho_i/dp$ should be three times larger at low temperatures than at high temperatures, a trend which has indeed been found in Li, Na, and K at relatively low pressures.[135,139]

A theoretical interpretation of the observational data has been attempted only for the alkali metals and for Cu, and then only at low pressures ($< 3$ kb), because, in contrast to the hard, high-melting-point transition metals, the alkalis, with their high compressibilities and low melting points, are very severely affected by even moderate pressures of 15 to 30 kb. It is quite clear that even for Na, the metal whose Fermi surface at effectively zero pressure is nearest to being spherical, pressures exceeding 25 kb distort the Fermi surface markedly, so that it is no longer valid to take $\kappa$, the so-called electron–phonon interaction parameter, as being pressure- or volume-independent. Consequently, in order to be able to understand the behavior

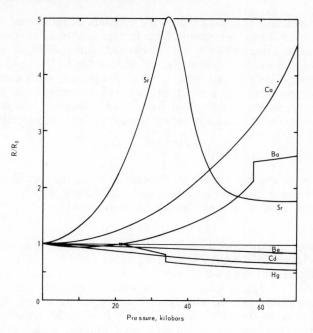

Fig. 45. Reduced resistances of IIA and IIB metals at room temperature as a function of pressure (Bridgman's data, amended by Bundy and Strong[96]). Mercury is liquid at room temperature up to 13 kb. In this diagram the resistance of Hg is compared with its resistance at 21.5 kb. Magnesium and zinc behave like Be and Cd and have not been included in this diagram.

of the simplest metals at pressures greater than atmospheric, we must assume that $\kappa$ and $\theta_R$ are functions of the volume, although we may continue to take them as being independent of the temperature. Then by differentiating equation (4.2) with respect to $\log V$ and $\log T$, we obtain for the relation between the volume and temperature coefficients of the ideal resistivity[184,136,139]

$$\left(\frac{\partial \log \rho_i}{\partial \log V}\right)_T = \frac{d \log \kappa}{d \log V} - \frac{d \log \theta_R}{d \log V}\left[1 + \left(\frac{\partial \log \rho_i}{\partial \log T}\right)_V\right] \quad (6.3)$$

With this equation, the form of $(d \log \kappa)/(d \log V)$ may be studied, as was done by Dugdale and Gugan[136,139] for Li, Na, K, and Cu. They plotted graphs of $(\partial \log \rho_i)/(\partial \log V)$ against $1 + (\partial \log \rho_i)/(\partial \log T)$

for these metals, employing their very accurate experimental results
which descend down to helium temperatures, and found that straight
lines resulted. Equation (6.3) is thus obeyed, and the slopes and in-
tercepts of the graphs give numerical values for $(d \log \kappa)/(d \log V)$
and $-(d \log \theta_R)/(d \log V)$. The latter quantity, but with a characteristic temperature $\theta_D$ instead of $\theta_R$, will be recognized as the
Grüneisen $\gamma$, which is deducible from a knowledge of the thermal
expansion coefficient $\alpha$ and other thermodynamic data, namely,

$$\gamma = -\frac{d \log \theta_D}{d \log V} = \frac{\alpha V_0}{\beta_0 C_v} \tag{6.4}$$

Here, $\beta_0$ is the compressibility at absolute zero, $C_v$ the specific heat at
constant volume, and $V_0$ the volume of 1 g of the metal ($= 1/$density).

For the abovementioned metals the correlation of

$$-(d \log \theta_R)/(d \log V)$$

with $\gamma$ turns out quite well,[135,139] so with a little confidence equation
(6.3) may now be used for extracting values of $(d \log \kappa)/(d \log V)$.
Positive figures for Na ($+2.0$) and K ($+3.1$) are found, and negative
ones for Li ($-2.3$) and Cu ($-1.0$). Using less reliable data for the
other monovalent metals, Dugdale obtained the following figures:
Rb ($+0.7$), Ag ($-0.9$), and Au ($-0.7$).[135] It is quite apparent that
some correspondence exists between each number and the known
degree of distortion of the Fermi surface from a sphere, Na and K
having the most nearly spherical Fermi surfaces and Li and the noble
metals the least spherical. The Fermi surfaces of these latter metals
always make contact with the Brillouin zone boundaries, and one of
the consequences of higher pressures is to distort the Fermi surfaces
further and to increase the areas of contact. These alterations, by
augmenting the Umklapp scattering and tending to increase the
electrical resistance, are probably the main factors causing the upward curvatures of the resistance–pressure dependences of the monovalent metals.

Qualitative discussions such as these cannot be carried very far,
even with the monovalent metals, and still less can be said about
more complicated metals. Evidently, the pressure or volume coefficient of resistivity is still more highly sensitive to exact details of
the electron–phonon interaction mechanisms than is the temperature coefficient, for which, as indicated in Chapter 3, theoretical
analysis is difficult enough. We shall therefore merely indicate what
factors may conceivably be operating and say that the observed resistance behavior of any given metal with change in pressure is the
result of the partial counterbalancing of effects of various origins.
Thus, in a particular metal, higher pressures may raise the Fermi

energy of the electrons and lead to a decrease in the scattering of these electrons and so to a fall in the resistivity. This would be additional to the lowering expected from the rising $\theta$. Yet both these effects may be more than offset by a higher resistivity associated with a more distorted Fermi surface, as explained above. Furthermore, in those metals in which more than one band is involved, such as the transition metals with their overlapping s- and d-bands, pressure changes may modify the Fermi surface geometries in both bands, and of course the interband scattering and resultant resistivity at the same time. In addition, a few of the resistivity maxima are no doubt due to electron transfer of the type probably existing in Yb.[260]

We shall conclude by giving some references for further reading. Paul[347] has given a fine summary of the present theoretical situation, and Swenson's description[417] of the apparatus and techniques of high-pressure research is very complete. Lawson's account of experimental data obtained up to 1955[260] is invaluable for its inclusion and referencing of the majority of Bridgman's results, while the review by Bundy and Strong[96] covers more recent published work. This review is also noteworthy for its inclusion in graphical form of some of Bridgman's data corrected to the new pressure scale, which is based on the Ba transition at 58 kb instead of at 78 kb. Bridgman's classic book [M13] was partially revised in 1949.

### 6.1.2. The Influence of Tension

This is a one-dimensional pressure effect obtained when a force of extension is applied to a wire carrying a current. The resistance is altered because the tension lengthens the wire and contracts its diameter. Assuming that the elastic limit is not exceeded, an equation relating the longitudinal (or, if desired, transverse) tension coefficients of resistivity and resistance with Young's modulus and Poisson's ratio may be derived quite simply for a conductor of rectangular cross section (see Gerritsen [M1]). Gerritsen also lists some of Bridgman's experimental results[89a] showing that positive values for the longitudinal and transverse tension coefficients of resistivity predominate. An application of this property is to be found in strain gauges, which have been previously mentioned in Section 1.1.

## 6.2. THE INFLUENCE OF A MAGNETIC FIELD AND MAGNETORESISTANCE

### 6.2.1. The Influence of a Magnetic Field

When an electric field $E_z$ is applied to a metallic specimen, a flow of current designated by the current density $J_z$ results which is parallel to $E_z$ and from which the normal *electrical resistance* may be determined; there is of course no net current flow in directions perpendicular to $E_z$. If a magnetic field $H_z$ is now applied in the same direction as $E_z$, the conduction electrons are constrained to follow helical instead of linear paths in between collisions, and it is found that the resistance is almost always higher than that obtained in the absence of a magnetic field. The fractional change in resistance that occurs is called the *longitudinal magnetoresistance*. But if instead the external magnetic field (now called $H_y$) is applied in a transverse direction to $E_z$, a different current density parallel to $E_z$ is found to result, causing a fractional change in resistance compared to the zero-field resistance, which is known as the *transverse magnetoresistance*. In addition, a potential gradient perpendicular to both $E_z$ and $H_y$ is set up, giving the phenomenon of the *Hall effect*. We shall not treat the Hall effect at all in this book, and neither shall we deal with the remaining galvanomagnetic and thermomagnetic effects not mentioned above. For these, Jan[227] and Putley [M28] are suggested as basic references.

### 6.2.2. Magnetoresistance

Except in the cases of certain ferromagnetic metals and alloys and in the resistance-minimum phenomenon (Section 3.9), longitudinal and transverse magnetoresistivities are positive. That is to say, the electrical resistance increases with increasing magnetic field. In weak fields it does so as $H^2$, but in large fields it usually tends toward a saturation value, although in a number of instances an increase proportional to $H^2$, or to $H$, continues up to the highest fields attainable ( > 300,000 Oersteds). It is on account of the possibility of this rather unexpected high-field behavior that the magnetoresistance occupies its place of importance in the realm of Fermi surface analysis. Yet, while much information on the magnetoresistance of metals has been gathered experimentally, not very much can at this time be explained theoretically. The real difficulty is that the magnetoresistance itself is a second-order effect compared to the normal resistance and is in fact nonexistent on the free electron model; consequently, it appears only when the ways in which real metals depart from the simple theoretical models are considered.

We now introduce the important rule originated by Kohler,[249] which can be most helpful when discussing experimental results. This states quite simply that the magnetoresistivity $\Delta\rho/\rho$, where $\rho$ is the zero-field resistivity and $\Delta\rho$ the increase due to the field $H$, is a function of the ratio $H/\rho$:

$$\frac{\Delta\rho}{\rho} = f\left(\frac{H}{\rho}\right) \tag{6.5}$$

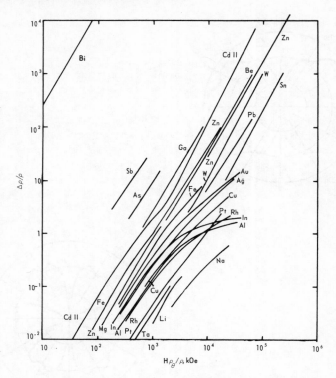

Fig. 46. The transverse magnetoresistivity of 22 metals plotted on a reduced Kohler diagram (taken from Olsen[M8] and based on the results of Justi and Ascherman[232] and Luthi[282]).

For a particular metal, $f$ depends on the orientation of $H$ and $E$, and, if a single crystal, also on the orientation of the crystal axes. Theoretically, Kohler's rule can be shown to follow directly from the Boltzmann equation, if a relaxation time solution can be employed; and experimentally it is usually found to agree fairly well with observation. Figure 46, given to illustrate it, with $H\rho_\theta/\rho$ as abscissa (where $\rho_\theta$ is the resistivity at $T = \theta_D{}^\circ$K), is called a *reduced Kohler plot* (Justi[231]). By using it, a rough estimate of the transverse magnetoresistivity may be deduced if, at any temperature $T_1$, $\rho_{T1}$, $\rho_\theta$, and $H$ are known. From the parameters in Kohler's rule, we note that in order to obtain as large a $\Delta\rho/\rho$ as possible for a given metal we must employ *pure* metals at low temperatures (to lessen $\rho$) and high fields. We note also that the magnetoresistivity effect is smallest in the simplest alkali metals

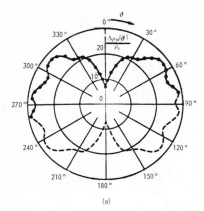

(a)

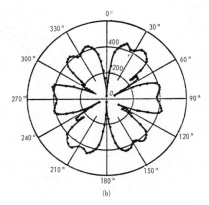

(b)

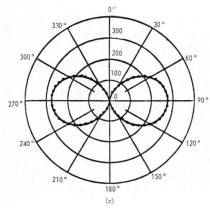

(c)

Fig. 47. The transverse magneto-resistivity as a function of the angle between the magnetic field and the crystal axes at 4.2°K and approximately 23,000 Oe for (a) Mg (cph),[44] (b) Pb (fcc),[43] and (c) Tl (cph).[43]

and greatest in the Bi-group metals. Last, we mention that, since deviations from Kohler's rule do occur and are large in high-purity Al at low temperatures, for example,[84] Jones and Sondheimer[230] have recently suggested a more generalized rule which is unwieldy but takes better account of anisotropic scattering in actual metals. This will not be considered, however, in this introductory discussion.

The analysis by Sondheimer and Wilson[407] of possible magneto-resistive effects arising from a two-band model for metals in which there are different conductivities and electron or hole densities in each band still leads to a zero longitudinal magnetoresistivity, but a transverse magnetoresistivity is now found to be possible under certain reasonable conditions. One special case gives a transverse magnetoresistivity that may be written in the form[250]

$$\frac{\Delta\rho}{\rho} = \frac{A(H/\rho)^2}{1 + B(H/\rho)^2} \tag{6.6}$$

From this equation it follows that $\Delta\rho/\rho \propto H^2$ in small fields, which agrees well with observation, but in high fields two alternative possibilities arise. If $B \neq 0$, $\Delta\rho/\rho$ tends toward a definite limit, but if $B = 0$, as when the numbers of electrons in the two bands are equal, $\Delta\rho/\rho$ has no limit and remains proportional to $H^2$ no matter how great the field. This is also in accord with observation, although experiments show that a linear and boundless increase with $H$ is yet a third possibility. The simple two-band theory does not provide for this at all, and, as just indicated, fails to account for the longitudinal magnetoresistivity, for which Kohler diagrams may also be plotted. It can, in addition, say nothing of the dependence of the magnetoresistivity on the orientation of the field with the axes of single crystals. In cubic metals this high-field effect is found only at low temperatures, but in noncubic metals it can be observed easily at even room temperature. The polar diagrams of Fig. 47 demonstrate the transverse magneto-resistivities found for single crystals of Mg, Pb, and Tl[43,44] at 4.2°K as the direction of the field is varied through 360°. The shapes of such figures vary according to the field strength, so an $H^2$ law cannot hold for all directions, except maybe for small fields. This is made clearer by Fig. 48, which shows the field dependence of $\Delta\rho/\rho$ along the directions of minimum and maximum variation for the Pb specimen. The magnetoresistivity tends to a saturation value for one direction, but rises as $H^2$ without limit for the other.

This is understood nowadays as follows:[M12] In large fields the electron paths in k-space (which are practically on the Fermi surface) follow lines of constant energy perpendicular to the direction of the magnetic field. When a crystal direction in which the magnetoresistivity does not saturate is found, this shows that the metal possesses

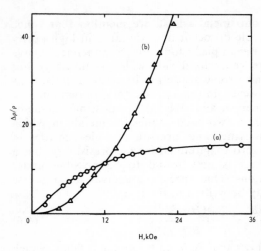

Fig. 48. The field dependence of the magnetoresistivity of Pb for the directions of (a) minimum and (b) maximum magnetoresistivity variation in Fig. 47(b) (Alekseevskii and Gaidukov[43]).

a multiply connected Fermi surface on which the electrons are traveling without bound, subject to the one restriction that they remain perpendicular to the field. Unbounded paths like these are called *open orbits*; they cannot occur if the Fermi surface does not touch the zone boundary, under which circumstances orbits are always *closed* and of quite short length. Theoretical considerations[266] show that for open orbits the magnetoresistivity in single crystals extends to infinity in proportion to $H^2$, but for closed orbits it has a limiting upper value. Herein lies the power of magnetoresistivity measurements in Fermi-surface mapping, because from high-field experiments on single crystals the directions in which contacts occur with the zone boundaries can be found by stereographic plotting of saturated and nonsaturated magnetoresistivity regions.

Such studies of the Fermi surface are further facilitated when they are combined with measurements of other properties that give additional clues about the nature of the Fermi surface. The *anomalous skin effect* (Section 6.3.2) and the *de Haas–van Alphen effect*[194] are two of these. The latter is the oscillatory fluctuation of magnetic susceptibility with $1/H$; the amplitude increases with decreasing temperature and with increasing field, and from the periods we can deduce the maximum or minimum cross-sectional areas of the Fermi surface that lie transverse to the field. We have mentioned this here because related oscillatory effects occur at low temperatures in the transport properties as well as in the susceptibility; the first to be discovered was in the magnetoresistivity of Bi (Schubnikov and de Haas[391]). All of these phenomena originate in the quantization of the electron orbits by a magnetic field.

Regarding the question of the linear increase in magnetoresistivity with $H$ so often found for polycrystalline specimens, Ziman[457, M12] has offered the explanation that this is caused by an averaging over the separate crystallites, for some of which $\Delta\rho/\rho \propto H^2$ while for others $\Delta\rho/\rho$ tends to constancy. Ziman's book should be consulted for further details of this and all other aspects of the theory of magnetoresistivity—in particular for a description of the present theory, based on the methods of Jones and Zener[229] and Davis,[127] in which longitudinal as well as transverse magnetoresistivities are obtained. The application of the methods of magnetoresistance measurement to a study of the Fermi surface has been described by Chambers[99] and recently fully reviewed by Fawcett.[152]

## 6.3. THE INFLUENCE OF SIZE

In the entire treatment up to this point we have ignored any effect that the size and shape of a given specimen may have in determining the observed electrical resistivity of a metal. This cannot be justified, however, if the conditions are such that the mean free path for the electron scattering is of the same order as one of the dimensions of the specimen. At room temperature, at any rate, there is no problem, since electron mean free paths are always very small ($10^{-5}$ or $10^{-6}$ cm) and the resistivity is never significantly affected. But at low temperatures, where free paths exceeding 0.1 mm are not uncommon in pure metals, the resistivity may be considerably raised in thin film and wire specimens less than $\frac{1}{2}$ to 1 mm thick, because of the increased surface scattering. Indeed, in the purest Sn specimen of Zernov and Sharvin,[455] the mean free path corresponding to the residual resistivity was calculated as 3 mm. Obviously then, in measuring resistivities of high-purity specimens at low temperatures, one must be careful to ensure that appropriate corrections are made for size effects. As both Sondheimer[406] and MacDonald[M4] have remarked, it is nevertheless a happy circumstance that merely by straightforward resistivity experiments at low temperatures one is able to deduce values of the mean free path for electron scattering, a parameter that has hitherto been a theoretical concept difficult to compute.

If we let $l$ be the mean free path for electron scattering in a material of bulk resistivity $\rho_b$, then by substituting $\tau = l/v$ in equation (3.6), we obtain the relation

$$\rho_b = \frac{mv}{ne^2} \cdot \frac{1}{l} \qquad (6.7)$$

In a thin wire of diameter $d$, where $d$ is comparable to or less than $l$, the observed resistivity $\rho$ will be greater than that of the bulk substance, and on a simple model[334] the additional resistivity may be taken as being inversely proportional to $d$, since the latter will, as a rough approximation, be the free path pertaining to the surface scattering. Consequently, by assuming Matthiessen's rule to hold, we obtain

$$\rho = \frac{mv}{ne^2}\left(\frac{1}{l} + \frac{1}{d}\right) \tag{6.8}$$

which, by using equation (6.7), gives

$$\frac{\rho}{\rho_b} = 1 + \frac{l}{d} \tag{6.9}$$

a relation that is found to be moderately well obeyed. A rigorous computation by Dingle[131] leads to a similar formula, though with a different constant, for cases when $d \gg l$:

$$\frac{\rho}{\rho_b} = 1 + \frac{3}{4}\frac{l}{d} \tag{6.10}$$

But if $d \ll l$,

$$\frac{\rho}{\rho_b} \rightarrow \frac{l}{d} \tag{6.11}$$

a result that is also derivable from equation (6.9).

For thin films, Fuchs[162] has given the following formulas:

$$\frac{\rho}{\rho_b} = 1 + \frac{3}{8}\frac{l}{d} \quad \text{when } d \gg l \tag{6.12}$$

and

$$\frac{\rho}{\rho_b} = \frac{4}{3}\frac{l}{d}\frac{1}{\log_e(l/d)} \quad \text{when } d \ll l \tag{6.13}$$

where $d$ is now the film thickness.

The foregoing formulas assume that the surface scattering is diffuse, the electrons losing all of their drift velocity on meeting the surface. This is generally the case, but specular reflection undoubtedly occurs in Bi,[161] as borne out by agreement between experiment and the modified theory that allows for specular reflection in this metal.[203,369] Olsen [M8] has computed a table comparing the ratios

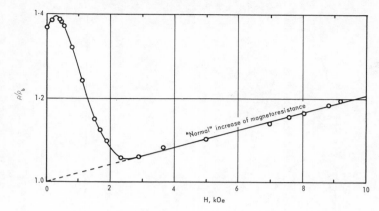

Fig. 49. The influence of size at low fields on the transverse magnetoresistivity of a Na wire (MacDonald[M4]).

$\rho/\rho_b$ for diffuse scattering, calculated for a range of $d/l$ values from the equations given above, with those for 50% specular reflection.

It has also been assumed in the above formulas that the temperature-dependent part of the resistivity is not itself influenced by the size of the specimen, but from the experimental observations of Olsen[335] it is now clear that some mechanism is at work which slightly modifies the electron–phonon scattering contribution. Olsen's suggestion that it is caused by electrons being further diffusely scattered at the surface after normal small-angle lattice scattering has since been supported theoretically to some extent.[80,283]

### 6.3.1. The Magnetoresistance Size Effect

Since a longitudinal magnetic field applied to a conductor tends to direct the electrons into helical orbits with axes parallel to the axis of the specimen, we intuitively expect that the application of high longitudinal magnetic fields will partially, and for large-enough fields wholly, annul the size-effect resistive component of thin wires and films. A big-enough field applied parallel to the plane of a film but *transverse* to the direction of the current flow will also reduce the resistivity to its normal bulk magnetoresistive value, but the reduction will not be complete in the case of a wire. This is because the electron velocity component parallel to the field remains unchanged, and so in a wire some electrons will still collide with the walls. These various effects have been investigated theoretically by Chambers[98] and MacDonald and Sarginson,[290] and experimentally by Mac-Donald[285, M4] and White and Woods[437] on Na wires, Cotti, Olsen,

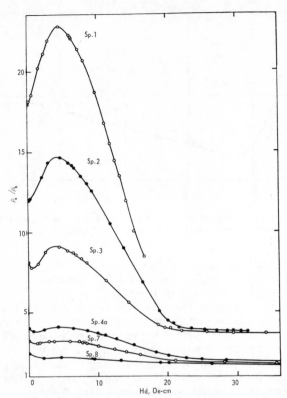

Fig. 50. The size contribution to the resistivity of Al films in a transverse magnetic field. The normal "bulk" magnetoresistivity has been subtracted (Försvoll and Holwech[155]). The thicknesses of the films were 0.0125 mm (Sp.1), 0.025 mm (Sp.2), 0.04 mm (Sp.3), 0.063 mm (Sp.4a), 0.103 mm (Sp.7), and 0.21 mm (Sp.8).

Daunt, and Kreitman[111] on In films, and Försvoll and Holwech[155,156] on Al and In films (naming only the principal papers). As examples, we illustrate in Fig. 49 MacDonald's results obtained on a Na wire in a transverse field and in Fig. 50 Försvoll and Holwech's results for Al films. The slight increase in resistivity seen at low fields is due to an initial predominating effect from the relatively few electrons which have directions such that they actually suffer reductions in free paths at these low fields.

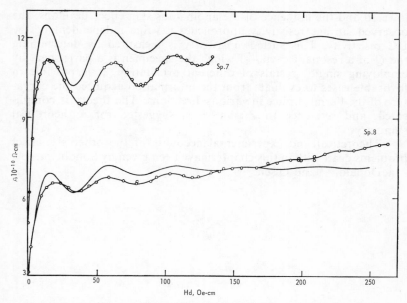

Fig. 51. Experimentally observed Sondheimer oscillations in Al films compared to theory (to which approximate magnetoresistivities have been added to make the comparison more exact) (Försvoll and Holwech[155]). The thicknesses of specimens 7 and 8 were 0.103 mm and 0.21 mm, respectively.

Försvoll and Holwech[154,155,156] have also studied the effect predicted by Sondheimer[404] which arises when magnetic fields are applied in a direction perpendicular to both the current and the film. Their results for two Al samples are compared to Sondheimer's theory in Fig. 51. The remarkable oscillatory variation with the field strength is due to fluctuations in the electron velocities, causing the distribution function to vary periodically with distance from the surface.

### 6.3.2. The Anomalous Skin Effect

Finally, we come to the *anomalous skin effect*, which is another size-effect phenomenon of great importance in the theory of metals. It was H. London[275] who first pointed out (in 1940) that the classical theory of the skin effect would no longer hold and that changes in the skin resistivity would occur when the electron mean free path in a metal exceeds the penetration depth of a high-frequency magnetic field. Normally, at high frequencies the surface resistivity varies as the square root of the bulk DC resistivity, but as the temperature is lowered and the influence of the anomalous skin effect develops, the observed surface resistivity approaches a value independent of the DC resistivity. This surface resistivity is measured by determining the $Q$ of a resonant cavity of which the specimen is a part; then, by employing single crystals of different orientation, it is possible in favorable cases to evaluate from the information acquired the curvature of the Fermi surface in various directions. The theory is complicated, and reference to Ziman [M12] is suggested for a theoretical summary.

Theoretical and experimental accounts of the other size-effect problems dealt with in this chapter have been given by Sondheimer,[406] MacDonald, [M4] and Olsen. [M8]

*Chapter 7*

# Resistance Measuring Techniques at Ordinary and Low Temperatures

## 7.1. GENERAL PROBLEMS

The account given here must necessarily embrace methods for measuring electrical resistances of all magnitudes from less than $10^{-6} \, \Omega$ to more than $10^6 \, \Omega$.

On the one hand, determination of temperature by use of the electrical resistance thermometers to be discussed in the next chapter requires measurement of resistances which are invariably larger than $1 \, \Omega$. A typical ice-point value for a platinum resistance thermometer is $25 \, \Omega$, while resistances of carbon or doped-germanium resistors in the liquid-helium region usually lie between 50 and 50,000 $\Omega$.

On the other hand, electrical resistances of metal or alloy specimens are rarely greater than $1 \, \Omega$, even at room temperature, and, in the case of very pure material, are perhaps as small as $10^{-7} \, \Omega$ at helium temperatures. Since the resistance of a sample of length $l$ and cross-sectional area $A$ is equal to $\rho l / A$, where $\rho$ is the resistivity, and $l$ is normally made as big and $A$ as small as possible. The principal factors limiting the choice of these dimensions are, in practice, the working space within the cryostat, the quantity of the substance actually available, and the metallurgical and chemical properties of the substance—for example, its workability and reactivity. With high-purity samples of metals such as Au or Na, there is also the effect of size to be considered at low temperatures. If we wish to study these metals in the impurity-scattering region ($< 10^\circ$K) and yet make sure that size effects remain unimportant, wire diameters of about $\frac{1}{2}$ to 1 mm are the smallest that can be tolerated (Section 6.3).* Therefore,

* For very high-purity specimens of certain other metals such as Sn, In, and Pb, even thicker wires may be needed to ensure that effects of size will not arise at low temperatures (Section 6.3).

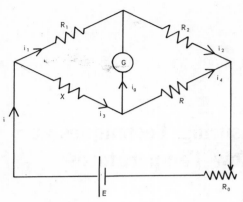

Fig. 52. The Wheatstone
bridge.

taking as examples the reasonable values of $l = 20$ cm and $d = \frac{1}{2}$ mm
for Au wire, and $l = 5$ cm and $d = 2$ mm for a metallurgically more
difficult element such as Bi, we find by calculation their room-
temperature resistances each to be about $2 \times 10^{-2}$ Ω. At helium
temperatures the resistance of the Au, if extremely pure, will become
about $10^{-5}$ Ω.

The following account of the resistance measuring techniques is
concerned with those methods best suited to meet the requirements
of cryogenic work, where further difficulties are provided by the
high-resistance specimen leads that sometimes have to be used, and
where, without special precautions, the presence of stray thermal or
contact emfs is sometimes ruinous. We shall begin with the simple
Wheatstone bridge and its more important modifications, before
passing on to the more precise and elaborate potentiometers.

## 7.2. WHEATSTONE BRIDGE*

Even in its simplest form, the Wheatstone bridge can without
difficulty be used to measure resistances in the range between 10 and
10,000 Ω with an accuracy of 0.1 % if reasonably good components
are used. With a little care and some detailed improvements, resistances between 1 Ω and 100 MΩ may be measured to the same degree
of accuracy.

The basic Wheatstone circuit, but with switches and the usual
galvanometer shunt omitted, is shown in Fig. 52. $R_1$ and $R_2$ are fixed

* The principle was first applied by S. H. Christie[100] and reported by him
in 1833. He called it a "differential arrangement." It was developed and popu-
larized through the efforts of C. Wheatstone from 1843 onward.

known resistors called the ratio arms. $X$ is the unknown resistor and $R$ a variable known one. $G$ represents a null-detecting instrument such as a galvanometer, $E$ a supply of constant emf, and $R_0$ a rheostat for controlling the current to the bridge.

Let the currents in the various parts of the circuit be as indicated in the figure. When $R$ has been adjusted so that no current flows through $G$, $i_1 = i_2$, $i_3 = i_4$, and $i_g = 0$. The potential drops in arms $R_1$ and $X$ are then equal, as are the potential drops in arms $R_2$ and $R$.

We then have

$$i_1 R_1 = i_3 X \tag{7.1}$$

and

$$i_2 R_2 = i_4 R$$

which may be written

$$i_1 R_2 = i_3 R \tag{7.2}$$

Dividing equation (7.1) by (7.2), we finally obtain

$$\frac{X}{R} = \frac{R_1}{R_2} \tag{7.3}$$

from which the unknown resistance $X$ may be calculated.

A reversing switch provided in the battery circuit can be used to reverse the current to the bridge and therefore permit two separate measurements of $X$, largely eliminating thermal emfs. This effect can be still further reduced by employing standard resistors as the ratio arms $R_1$ and $R_2$, and arranging a second commutator to interchange their positions.

A galvanometer touch key should be provided and also a high-resistance shunt to protect the galvanometer from possible excessive deflections during the early stages of the balancing procedure. The variable resistor $R$ should preferably be a decade resistance box. If the smallest decade is in steps of 0.1 $\Omega$, it is then quite possible that the sensitivity of the bridge will be limited not by the decade resistance box but by the sensitivity of the galvanometer, if this is, say, an inexpensive portable model. To increase the sensitivity, one must either select a better galvanometer or arrange the bridge components in the most efficient manner so as to give the maximum current through the galvanometer.

An estimate of the galvanometer current when near the balance point can easily be obtained by applying Kirchhoff's laws to the circuit of Fig. 52. Let $G$ be the galvanometer resistance and assume that the resistance in the battery circuit, including that of the battery, is zero.

Six simultaneous equations can be obtained, which, on reduction, give the six unknown currents. The current through the galvanometer, $i_g$, is found to be given by

$$i_g = \frac{V(RR_1 - XR_2)}{G(XR_1 + RR_1 + XR_2 + RR_2) + RR_1(X + R_2) + XR_2(R + R_1)}$$

(7.4)

We see at once that at the actual balance point, where $i_g = 0$, $RR_1 = XR_2$, as obtained before in (7.3).

Now, the sensitivity $S$ of the bridge is at its greatest when a given fractional change of the variable resistor $R$ causes the greatest possible deflection of the galvanometer. If the galvanometer has a sensitivity of $S_g$ per unit current, we may then write

$$S = S_g R \frac{\partial i_g}{\partial R}$$

(7.5)

where $R = XR_2/R_1$.

As the balance point is approached, $\partial i_g/\partial R$ becomes simply

$$\frac{VR_1}{G(XR_1 + RR_1 + XR_2 + RR_2) + RR_1(X + R_2) + XR_2(R + R_1)}$$

(7.6)

therefore

$$S = \frac{S_g RR_1 V}{G(XR_1 + RR_1 + XR_2 + RR_2) + RR_1(X + R_2) + XR_2(R + R_1)}$$

$$= \frac{S_g V}{G(2 + X/R + R/X) + R_1 + R_2 + R + X}$$

(7.7)

The quantity $S$ is greatest when the denominator of equation (7.7) is least—that is, when

$$\frac{\partial}{\partial R}\left[G\left(2 + \frac{X}{R} + \frac{R}{X}\right) + R_1 + R_2 + R + X\right] = 0$$

$$-\frac{GX}{R^2} + \frac{G}{X} + 1 = 0$$

or

$$R = X\left(\frac{G}{G + X}\right)^{1/2}$$

(7.8)

Thus, if $X$ is known very approximately, for a given $G$ the best value of $R$ and hence $R_1/R_2$ [by means of equation (7.3)] may be estimated. As an example, we see from equation (7.8) that if $G \gg X$, the most sensitive arrangement of the bridge occurs for $R = X$. This obtains when the ratio arms $R_1$ and $R_2$ are equal. Also, from equation (7.7) we see that for best sensitivity $R_1 + R_2$ should be made as small as possible. There is, however, a limit to be observed here because of the maximum current that these resistors can pass safely without heating and changing their resistance values.

The effect on the bridge sensitivity of varying the galvanometer resistance $G$ and the sensitivity $S_g$ may also be studied by means of equations (7.7) and (7.8). In general, galvanometers of more than adequate sensitivity should not be used, as excessive sensitivity leads to time wasted in handling an unnecessarily delicate instrument, especially if it is of long period. A galvanometer having a sensitivity of a few millimeters per microampere should suffice for most purposes. For bridges intended for measurements of a few ohms, a low-resistance galvanometer is best, while for high-resistance measurements, a galvanometer of high resistance should be used. One of 100 $\Omega$ or so should be satisfactory for general purposes.

The above comments should give some idea of the criteria to be considered when choosing the various bridge components. The task is easier when the range within which the unknown resistances will normally lie is fairly narrow. Commercial Wheatstone bridges necessarily have wide practical measuring ranges. There are some which can be used between 0.01 $\Omega$ and 100 M$\Omega$ with accuracies of the order of 0.01 %. In such bridges, refined techniques of construction are employed which minimize the temperature coefficients of the resistors, the generation of thermal emfs at the switches and terminals, and the actual temperature changes occurring within the box in which the bridge components are housed.

For a fuller discussion of some of the topics outlined above, reference should be made to the book *Electrical Measurements*, by F. A. Laws. [M24]

## 7.3. FOUR-TERMINAL RESISTORS

The chief drawback of the Wheatstone bridge is that one measures the *total* resistance in the unknown arm, which besides $X$ includes contact resistances and the resistances of the two leads. In precision measurements of less than $10^{-1}$ $\Omega$, the resistances of the leads are no longer unimportant, since they are of the order $10^{-3}$ to $10^{-4}$ $\Omega$ at room

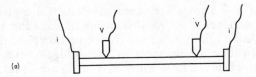

(a)

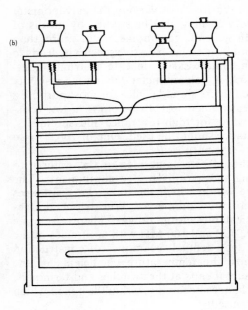

(b)

Fig. 53. (a) Rod specimen set-up as a four-terminal resistor. The four contacts must be spot welded, soldered, or spring-loaded to ensure that they are in good contact with the specimen. (b) Diagrammatic representation of a commercial four-terminal standard resistance.

temperature, even for short, thick copper leads. At the same time, possibly large and variable contact resistances resulting from oxidation, corrosion, or residual enamel on the wire surfaces where they contact the specimen (or the terminals with which it is provided) would render reliable measurements of low resistances impossible. However, these problems can be overcome by setting up the unknown resistor as a four-terminal resistor, supplying it with separate current and potential leads, as shown in Fig. 53(a).

The resistance determined by this method is the resistance of that part of the unknown resistor lying between the two points where the potential wires make contact with it. With the four-terminal arrangement, it is ensured that the potential leads themselves are not a part of the circuit whose resistance is to be measured, and in the null potentiometric methods most often used (see next section) these leads carry no current in the balance position. Thus, contact resistances in that part of the circuit can have no effect on the measurements, while contact resistances which will be present in the current leads are fortunately of very little significance. Another feature of the four-terminal arrangement is that the potential lead contacts are usually positioned at least a few millimeters away from the current lead contacts, because near the latter the equipotential lines of the electric field in the specimen are very often not uniform. It is for such reasons as these that commercial standard resistors of less than 1 $\Omega$ are invariably supplied with four terminals [Fig. 53(b)], and why, for precision work on the measurement of low resistances, specimens must be set up with four leads.

The unmodified Wheatstone bridge cannot be used to measure the resistances of four-terminal resistors. For such measurements at room temperature in the range $10^{-5}$ to 1 $\Omega$, where lead resistances are of the order $10^{-3}$ to $10^{-4}$ $\Omega$ and where an accuracy to 0.5 % or better is desired, recourse can be made to the Kelvin double bridge. [M24] This is an elegant modification of the Wheatstone bridge, but we shall not describe it here because its use is normally limited to comparisons in the steady state of like resistors, and because the lead resistances with which we are concerned are more likely to be in the range 1 to 100 $\Omega$. This is because in low-temperature work it is necessary to utilize long leads of wire, sometimes very fine, in order to reduce heat leaks. In some cases, one must go further and use for leads, instead of copper wire, wire of high electrical resistivity, such as constantan or manganin, since these alloys have particularly small thermal conductivities. Consequently, a Kelvin bridge cannot be used for low-temperature work, since the thick copper leads essential for its use would introduce truly excessive heat leaks into the cryostat.

For platinum resistance thermometry, precision bridges of very high performance have been especially developed (refer also to Section 8.5). The most widely used of these bridges are the Smith bridge (a form of Kelvin double bridge) and the Mueller bridge. The circuitry of the former is such that once three of the lead resistances have been adjusted to equality, the resistance of the thermometer is thereafter found from one balance position only. In the Mueller bridge, carefully designed and well-sited resistors are used, and lead and contact resistances are eliminated by current reversal. However, the lead resistances do need to be fairly small and in the case of the Smith bridge nearly equal in value. The range of the

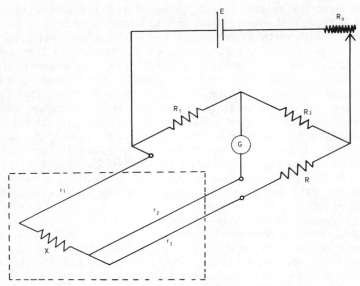

Fig. 54.   Method of setting up a resistor with three leads for the rough
elimination of high lead resistances.

Smith bridge is 111 $\Omega$ and that of the Mueller bridge 400 $\Omega$; both are
accurate to $10^{-4}$ $\Omega$. Full details of the design and operation of these
bridges may be obtained by referring to the original papers[401,327,63]
or to the descriptions to be found in Laws [M24] and the volumes of
*Temperature: Its Measurement and Control in Science and
Industry.* [M34-M37]

Even with platinum resistance thermometers, the use of potentiometers is recommended for resistance measurements below about
50°K. But before we pass on to describe potentiometric methods,
mention will be made of one particularly simple, though rather
rough, Wheatstone bridge method that eliminates the effect of high-
resistance leads sufficiently well for the purposes of measurements on
large resistances such as carbon resistors at low temperatures.

The resistor under test is connected by three wires into an ordinary
Wheatstone network, so that one of the leads is in the galvanometer
branch and the other two leads are in the adjacent $X$ and $R$ branches
(Fig. 54). If the resistances of these leads are $r_1$, $r_2$, and $r_3$, then the
condition of balance is

$$\frac{X + r_1}{R + r_3} = \frac{R_1}{R_2}$$

If, furthermore, the leads are carefully chosen to be identical as far as possible and if the ratio of $R_1$ and $R_2$ is unity, then $X$ is simply equal to $R$. A method of this type was first suggested by Siemens.[398]

## 7.4. POTENTIOMETERS

Potentiometric methods afford the most accurate and convenient means of determining the resistances of four-terminal resistors whatever the temperature and the resistances of the leads. An accuracy of better than 1 % can even be obtained with resistances of the order of $10^{-6}$ $\Omega$.

The presence and effect of high-resistance leads is rendered quite unimportant, because in the final balance position no currents flow in the potential leads, while the effect of any stray emfs that may be present is eliminated by current reversal in the current leads.

### 7.4.1. Principle of the DC Potentiometer

Essentially, a potentiometer is a means of comparing emf values. If one of the emfs is already known, say, the emf of a standard cell, then the other may be determined. In the application of the method to the measurement of low resistances, the same steady current is passed through both the unknown resistance and a standard known resistance connected with it in series. The potential drops across the two are then compared.

To understand the principles involved, consider first the elementary form indicated in Fig. 55.

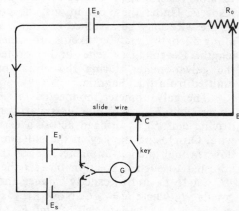

Fig. 55. Diagram to illustrate the principle of the DC potentiometer.

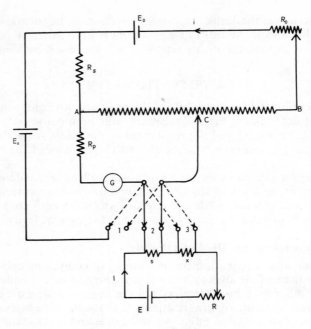

Fig. 56. Circuit diagram to illustrate the comparison of
two resistances, $X$ and $S$, by means of a potentiometer.

A steady current $i$, whose value is controlled by means of a
variable resistor $R_0$, is passed through a slide-wire $AB$, uniform in all
respects. Under these conditions, the potential drop per unit length
of the wire may be assumed constant, and the total potential drop
along a length $l$ may be taken as $rli$, where $r$ is the resistance per unit
length. Reversing switches and a protecting resistor, necessary for
the galvanometer during the initial balancing stages, have been
omitted from this diagram.

The galvanometer, connected in series with the source of unknown emf $E_1$, which has its polarity in opposition to that of the
driving emf $E_0$, is bridged across a certain length $AC$ of the slide-
wire. On closing the key in the galvanometer circuit, a current will
flow through the galvanometer, unless the sliding contact $C$ has been
adjusted to such a position on $AB$ that the potential drops along
$AC$ due to $E_0$ and $E_1$ exactly balance and annul one another. $E_1$ then
equals $irl_1$, where $l_1 = AC$. Now, if $E_1$ is replaced by a second source
of emf, say a standard cell of emf $E_s$, and the new balance position

found, $E_s$ is given by $irl_s$, where $l_s$ is the new length of $AC$. Finally, by division we obtain for the ratio of the two emf values:

$$\frac{E_1}{E_s} = \frac{l_1}{l_s} \tag{7.9}$$

Often it is desired that the current through the slide-wire resistance should be identical on each occasion that the potentiometer is used. This can be achieved by an initial standardization in which the emf $E_s$ from a standard cell is applied to a suitable fixed resistor which is in the driver-cell circuit. $E_s$ is in opposition to $E_0$, and the precise balance position is found by adjusting $R_0$ so that no current flows through the galvanometer. $AB$ can then be calibrated to read directly in volts.

This principle is illustrated in the more fully developed potentiometer shown in Fig. 56, which will also serve to indicate the working principles of commercial potentiometers with which emf values of $1 \, \mu V$ can be measured.

In this figure $AB$ represents several decades of manganin-wound resistors in series. $R_s$ is the resistor used in conjunction with the standard cell for establishing the standard driver current through the potentiometer.* $R_s$ is not quite a fixed resistor, but is made variable over a small range in order that allowance may be made for the effect of small temperature changes on the standard cell. $R_0$ represents the coarse and fine adjustments in the driver cell circuit. Then with the double-pole, double-throw switch in position 1, $R_0$ is adjusted to give the standard current to the potentiometer.

In position 2, the emf across a standard resistor $S$, which is in series with the unknown resistor $X$, is applied to the galvanometer circuit, and the potential drop $V_s$ across it is read from the calibrated dials of the potentiometer. Last, the switch is moved to position 3 and the potential difference $V_x$ across $X$ obtained.

We may therefore write for equation (7.9),

$$\frac{IX}{IS} = \frac{V_x}{V_s}$$

where $I$ is the current through $X$ and $S$.

* A series arrangement of this type, though the simplest, is not employed in commercial potentiometers because a 4 V emf source would be needed in order to produce the necessary voltage drops across $R_s$ and $AB$. To avoid this, an alternative means would be to arrange the switching so as to have $R_s$ much smaller than the desired value and to make up the remainder by using a part of the slide-wire circuit.

The unknown resistance $X$ can now be simply calculated from

$$X = S\frac{V_x}{V_s} \qquad (7.10)$$

### 7.4.2. Precautions to be Observed in Achieving the Best Accuracy

To obtain the greatest precision in measurement, some details of procedure and construction require elaboration.

First, the use of the potentiometer in the manner described above assumes that the currents in the various circuits remain perfectly constant. If, however, it is considered that the currents may have changed while the potential measurements across the specimen were being taken, the measurements of the former should be repeated and averaged. The current in the driver circuit is often 10 mA or 1 mA, depending on the sensitivity range being used. With these small currents, no important change in standardization should occur over a period of minutes for a 2 V lead–acid accumulator in good condition. It is in any case best to connect the latter to the potentiometer at least 10 or 15 min before use to allow its current when under load to become steadier, and good practice to leave it permanently connected, until such time, of course, as it requires recharging. After several hours' connection, the current it is delivering will be stable to a few parts in a million.

In order to ease the problem of maintaining very steady currents, Tinsley and some other companies manufacture current stabilizers for potentiometric use. These instruments are particularly useful in circuits where the circuit resistance is not constant. The working principle is the familiar one in which the potential drop across a resistor placed in the desired stable-current circuit is compared with the emf of a standard cell. The error signal, or difference between the two, is amplified by a DC photoelectric-amplifier, which causes the current to change so as to reduce the error. Under steady conditions, the current is stabilized almost indefinitely by this means to within 1 part in $10^6$. Currents stable to this degree are obligatory if the accuracy of potential measurement is to be of the order of 1 in $10^5$.

A description of a current stabilizer that can be constructed without much difficulty has been given by Thompson.[423] It was able to supply 50 mA constant to within 1 part in $10^5$ for periods of about 10 min.

It is also best to have reversing switches in both the potential and current circuits of the specimen, particularly if small emf values are to be measured. By reversing the currents after each reading of $X$ and $S$ and taking the readings again, spurious thermal emfs present in the potential circuit and current leads may be effectively eliminated. In dynamic experiments (next chapter) in which potential measurements are made while the specimen temperature is slowly changing, there often occurs an unwanted temperature gradient along the specimen itself. Nevertheless, the effect of this on the precision of the resistance determination can be virtually annulled by current reversal.

It must be remembered that after current reversal in the specimen potential circuit the polarity of the battery of the potentiometer must be changed before the potential can be rebalanced. The Tinsley design of reversing switch is extremely useful in this respect because it will simultaneously reverse the current in the battery circuit plus currents from two other sources of emf, and in addition cut out the galvanometer at the moment of reversal. This ensures rapid commutation and a minimum "kick" of the galvanometer on reversal.

It is, of course, obvious that there should be no appreciable generation of thermal emfs within the potentiometer itself, and the resistances of all the resistance coils, especially those in the battery circuit ($R_0$), should remain constant. Good design of coils, switches, and moving contacts and their placement in a box, oil-filled and stirred, if necessary, to ensure a more uniform temperature distribution are features of modern commercial potentiometers, further details of which we shall not go into here. If the reader requires such information, reference should be made to Laws[M24] and to the electrical instrument catalogs of the leading manufacturers.

In these references, there is also information on the very high precision potentiometers such as the Diesselhorst, in which the effect of thermal emfs on the performance of the potentiometer is further reduced by excellent circuit design. The Diesselhorst potentiometer, for example, can measure emf values to the nearest 0.1 $\mu$V, and the best of the Honeywell–Rubicon instruments (Models 2768 and 2773) to the nearest 0.01 $\mu$V. The accuracy of Model 2773 is to within 0.01 $\mu$V, plus 0.01 % of the potentiometer reading. Variable contacts in the potential circuit, a defect of the simpler potentiometers, are avoided altogether, and the parasitic thermal emfs, inevitably generated in the switches, arise only in the battery circuit, where they do much less harm. In the Diesselhorst, these emfs are made to neutralize one another so far as the potential circuit is concerned by a differential circuit arrangement.

In the more expensive instruments, double-decade resistance coils are used for $AB$, the purpose of which can be understood from the simplified diagram of Fig. 57. No matter what the position of the contact $C$, a constant resistance in the galvanometer circuit is ensured and hence a constant sensitivity of the potentiometer. This principle is used in the Diesselhorst potentiometer, although, as mentioned

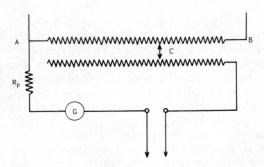

Fig. 57. A part of Fig. 56 redrawn to show a method by which the resistance of the galvanometer circuit may be made to remain constant.

above, it is there arranged that $C$ comes in the battery and not in the galvanometer circuit.

## 7.5. SELECTION OF GALVANOMETERS AND GALVANOMETER AMPLIFIERS

For general potentiometric work, a low-resistance galvanometer is best. If its resistance is not low, the galvanometer will be over-damped by the resistance of the potentiometer. This is particularly the case when the lower voltage settings are being used on the cheaper potentiometers. The question is not so important in high-resistance external circuits, but when the external circuit has a low resistance a galvanometer of low resistance, say, 10 $\Omega$, should always be chosen. The advice given in Tinsley's catalog is that the galvanometer resistance should be about one-third of the resistance of the circuit which is shunting it in order to prevent overdamping.

The periodic time quoted for a ballistic galvanometer is that for when it is critically damped, i.e., when the galvanometer circuit itself, including the galvanometer resistance, potentiometer resistance, and specimen leads resistance has a total value equal to the critical damping resistance. If the latter has not been matched, the galvanom-eter will appear more sensitive, but it will have a very much longer period and will be more difficult to handle. The quoted sensitivity also assumes that there is a 1 m beam throw. Obviously, increased sensitivity may be obtained quite simply by lengthening the path of the light beam to 2 or 3 m.

The best galvanometers of reasonably short period (less than 5 sec) have sensitivities of the order of 0.03 $\mu$V/mm for a beam throw of 1 m. If higher sensitivities are desired, the voltage signal must first be magnified. One method of doing this is by photoelectric amplifica-tion, using an instrument known as a *galvanometer amplifier*. It

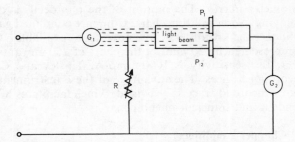

Fig. 58. Diagram demonstrating the principle of a galvanometer amplifier.

normally consists of a primary galvanometer $G_1$, which deflects a light beam over the surfaces of twin photocells connected in parallel (Fig. 58). Due to their differential illumination, there is a resultant flow of current from the cells which is considerably larger than the initial current. This deflects a secondary indicating galvanometer and is also used to apply negative feedback to the primary galvanometer. That is to say, a large fraction of the magnified current is fed back in opposition to the original input voltage in order to achieve better stability and rapid response. The feedback may be provided either as parallel or series negative feedback. The former is best for measuring the emf from a low-voltage source, such as a thermocouple, while the latter is used to avoid overdamping. Net current amplifications exceeding 100, together with a stable sensitivity of 5000 mm/$\mu$V or $2 \times 10^{-4}$ $\mu$V/mm, are not very difficult to obtain. The galvanometer amplifier should, however, always be mounted on a rigid stand. With very large feedbacks the period of the primary galvanometer becomes much smaller, and the instrument is more likely to be influenced by the vibrations normally found in a building.

A good account of galvanometer amplifiers has been given by MacDonald.[M4] If it is desired to construct one's own, then information on design details can be found from the literature.[368,284,158,212,132,328] Otherwise, there is now available a very wide commercial selection.

### 7.5.1. Spot-Followers

For some years the French company SEFRAM has manufactured recording instruments known as *spot-followers*, with which a permanent record of the movement of the mirror of a distant galvanometer may be obtained. This is a photoelectric device which, being free to move laterally, keeps in line with the light beam reflected from the galvanometer mirror. The motion of the photocells is displayed by a pen moving over a rotating chart. Compact combined galvanometer amplifiers and recorders are now also available. On one, 0.1 $\mu$V is represented by 10 mm on the chart of 250 mm total width. On another, the sensitivity is 1000 mm/$\mu$A. Tinsley and Co. make similar recording devices. The advantage of these instruments is that a continuous recorded trace is provided, which facilitates a study of time-dependent and transient phenomena.

### 7.5.2. DC Chopper Amplifiers

An alternative and sometimes preferable means of amplifying small voltages is by using a suitably chosen DC amplifier of low noise level. A high-gain electronic amplifier has the advantages of fast response and low vulnerability to vibration, besides also providing a signal suitable for recording or for control purposes, such as automatic bridge balancing. Chopper amplifiers are commonly used. The DC signal is chopped to produce AC, which is then amplified and synchronously rectified to give a DC output voltage.

In the widely used Model 14 Liston–Becker amplifier,[270,271] the input voltage is mechanically chopped at 8 cps. The maximum voltage gain available is $10^7$, and the noise with respect to the input does not exceed 0.005 $\mu$V. An input signal of 0.1 $\mu$V can therefore give an output of 1 V at full gain. It is consequently ideal as a high-resolution null detector in precision potentiometer and bridge circuits.

Dauphinée and Woods[125] have also described a very stable, fast chopper amplifier of $10^7$ gain and low noise level with which inputs of 0.01 $\mu$V are readily detectable.

## 7.6. SPECIAL SWITCHES AND OTHER DEVICES OF PRACTICAL INTEREST

### 7.6.1. Templeton's Methods of Eliminating Parasitic emfs

When potential differences of the order of microvolts across a specimen at liquid-helium temperatures are to be measured, the small parasitic emf inevitably present in the long leads that pass from the cryostat to room temperature assume considerable importance. Their effect on measuring instruments may, however, be eliminated by various methods, including the two described below due to Templeton. Both these instruments work at the temperature of liquid helium and make use of the property of superconductivity.

*7.6.1.1. Superconducting Reversing Switch.*[421] This switch utilizes four small flat coils of tantalum wire $a$, $a'$, $b$, $b'$, arranged as indicated in Fig. 59. At 4.2°K, tantalum is superconducting, but its normal

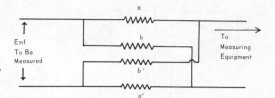

Fig. 59. Diagram illustrating the principle of Templeton's superconductivity reversing switch.[421]

electrical resistance is restored by a magnetic field of about 60 Oe. Therefore, one pair of coils $a$, $a'$ is set up between the poles of a small electromagnet and $b$, $b'$ between the poles of a second; either one electromagnet or the other is energized at any one time so that the critical field of 60 Oe is exceeded at the coils. Thus when one pair of coils is superconducting, the other pair is in the normal state, each normal coil in Templeton's design having a resistance of 2 $\Omega$. In this simple way, the switch may be operated to reverse the direction of the input current. Since it is desirable that a reversing switch have a high parallel resistance in comparison to the output impedance of the source, this particular switch is perfectly satisfactory for use with specimens of $10^{-3}$ $\Omega$ or less.

*7.6.1.2. Superconducting Modulator.* Templeton[422] has improved the sensitivity of small-voltage detection still further by having the actual detector itself also operating in liquid helium alongside the reversing switch. An extra reduction in primary circuit resistance and noise level is achieved, and specimen resistances of even $10^{-7}$ $\Omega$ can be measured with considerable precision and yet using only moderate currents (30 mA), if desired.

The low-resistance source whose emf is to be measured is connected in series with both a length of superconducting tantalum wire (whose normal resistance is $10^{-1}$ $\Omega$) and the primary of a miniature transformer. The tantalum wire is held near its transition temperature by a field of suitable magnitude (more than 60 Oe), and a modulated field of 800 cps impressed upon it causes the wire to act as a chopper by switching its resistance between 0 and $10^{-1}$ $\Omega$. The modulated signal is stepped up by the transformer and then led to a synchronized amplifier which is at room temperature. Any parasitic DC thermal emfs present do not affect the AC measurements, and the limiting noise level in Templeton's experiments, which was from the amplifier, was equivalent to about $4 \times 10^{-12}$ V at the transformer primary. The inclusion of a superconducting reversing switch enables the amplified signal to be more easily discerned, since there is still some spurious pick-up.

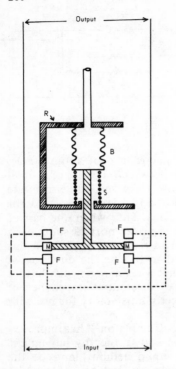

Fig. 60. A mechanical reversing switch for use at low temperatures (Haen and Weil[199]). F: fixed copper contacts, M: mobile copper contacts, B: bellows, R: rigid support, S: spring.

## 7.6.2. Bellows-Operated Reversing Switch

The action of this switch[199] may be understood by referring to Fig. 60. The pressure-actuated bellows moves a pair of copper contacts between two pairs of fixed contacts connected in opposite senses, as shown. Like Templeton's superconducting switch, it is placed within the cryostat close to the specimen and precedes the exit of the potential leads to the measuring equipment. Because it does not utilize the property of superconductivity, it has the distinct advantage of not being limited to very low temperatures, as is Templeton's switch.

## 7.6.3. Superconducting Galvanometer

Finally, in this section we shall mention the specialized and highly sensitive galvanometer constructed by Pippard and Pullan.[353] It consists of a tiny magnet 2 mm in length and of moment 0.2 emu, suspended between a pair of one-turn superconducting Helmholtz coils. Because the circuit resistance is extremely low, about $10^{-7}\ \Omega$, small voltages give comparatively high currents, and the limit of detection is as small as $10^{-12}$ V. The period of the galvanometer is long, however (12 to 15 sec), owing to a relatively high inductance.

## 7.7. ALTERNATING CURRENT METHODS

### 7.7.1. AC Potentiometers

AC methods have been developed which can equal and even excel the accuracy and performance of the best DC potentiometers. The procedure involved when employing AC methods is, however, complicated by the fact that not only must the magnitudes of the potentiometer and unknown voltages be matched in order to obtain balance, but their phases must as well. For this to be possible, both the potentiometer resistance and the unknown resistance must be supplied with current from the same initial source. AC methods are nevertheless sometimes preferred to DC ones for electrical resistance measurements, particularly when very small heat dissipation in the specimens is desirable or when the actual specimen resistance itself is extremely small. Such measurements are also quite unaffected by stray thermal emfs since these are essentially of DC origin.

The two fundamental forms of AC potentiometer are represented by the Gall and the Drysdale instruments. The simpler one is the latter, in which the unknown voltage is measured in terms of its magnitude and relative phase, i.e., it is measured in polar form. Basically, it consists of a DC type potentiometer with noninductively wound resistors, a phase-shifting transformer, and, for purposes of standardization, a dynamometer milliammeter which reads correctly on both direct and alternating current. When balance conditions have been obtained, the magnitude of the unknown voltage is found directly from the potentiometer dials and its phase relative to that of the supply read from the phase-shifter. Resistances can be compared if measurements are also taken on a standard known resistor included in the circuit of the unknown one.[134]

In the Gall potentiometer, on the other hand, the unknown voltage is measured in terms of its rectangular coordinates.[164] There are two distinct potentiometer circuits, and these are supplied with currents having a phase difference of 90°. One is called the *in-phase* potentiometer and the other the *quadrature* potentiometer. Each is used to measure that component of the unknown voltage in phase with the phase of its own current supply. The sum of the squares of these two measured values is then equal to the square of the actual unknown voltage.

Potentiometers of both the Drysdale and Gall types are made by H. Tinsley and Co., Ltd. For complete details of the basic potentiometers and their principal modifications with regard to the measurement of resistance, reference should be made to the original articles by Drysdale[134] and Gall,[164] to the books by Gall [M17] and Laws, [M24] and also to more recent scientific instrument journals.

### 7.7.2. AC Bridges

To illustrate the possibilities available in the measurement of medium to high resistances (1 to $10^5$ $\Omega$) by means of alternating current bridges, we shall briefly mention a fairly convenient though expensive one described by Green.[181]

He reported that a standard Liston–Becker DC chopper amplifier (Model 14, 8 cps) could easily be converted to provide both a source and a detector for a low-frequency AC bridge (reactance can be ignored if the frequencies used are low). Resistors of 150 $\Omega$ were used for the ratio arms and a six-dial decade resistance box for the variable arm. It was found that the rms noise level in a $\frac{1}{10}$ W Allen–Bradley carbon resistor of nominal resistance 47 $\Omega$ whose resistance at liquid-helium temperatures lay in the range 500 to 5000 $\Omega$ was very low and equivalent to 1.5 to $6 \times 10^{-6}$ °K. In addition, the measuring powers employed in the measurements were very small, less than 0.05 $\mu$W, in fact.

This level of performance was very similar to that of a more complex 33 cps AC bridge system especially designed for such measurements by Blake, Chase, and Maxwell.[77] Further details on these bridges can be obtained from the original papers, and information on other AC bridges by referring to handbooks and journals on electrical engineering and scientific instruments.

### 7.7.3. Induction Methods

Induction or eddy-current methods of resistance measurement offer certain considerable advantages over conventional DC or AC four-terminal methods. Since no wires have to be attached to the specimen, there is no possibility of contamination. Also, fabrication of the specimen into thin rods or wires, which can be a difficult procedure for brittle materials, is unnecessary, and in some induction methods no particular size or shape is demanded of the specimen, although often a thick cylinder or bar is preferable. In many of the methods, too, measurements can just as easily be carried out if the specimen is in the liquid state. Nevertheless, despite these and certain other advantages, electrodeless induction methods have not as yet proved very popular for purposes of resistance measurement. This is perhaps because they are essentially comparison methods and do not always give the resistance directly and simply. In some cases, also, the auxiliary equipment is rather elaborate, and possibly the procedure is considered laborious. Such objections have been shown to be not necessarily valid, and for certain specialized applications such as measuring the resistances of parts of rods or of molten columns these methods can be fast and very accurate.

A variety of different approaches have been tried, and recent discussions and descriptions have been given by Bean, Deblois, and Nesbitt,[67] Zimmerman,[459] and Khotkevich and Zabara.[242] In Zimmerman's method the resis-ance and inductance of a coil are first measured by a suitable AC inductance bridge, such as a Maxwell $L_1/L_2$ bridge. The specimen is then introduced into the field of the coil, and, because eddy currents are induced within the specimen, the resistance and inductance of the coil change and the new values are measured. For specimens of simple geometry, including a cylinder of circular cross section, relations have been obtained theoretically from which the electrical resistivity may in principle be calculated. The equations are complicated, however, and it is usual to use them for the comparison of resistivities. Audio, not radio, frequencies must be used in order to ensure that the currents flow through the entire mass of the conductor and are not just limited to regions near the surface.

A more convenient approach with wider applications is due to Bean *et al.*[67] The method is to apply a current to a coil within which the specimen is placed for a time long enough to cause a flow of eddy currents in the specimen, and then to stop the current. As the flux emerges, the voltage across a small pick-up coil is observed on an oscilloscope (as a function of time) and the trace photographed for later analysis. Absolute resistivities may be calculated for specimens of regular cross section. The method is particularly useful for determining or comparing the resistivities of small regions of long bars, including, for example, a single crystal during preparation by zone-melting. For specimen diameters of 1 cm, it is estimated that resistivities of between $10^{-11}$ and $10^{-3}$ $\Omega$-cm can be obtained to better than 3%.

Khotkevich and Zabara prefer the rotating magnetic field method due to Regel'.[372] The electrical resistivity of a spherical or cylindrical specimen is determined by measuring the moment of the forces acting on it due to induced currents when placed in a rotating field. It is claimed that resistivities between $10^{-8}$ and $10^6$ $\Omega$-cm can be measured to 0.1% accuracy. The main drawback is the very elaborate and costly subsidiary equipment needed.

For more details and earlier references on induction methods of resistance measurement, the reader is referred to the papers of the above authors.

## 7.8. SPECIMEN HOLDERS FOR RESISTANCE EXPERIMENTS

We shall now discuss briefly the means by which specimens may be held in position with their four electrodes attached for conventional resistance measurement at cryogenic temperatures. Since there are so many possible varieties of holders, we shall in fact do little more than summarize the criteria relevant to the design of a holder for any particular specimen.

The first considerations are due to the nature of the specimen itself—for instance, its quantity and shape, its hardness and strength, its radioactivity, if any, and whether it oxidizes readily or can, if necessary, be soldered.

In most cases the sample is in the form of a cylinder or a bar of round, square, or rectangular cross section, and it is possible to use spring-loaded blocks for the current contacts and spring-loaded cones or knife-edges for the potential contacts. With sharp edges for the potential contacts, the probe separation can be determined with greater precision. Alternatively, if the possible risk of surface contamination or perhaps even damage to the specimen can be taken, then the leads may be either soldered or spot-welded directly to it. Spot-welding is a most useful procedure and is described in Section 7.10; with good technique, contamination need never result. If it is desired to make resistance measurements below 7 or 8°K using soldered wires, a nonsuperconducting solder such as Bi-Cd or Zn-Cd eutectic should always be chosen. Otherwise, with soft-solder or Wood's metal there is a danger that the effective distance between the potential probes will change when the solder becomes superconducting. When very fine wire leads are employed, it is sometimes difficult to spot-weld them to much thicker specimens, and soldering may also not be possible. A solution in such cases is to solder them onto thicker platinum or nickel wires which have instead been previously spot-welded to the specimen.

To raise the resistance of ductile metal specimens of low resistivity, very long wires of small diameter must be used. The difficulty lies in mounting them in a strain-free manner. This has been done by constructing cylindrical copper formers with an external spiral groove to support 0.5 mm diameter specimens 50 or 100 cm in length.[211,137] Soft and reactive metals like the alkalis can be cast or

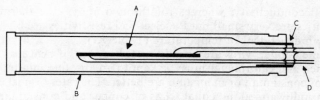

Fig. 61. Method of sealing a radioactive specimen in a capsule (Meaden and Lee[307]). A: sample, B: brass cylinder, C: platinum tube, D: platinum wires. For purposes of insulation and increased strength, the platinum wires are enclosed within fine glass tubes for most of their lengths.

distilled into glass capillary tubes which have been previously furnished with suitably located platinum wires to serve as current and potential leads. [M4] Such specimens may not always be entirely free from strain at low temperatures, and the method has been criticized by Dugdale and Gugan,[140] who have demonstrated how it is possible to extrude and mount 100 cm lengths of these metals.[137]

Even radioactive metals, as long as the activity can be stopped by a few tenths of a millimeter of copper, may be investigated by the four-terminal method in a standard cryostat using the method of Meaden and Lee.[307] After attaching platinum leads by spot-welding, the active specimen (Pu or Np, for instance) is sealed into a thick-walled copper container, as indicated in Fig. 61. Helium exchange gas within the container and the use of thick platinum wires ensure that the temperature of a thermocouple or other thermometer placed on the outside surface of the container closely follows that of the specimen.[304,310] Wigley's improved design[447,448] includes two fine platinum tubes at the platinum–glass seal so that thermocouple wires can pass through the seal directly to the specimen.

For rods and wires of ordinary metals less than 10 cm in length, it is no great problem to design a multiple holder that will take as many as six, or even twelve or more, specimens at the same time. In such a case the heat entry along the numerous leads would require consideration. Generally speaking, of course, a specimen holder has to be designed specially for the case in hand, the ultimate factor influencing the design, so far unmentioned, being the space available in the cryostat.

## 7.9. SELECTION OF WIRES FOR CURRENT AND POTENTIAL LEADS

Most commonly, the choice lies between copper and either constantan or manganin. Copper has a low electrical resistivity and high thermal conductivity, whereas for the two alloys, the thermal conductivities are very small but the electrical resistivities are big, though largely independent of temperature (Table XI).

Fine copper wires are usually preferred, but, if heat leaks to the specimen and calorimeter must be kept to an absolute minimum, thin wires of constantan or manganin are better. The rates of heat conduction in milliwatts along equal wires of copper and constantan 10 cm in length and 1 mm in *diameter* are compared in Table XII. It is seen that for wires held with their ends at 300 and 4°K, the heat flow along a copper wire is thirty times greater than along one of constantan. The importance of thermally anchoring copper wires at intermediate temperatures, such as at 77 or 20°K, is quite evident. For the above calculations, use was made of the data given by White, M9 (p.186) whose original sources were Powell, Rogers, and Roder[360] for the electrolytic copper and Berman[73] for the constantan. The electrolytic tough-pitch copper is widely used for drawing wire. Compared to the data of White,[434] the behavior of Johnson–Matthey cold-worked high-purity copper would be judged to be similar, but if annealed it would certainly possess a much higher thermal conductivity, especially at low temperatures in the region of the thermal conductivity maximum. Manganin would be expected to behave very like constantan.

Data for the important thermocouple wire Au–2.1 at.-% Co have also been included. The thermal conductivity has been measured

### Table XII. Comparison of Heat Conduction Along Various Wires*

(The amount of heat in milliwatts conducted along wires 10 cm in length and 1 mm in *diameter* with their ends at the temperatures indicated.)

| Temperature (°K) | Copper | Constantan | Au–2.1 at.-% Co |
|---|---|---|---|
| 300-77 | 720 | 38 | — |
| 300–20 | 1190 | 46 | — |
| 300-4 | 1320 | 46 | — |
| 77-20 | 430 | 7 | 7.5 |
| 77-4 | 560 | 8 | 8.5 |
| 20-4 | 125 | 0.6 | 0.63 |
| 4-2 | 6 | 0.009 | 0.011 |

* Copper—electrolytic, tough-pitch, as received. Constantan—60 Cu, 40 Ni, as received. The behavior of manganin would be similar to that of constantan.
For references and further details, see text.

below 100°K by Powell, Bunch, and Gibson.[358] Below 80°K, the conductivity is not very different from that of constantan, but at room temperature it is probably roughly double. A few measurements on Ag–0.37 at.-% Au (normal silver) in the regions of 20°K and 80°K by Grüneisen and Reddemann[190] show the thermal conductivity to be very low and worse than that of impure, cold-worked copper. Typical values are 3 W/cm-deg K at 23°K and 3.45 at 80°K.

Last, we point out that for resistance-measuring experiments at liquid-helium temperatures, wires of a superconductor such as niobium or lead are occasionally used for the current leads. Since the Joule heating in a wire in the superconducting state is zero, such wires are particularly desirable if high currents are to be passed.

## 7.10. SPOT-WELDING TECHNIQUES

We shall include some remarks on this subject because spot-welding is the only satisfactory method of attaching leads securely in the cases of a large number of metals and alloys that are difficult to solder and that surface-oxidize readily. Also, contact-resistance troubles may arise with spring-loaded probes if there is appreciable oxidation of the specimen surface, a problem more likely to be encountered at temperatures above room temperature, it is true.

In spot-welding, a joint between two wires is achieved by their mutual fusion when an arc is struck between or in the region of the wires concerned. The principle underlying the operation of most commercial machines can be understood by referring to Fig. 62. First, a condenser is charged from a source of direct current to a voltage whose value is controlled by a variable resistor R. The switch is then opened and the condenser discharged at the welding site simply by bringing the electrodes A and B together, at which moment an arc strikes between them.

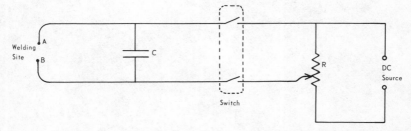

Fig. 62. Diagram illustrating the principle of a spot-welding machine.

The fusion of two fine wires together, as in a thermocouple, or of one fine wire to a much thicker one, as of a potential lead to a specimen, is not easy with commercial spot-welding instruments, because of their large electrodes and often high welding pressures. In particular, it is desirable that thermocouple wires should not be distorted or strained near their junctions. Simple welding arrangements including circuit details that solve this problem and enable wires of 0.05 mm diameter to be joined without difficulty have been described by Hill[213] and Radcliffe and White.[370] The principles involved are similar to the above, but more control over the welding operation is obtained.

*Chapter 8*

# Techniques of Low-Temperature Control and Measurement

In this chapter we shall describe just a few of the many possible cryostats in which electrical resistivity experiments over the entire temperature range from helium up to ordinary temperatures may be carried out. We also describe some thermometers and procedures in common use for determining temperatures down to about 1°K, although, in keeping with the nature of this book, we deal chiefly with resistance thermometers. An account of the principal low-temperature thermocouples is nevertheless included, since they are the most practical of all low-temperature thermometers.

## 8.1. CRYOSTATS

First, we point out that, if only the residual resistivity ratio $\rho_{4.2}/\rho_{295}$ of a specimen is wanted, a proper cryostat is not needed at all, because a simple method based on direct dipping into the liquid helium of a transport or storage dewar may be arranged without any difficulty. The specimen is merely attached in a strain-free manner to a suitable holder small enough to pass through the narrow neck of the dewar, there also being provision made for the exclusion of the entry of air, the safe entry of the leads, and, if necessary, the collection of escaping helium gas. These dewars commonly have volumes of 10, 15, or 25 liters and they have long, narrow necks. Since a fairly stable vertical temperature gradient exists in the helium gas above the liquid-helium level and in the neck of the dewar, the sample resistance may also be measured as a function of temperature (up to 100°K at least) by gradually pulling the holder and the specimen upward and using a previously calibrated thermocouple or carbon resistance thermometer for temperature measurement.

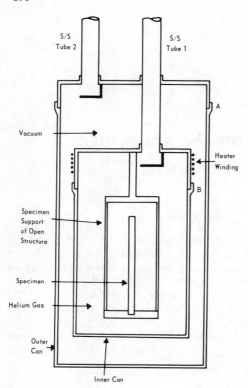

Fig. 63. An electrical-resistivity cryostat for use between 1 and 300°K.

Next we turn our attention to true cryostats for the achievement and control of low temperatures. However, for descriptions of the most basic cryostats and the fundamental procedures involved in low-temperature research, the reader is referred to the books of White [M9] and Rose-Innes [M29]; those of Hoare, Jackson, and Kurti [M19] and Scott [M31] are also very helpful. Here we shall simply describe a range of different research cryostats that can be used in resistance experiments over a wide range of low temperatures. Some of them are dual-purpose cryostats in which one or more transport properties may be determined either simultaneously or in separate experiments.

In Fig. 63 is shown an apparatus which may be used for resistivity measurements between 4 and 300°K and which illustrates the conventional principles that have been employed for many years. Initially, the two copper cans are filled with helium gas, and the outer bath contains liquid helium, hydrogen, or nitrogen, according to choice.

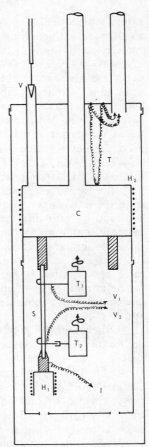

Fig. 64. A thermal-conductivity cryostat used by White and Woods.[436]

When temperatures above the boiling points of these liquids are required, the outer can is evacuated and the inner one is heated, but a low pressure of helium gas is retained in the latter chamber in order to preserve thermal equilibrium within it. In Anderson's arrangement[48] (see also ref. 51 and 108) the stainless steel tube number 1 is made so wide that the specimen may be lowered down through it directly into the central chamber. This increases heat leaks, but it avoids the Wood's metalled joints A and B. In the apparatus of Fig. 63, gases can be condensed or siphoned directly into the inner can, if desired, for accurate calibration of the thermometers, and afterwards boiled away by means of a heater. However, it is preferable to provide a third chamber, in the upper part of the inner can, to receive such liquid gases, as in the typical thermal-conductivity cryostat of Fig. 64 (White and Woods[436]). Thermal-conductivity experiments are invariably more complicated than electrical-resistivity ones, since strictly adiabatic conditions are essential for the steady-state methods of measurement that are usually employed. At every stage of a run, temperatures must be steady while readings are being taken. Dynamic experiments with drifting temperatures cannot be used, as they so often are in electrical-resistivity runs.

The extra chamber C of Fig. 64 may be filled with liquid helium, hydrogen, or nitrogen from the dewar by opening the valve V. Then, with the calorimeter evacuated, control of the specimen temperature over certain ranges of temperature which depend on the liquid is achieved by reducing the pressure of the boiling liquid in C. Inter-mediate temperature ranges are covered by using the heater $H_2$ to raise the temperature above that of the dewar bath. The purpose of the heater $H_1$ is to establish a temperature gradient along the speci-men, and $T_1$ and $T_2$ are thermometers (such as gas thermometers) for determining the temperature gradient. The electrical resistivity is measured at the same time in this apparatus using the wires $V_1$, $V_2$, and I.

Other thermal-conductivity cryostats, which are described in the literature of the last twelve years and which can be used equally well for measurements of electrical resistivities, include those of White [M9 (p.158)] (see also ref. 434 and 435), Powell, Rogers, and Coffin,[359] and Slack,[400] among others. There are also thermoelectric-power cryostats based on the same principles and described by Tyler and Wilson[428] and Born, Legvold, and Spedding.[83] Before about 1953, constructional details were more complicated than they are nowadays, since most thermal- and electrical-conductivity cryostats were associated with small helium liquefiers (e.g., Rosenberg[384]). When temperature stability of a high order and for long periods is desired outside of the range of the available cryogenic liquids, servocontrol instead of manual control is needed for the adiabatic calorimeter. White [M9(p.208ff)] discusses this and gives references. Some other references are given in ref. 378.

If the magnetoresistivity or the Hall effect is to be measured, that part of the cryostat containing the specimen, including the tails of the metal or glass dewars, is made very narrow in order to permit achievement of the highest-possible fields by an external magnet. The recent development of superconducting solenoids somewhat simplifies the high-field question, and a new Hall-effect cryostat for the temperature range 1.5 to 100°K, which has also been designed for

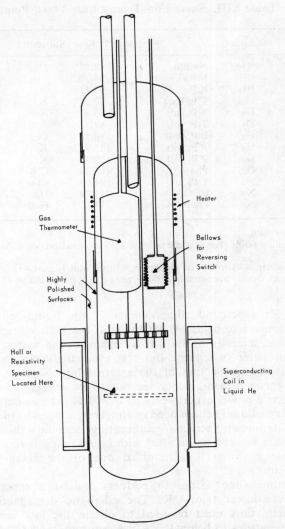

Heater

Gas
Thermometer

Bellows
for
Reversing
Switch

Highly
Polished
Surfaces

Hall or
Resistivity
Specimen
Located Here

Superconducting
Coil in
Liquid He

Fig. 65.   A Hall-effect and electrical-resistivity cryostat
for use between 1 and 100 or 300°K that includes a
superconducting solenoid (Meaden and Pelloux-
Gervais[309]).

measuring electrical resistivities and thermoelectric powers, is
illustrated in Fig. 65 (Meaden and Pelloux-Gervais[309]). A small

## Table XIII. Some Low-Temperature Fixed Points

| °K | Substance | | °K | Substance | |
|---|---|---|---|---|---|
| 2.172 | $^4$He | λ-point | 43.81 | $O_2$ | Phase tr. |
| 3.19 | $^3$He | B.P. | 54.36 | $O_2$ | T.P. |
| 4.125 | $^4$He | B.P. | 63.15 | $N_2$ | T.P. |
| 13.80 | $H_2$ | T.P. (eq) | 77.35 | $N_2$ | B.P. |
| 13.95 | $H_2$ | T.P. (nl) | 83.9 | A | T.P. |
| 18.72 | $D_2$ | T.P. (nl) | 87.3 | A | B.P. |
| 20.26 | $H_2$ | B.P. (eq) | 90.17 | $O_2$ | B.P. |
| 20.38 | $H_2$ | B.P. (nl) | 115.97 | Kr | T.P. |
| 23.57 | $D_2$ | B.P. (nl) | 119.93 | Kr | B.P. |
| 23.88 | $O_2$ | Phase tr. | 161.26 | $CS_2$ | M.P. |
| 24.56 | Ne | T.P. | 194.69 | $CO_2$ | S.P. |
| 27.09 | Ne | B.P. | 234.29 | Hg | M.P. |
| 35.4 | $N_2$ | Phase tr. | 273.15 | $H_2O$ | M.P. |

$D_2$—deuterium.

B.P.—boiling point, T.P.—triple point, S.P.—sublimation point, M.P.—melting point.

eq—equilibrium hydrogen at low temperatures, mostly para-$H_2$.

nl—normal, freshly prepared hydrogen, about 25 % para-$H_2$ and 75 % ortho-$H_2$.

Nb–25 % Zr superconducting magnet in the liquid-helium dewar provides transverse fields of 30,000 Oe at the Hall specimen, which is positioned laterally as shown. By means of the heater, the innermost calorimeter (when the outer is evacuated) can be raised in temperature to above that of the external liquid-helium bath, and when magnetic measurements are not to be made, resistivity and thermoelectric-power experiments up to 300°K become quite straightforward, since liquid helium need no longer be conserved in the dewar. The gas thermometer serves for calibrating secondary thermometers, and the inner vessel may be filled with liquid gases, if this is desired. The reversing switch is a modified one of the Haen–Weil type (Section 7.6).

Sometimes one wishes to perform resistance experiments at temperatures lower than 1°K. The adiabatic demagnetization of paramagnetic salts must be used to obtain the low temperatures when temperatures to below 0.3°K are required.[114,316] Otherwise, the employment of helium-3 cryostats is altogether simpler and is fairly widely used nowadays. Methods and apparatus have been reviewed by Peshkov and Zinoveva[350] and Rose-Innes.[M29] One recently described helium-3 cryostat was used for resistance experiments on radioactive metals, but it is of course equally suitable for use with ordinary metals.[310]

Finally, we give reference to a specialized but simple cryostat used for the dynamic measurement of the resistivity and thermoelectric power of radioactive metals between 1 and 360°K.[307,304] While this apparatus was designed and built for these particular purposes, it is basically of the most elementary type, and without the associated overhead glove-box it can instead be used for normal metals, if desired.

## 8.2. FIXED POINTS AND CONSTANT-TEMPERATURE BATHS

When it is necessary to calibrate or to check the calibration of thermometers, a knowledge of suitably located fixed points is required. We therefore list in Table XIII some of the points that, depending on the nature of the experiment, might prove useful for such purposes. Each temperature given represents what is considered to be the best value or, in cases where a choice between slightly different published figures is difficult, the mean value of the best reliable data. The articles by van Dijk[130] and Orlova[342] aided in selection of most of the data.

Vapor-pressure tables of helium-3, helium-4, hydrogen, nitrogen, and oxygen may be used in addition, and at low temperatures the superconducting transition temperatures of high-purity metals such as Pb, Sn, Al, and other so-called soft superconductors that have sharp transition regions.

Above 120°K, steady temperatures may be obtained in a bath by slowly passing liquid nitrogen through a copper tube immersed in well-stirred isopentane (2-methyl-butane) or ethyl or methyl alcohol. Unfortunately, such baths do not produce known temperatures,

## Table XIV. Melting Points of Some Organic Liquids

| °K | Substance | °K | Substance |
|---|---|---|---|
| 113.2 | isopentane (2-methyl-butane) | 178 | acetone |
| 132 | methyl cyclopentane | 189.6 | ethyl acetate |
| 146.8 | methyl cyclohexane | 200 | p-cymene |
| 154.2 | ethyl bromide | 219.5 | m-xylene |
| 156.9 stab. (149.9 unst.) | diethyl ether | 231.48 | pyridine |
|  |  | 250.3 | carbon tetrachloride (tetrachloromethane) |
| 175.0 | methyl acetate | 278.68 | benzene |

which therefore still have to be measured by other means. Consequently, we give in Table XIV the melting–freezing points of several organic compounds which, because they are liquid at room temperature (and thus are easily stored and handled), are convenient to employ as constant-temperature baths between 90 and 280°K, since they have melting–freezing temperatures that are moderately well reproducible. The comments we give here as to their suitability are in part due to Wigley.[448] Isopentane, ethyl alcohol (155.9°K), and methyl alcohol (176°K) are not at all good for providing steady temperatures because they become extremely viscous near their freezing points and solidify only slowly (luckily, alternatives are available in the cases of ethyl and methyl alcohol). The others are fairly good, although cymene and pyridine do have appalling smells. However, almost all are inflammable and must be handled with great care. Finally, it should be made clear that the freezing–melting points of these liquids cannot be regarded as true fixed points because the change of state usually occurs over a relatively wide temperature interval (0.1 to 0.3°K, or perhaps even more), thus limiting the precision with which the freezing–melting temperature may be maintained or reproduced.

## 8.3. TEMPERATURE MEASUREMENT BY RESISTANCE THERMOMETERS

In this section we shall consider platinum and other metallic resistance thermometers, as well as germanium and carbon resistance thermometers. All are secondary thermometers and in practice are calibrated against a primary gas thermometer or a certified platinum resistance thermometer, or with respect to fixed points such as those given in Table XIII and discussed in the preceding section.

### 8.3.1. Platinum Resistance Thermometers

For many years, because of their sensitivity and reliability, platinum resistance thermometers have been used to define the International Temperature Scale between 90 and 900°K. Their range of usefulness is even wider than this, however, because in specially designed thermometers temperatures may be measured either down to 10°K or up to 1600°K. The selection of Pt in preference to other metals is because it has the following characteristics:

A. It has a roughly linear variation of temperature with resistance over a wide range of temperatures, free of phase transitions and magnetic anomalies. The temperature coefficient is fairly large, and while the resistance is not perfectly linear with temperature, it can at any rate be specified by straightforward theoretical formulas.

B. High purity is readily attainable, giving a low residual resistivity and making for easier fabrication of nearly identical thermometers.

C. It is a cubic metal with a very stable resistivity that is unaffected by aging and thermal cycling.

D. It is strong, ductile, and chemically inert.

The full specifications that determine the selection of the type and quantity, the strain-free mounting, and the containment of the Pt wire in a helium-filled enclosure are necessarily very involved if reproducible and practically identical thermometers that will realize the International Temperature Scale are to be constructed. The three volumes of *Temperature: Its Measurement and Control in Science and Industry* [M34-M37] contain a wealth of information on this subject, but for the busy reader the summaries given by White [M9] and Barber[62] of the techniques and problems that arise are worth consulting.

The International Temperature Scale does not extend to below the boiling point of oxygen, chiefly because a simple-enough formula for interpolation between agreed fixed points has not yet been proposed for this range. As it also happens, just below the oxygen point the sensitivity of a platinum thermometer, as defined by $(1/R_0)(dR/dT)$, starts decreasing, and at $25°K$ it has fallen by about $90\%$. In fact, platinum thermometers are rarely used below 10 or $15°K$ because of the still lower sensitivity obtaining at these temperatures and because any deviations from Matthiessen's rule that may occur are relatively more serious when the ideal and residual resistivities have become comparable in magnitude.[246]

To construct by oneself a platinum resistance thermometer for use below room temperature is no difficult matter when an accuracy in temperature measurement of only $0.1°K$ or so is acceptable, and White [M9(pp.112-115)] gives useful advice on simple calibration procedures that are accurate to within $0.05°K$. Otherwise, manufacturers of low-temperature platinum resistance thermometers (calibrated already, if desired) include Tinsley's of London, Leeds and Northrup Ltd. (Philadelphia), and Hartmann and Braun A. G., Frankfurt-am-Main, West Germany. The Tinsley instrument is accurate to within $\pm 0.001°K$ down to $20°K$, and can be used even down to $10°K$.

### 8.3.2. Other Metallic Resistance Thermometers

Resistance thermometers made of Cu have been utilized below room temperature from time to time, and Dauphinée and Preston-Thomas[123] once made one by winding enameled copper wire directly around a copper calorimeter, securing it with varnish. A high re-producibility was found because thermal-contraction effects, which often cause strains in resistance thermometers, were absent, and the arrangement served as a practical thermometer of adequate sensi-tivity between 20°K and room temperature.

The higher sensitivity of In over Pt (and Cu) below about 50°K was first pointed out by White and Woods.[442] This arises despite Pt and In having rather similar room-temperature resistivities and is due to the much lower characteristic temperature of In ($\theta_D = 108°K$ compared to 280°K for Pt) and thus the lower temperature to which the resistivity remains linear in temperature (roughly to $\theta_R/4$ or $\theta_R/3$). White and Woods experimentally demonstrated the feasibility of using In down to 3.4°K, which is the superconducting transition temperature, and James and Yates[225] have, with their improved former for supporting the wire, further shown In thermometers to remain reproducible after many repeated coolings to low temperatures. The difficulties which can arise with In are on account of its softness and its consequent vulnerability to outside shocks if it is not well supported. Also, whereas commonly used Pt wire is of 0.1 mm diameter, 0.25 mm appears to be the lower limit for In because of drawing difficulties—thus the resistance per unit length will always be much smaller for In than for Pt. In is, however, readily prepared in a very pure form with a residual resistivity ratio of about $10^{-4}$, although, unfortunately, in thin wires of such purity there is likely to be some interference from size effects at the lowest temperatures. All the same, it does show considerable promise as a single accurate thermometer that can cover the entire temperature range between helium and room temperatures. Other metals of low characteristic temperature are, for one or more reasons such as fragility, poor ductility, low purity, or anisotropic thermal expansion, less satisfactory than In. High-purity Mn may nevertheless prove to have limited applications as a thermometer between 1 and 65°K (Fig. 7).[306]

Certain metallic alloys have also been used for resistance ther-mometers at low temperatures. For example, constantan and man-ganin show steady though slow increases in resistance with rising temperature between 4 and 150 or 200°K (the temperature coefficient is about $10^{-3}$ per deg K), and very dilute alloys of Fe in Cu or Au show decreases in resistance with rising temperature up to about 20°K (Section 3.9). Again, there are phosphor–bronze and brass alloys containing Pb inclusions, which, when drawn into wires, are found to have very spread-out superconducting transitions. These have proved to be sensitive indicators of temperature in the transition region between 1 and 6 or 7°K,[236,58,345] but obviously they are also very field-sensitive and unfortunately must be calibrated afresh at every run. Further information may be obtained from the accounts of Daunt[120] and White.[M9]

### 8.3.3. Germanium Resistance Thermometers

It is characteristic of semiconductors that with falling temperature they increase in resistance and in temperature coefficient of resistance, so that in contrast to metallic resistors they become more, not less, sensitive at low temperatures. In particular, suitably doped Ge single crystals have already proved themselves to be highly reproducible, as well as highly sensitive, low-temperature thermometers. The relatively large resistances of such crystals ($10^2$ to $10^5$ $\Omega$, as a rule) are much easier to measure than are the low resistances of metallic thermometers, and leads and contact resistances have a lesser and often negligible effect on the measurements.

Arsenic, gallium, and indium are the doping impurities that have received most attention so far in germanium thermometers. Naturally, the working temperature range of the resulting thermometer is critically dependent on the choice and amount of the impurities used, but the range that is available in thermometers made up to the present time is all or part of the temperature range between 1 and 100°K. It is unfortunate that at this moment the resistance behavior of these crystals cannot be described by straightforward theoretical formulas, because this means that every thermometer must be calibrated individually against a standard thermometer. This, together with the expense of chemically preparing the crystals under well-controlled conditions, makes the prices of commercial thermometers rather high (Texas Instruments Inc., Minneapolis-Honeywell Regulator Co.). There are, in addition, certain constructional difficulties in overcoming contact problems and in guarding the Ge crystal from mechanical strains and external contamination. Another disadvantage is the high magnetoresistivity of Ge (compared to carbon, say), a magnetoresistivity which, because single crystals are employed, is anisotropic. Nevertheless, the desirable features of germanium resistance thermometers are sufficiently important that with the further developments which seem indicated in the next few years, they may well eventually become commonplace in low-temperature laboratories. It may happen instead, however, that some other elemental or compound semiconductor will prove to be of more utility. Useful accounts of this subject have been given by Friedberg,[159] Kunzler, Geballe, and Hull,[255] Blakemore,[78] and Lindenfeld.[269]

### 8.3.4. Carbon Resistance Thermometers

The popularity of certain varieties of carbon radio resistors as low-temperature thermometers is due to their high temperature sensitivity, low field dependence, cheapness, and compactness and because they closely obey mathematical expressions of greater or less complexity. Their one grave disadvantage is that of irreproducibility caused by slight variations in the pressure contacts occurring at intergrain boundaries and with the terminals, so that, except for rough work, fresh calibrations are required after every warming to room temperature.

Most commercial radio resistors have been tested for their suitability at one time or another since the original work of Clement and Quinnell in 1950,[102] and Allen–Bradley, Speer, and LAB resistors are currently the most satisfactory. Allen–Bradley resistors are usually used between 1 and 4°K or between 1 and 20°K, although some are suitable for use down to 0.3°K and others have been used up to 100°K. For work below 1°K, Speer resistors are the best because they have a much lower temperature coefficient of resistance and can actually be used to temperatures as low as 0.02 or 0.03°K.[75]

The resistance–temperature relationship for Allen–Bradley resistors between 2 and 20°K was originally given by Clement and Quinnell as

$$\log R + \frac{K}{\log R} = A + \frac{B}{T} \tag{8.1}$$

where $K$, $A$, and $B$ are constants. Temperatures calculated from this formula were correct to within 0.5% for the eight 1 W resistors studied. Since that time, equation (8.1) has been verified many times; other equations have also been suggested, and 0.1 and 0.5 W resistors have been studied, too. For details of these other formulas and how the resistors are normally prepared for use, we refer the reader to the reviews of Friedberg,[159] White,[M9] Hudson,[219] and Lindenfeld.[269]

In Britain, LAB resistors have been used with some success,[318,453] and in general much simpler formulas are found to hold, although often only over very limited temperature ranges. Thus, Lounasmaa[279] has reported that the temperature dependence of a 0.25 W, 47 Ω LAB resistor is given by the equation

$$T - \theta = \frac{A}{R - R_0} \tag{8.2}$$

between 4 and 14 or 15°K. Here, $\theta(\sim 1°K)$, $A(\sim 1000\ \Omega\text{-deg})$, and $R_0(\sim 94\ \Omega)$ are constants of which only $R_0$ needs to be redetermined after warming to room temperature. For a 0.25 W, 56 Ω LAB resistor, the author[303] has found a yet simpler formula to hold between 1.4

and 4.2°K (the limits to which this resistor was tested). The formula was $T - \theta = A/R$, where $\theta = 0.79°K$ was constant from run to run. $A$, which was about 940 $\Omega$-deg, could be redetermined at each run from a single measurement taken at 4.2°K. The same equation also held for a second resistor from the same batch, but unfortunately was not obeyed very well by resistors from a new batch several months later.

Previous to the advent of radio resistors as popular low-temperature carbon resistance thermometers, thin carbon films had occasionally been used.[176,167] These were formed by painting colloidal suspensions of carbon, such as Aquadag and Indian ink, onto strips of absorbent paper or some other suitable surface. Such thermometers possess many of the advantages of radio resistors, but are unfortunately even less reproducible. Their possibilities have recently been reinvestigated by Hornung and Lyon.[216]

## 8.4. THERMOCOUPLES

Thermocouples, like carbon resistors, offer a very practicable means of measuring temperature, especially when high accuracy is not required, as in the case of dynamic experiments in which the specimen temperature is steadily rising or falling. This is because they provide for measurement a simple emf that can be readily studied and analyzed by the potentiometric and recording methods of Chapter 7; it is largely on this account that they are frequently employed in cryostats in which electrical resistances of metals and alloys are to be measured over wide ranges of temperature (Section 8.1). Thermocouples also have the inherent advantages of very small size and negligible thermal capacity and heat generation; on the whole, they are reliable, reproducible, and inexpensive.

Perhaps the most commonly used ones are copper–constantan thermocouples, since wires of these materials are cheap and easy to obtain and the sensitivity is sufficiently large for most purposes down to 20°K, where the thermoelectric power is 6 $\mu$V/deg K, compared to the room-temperature value of some 40 $\mu$V/deg K. In the literature, reliable tables may be found for both the thermoelectric power and the total emf with respect to the ice-point down to 10°K,[174,175] to 12°K,[57,408] and to 1°K.[357] These tables sometimes differ widely from each other because the basic compositions of the constantan alloys used were not quite the same. The best procedure is to find which of the tables corresponds most closely to one's own thermocouple by means of an initial calibration at a few low-temperature fixed points, and then to construct a deviation curve. This is normally a straight line, or nearly so, and is thereafter used in conjunction with the selected

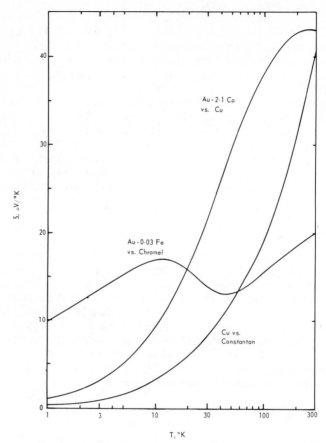

Fig. 66. The thermoelectric powers of three useful low-temperature thermocouples compared with each other. (a) Au–2.1 at.-% Co against Cu,[357] (b) Cu against constantan,[357] and (c) Au–0.03 at.-% Fe against chromel.[74]

table. In these thermocouples, most of the sensitivity arises from the high thermoelectric power of the constantan, and it is therefore important that this wire in particular should be entirely homogeneous and strain-free. If, also, the reference junction is held constant at the temperature of liquid helium instead of at the ice-point, it becomes quite possible to use copper–constantan thermocouples for temperature measurement at 10°K or even down to 4°K, at which point the power has fallen to only 1.3 $\mu$V/deg K.

Two rivals to copper–constantan which are more sensitive at the lower temperatures have appeared in the last few years. The first of these, an alloy of Au containing 2.1 at.-% Co unfortunately has a tendency to age, since the Co is in unstable supersaturated solid solution.[357] Thus, recalibration may be needed from time to time. The alloy is used against copper or, if instead a wire of poor thermal conductivity is wanted, against "normal" Ag (this contains 0.37 at.-% Au). The thermoelectric power of the Au-Co alloy against Cu is 4 $\mu$V/deg K at 4°K and 16 $\mu$V/deg K at 20°K. Full tables from 1 to 300°K have been given by Powell, Bunch, and Corruccini,[357] and their paper should be consulted for general advice and earlier references. The characteristics of normal Ag and other secondary thermocouple elements have been discussed by Crisp and Henry.[113]

Superior to the Au-Co alloy by being perfectly stable and by having a greater absolute thermoelectric power below 15°K is another Au alloy containing 0.03 at.-% Fe.[74] Used against chromel (Ni 90, Cr 10) it retains a thermoelectric power in excess of 10 $\mu$V/deg K at all temperatures higher than 1°K (Fig. 66). This combination consequently forms a single convenient thermometer of reasonable sensitivity that covers the entire temperature range below room temperature. In Fig. 66, we compare the performances of all three principal thermocouples discussed in this section.

## 8.5. MEASURING EQUIPMENT FOR RESISTANCE THERMOMETERS

The resistances of metallic and semiconductor thermometers are usually measured by Wheatstone-bridge methods, as discussed in Sections 7.2 and 7.3. In high-precision work, the thermometer is provided with four terminals, and the resistance of platinum resistance thermometers is measured by Smith or Mueller bridges (Section 7.3), or with reference to a standard resistance, using specialized potentiometric techniques. The latter are also used for accurate work on four-terminal germanium thermometers. The latest advances in these methods as applied to platinum thermometers have been reviewed by Dauphinée[121] and Evans.[150] A particularly interesting development is a direct-reading thermometer bridge[124,122] in which the temperature can be read directly from the bridge-dial readings with an accuracy of 0.001°K over the range 220 to 975°K. This is achieved by matching the quadratic temperature variation of the platinum thermometer with the linear variations of the bridge resistance elements employed.

# Notes Added in Proof

*(September 20, 1965)*

**β-Manganese** (p. 35). The electrical resistivity of β-Mn as a function of temperature between 2 and 300°K is currently being studied by MEADEN and PELLOUX-GERVAIS: a report will be published later in *Cryogenics*.[309]

**Technetium** (p. 35). The thermal conductivity of high-purity Tc has recently been measured by BAKER.[60a] From the character of his results at high temperatures and the behavior of adjacent transition metals, it is likely that any contribution to the thermal conductivity of Tc from the lattice is very small. Thus, assuming that the Wiedemann–Franz law may be applied and using the value $\kappa_{295} = 0.120$ cal/cm-sec deg K, we find that 14 or 15 $\mu\Omega$-cm is indicated for the electrical resistivity at 295°K.[305a]

**Samarium** (p. 42). ARAJS and DUNMYRE[55a] have measured the electrical resistivity from 4 to 300°K. We give here a few selected values for the *total* resistivity: $\rho_4$ 6.7 $\mu\Omega$-cm, $\rho_{20}$ 18.2, $\rho_{80}$ 51.1, $\rho_{100}$ 60.8, $\rho_{200}$ 76.4, and $\rho_{295}$ 91 $\mu\Omega$-cm. These authors suggest that the anomaly at 106°K occurs at the Néel point, while the anomaly at 14°K results from an order–order magnetic transformation.

**Superconductivity** (p. 57). WITTIG[450a] has shown that Si, Ge, and Se all become superconducting under pressures of 120 to 130 atm at temperatures of 7, 5, and 7°K, respectively.

# Appendix

### Table XV. Properties of the Metallic Elements

| Element and atomic number | Atomic weight | Crystal structure | Density (g/cm³) | Melting point (°K) |
|:---:|:---:|:---:|:---:|:---:|
| | | At 293°K | | |
| 3 Li | 6.939 | bcc | 0.534 | 454 |
| 4 Be | 9.0122 | cph | 1.82 | 1556 |
| 11 Na | 22.990 | bcc | 0.97 | 371 |
| 12 Mg | 24.312 | cph | 1.74 | 924 |
| 13 Al | 26.981 | fcc | 2.699 | 933 |
| 19 K | 39.102 | bcc | 0.86 | 336.8 |
| 20 Ca | 40.08 | fcc | 1.54 | 1123 |
| 21 Sc | 44.956 | cph | 2.99 | 1812 |
| 22 Ti | 47.90 | cph | 4.51 | 1941 |
| 23 V | 50.942 | bcc | 6.1 | 2180 |
| 24 Cr | 51.996 | bcc | 7.14 | 2140 |
| 25 α-Mn | 54.938 | cubic (complex) | 7.47 | 1516 |
| 26 Fe | 55.85 | bcc | 7.86 | 1807 |
| 27 α-Co | 58.933 | cph | 8.9 | 1768 |
| 28 Ni | 58.71 | fcc | 8.90 | 1726 |
| 29 Cu | 63.54 | fcc | 8.94 | 1356 |
| 30 Zn | 65.37 | cph | 7.14 | 692.6 |
| 31 Ga | 69.72 | ortho | 5.91 | 303 |
| 33 As | 74.922 | rhomb | 5.73 | 1087 |
| 37 Rb | 85.47 | bcc | 1.53 | 312.6 |
| 38 Sr | 87.62 | fcc | 2.6 | 1043 |
| 39 Y | 88.905 | cph | 4.47 | 1782 |
| 40 Zr | 91.22 | cph | 6.56 | 2125 |

**Table XV.** *Cont'd*

| Element and atomic number | Atomic weight | Crystal structure | Density (g/cm³) | Melting point (°K) |
|---|---|---|---|---|
| | | At 293°K | | |
| 41 Nb | 92.906 | bcc | 8.4 | 2740 |
| 42 Mo | 95.94 | bcc | 10.2 | 2890 |
| 43 Tc | (99) | cph | 11.50 | 2490 |
| 44 Ru | 101.07 | cph | 12.2 | 2690 |
| 45 Rh | 102.90 | fcc | 12.44 | 2249 |
| 46 Pd | 106.4 | fcc | 12.02 | 1825 |
| 47 Ag | 107.87 | fcc | 10.49 | 1234 |
| 48 Cd | 112.40 | cph | 8.64 | 594 |
| 49 In | 114.82 | bc tetr | 7.31 | 429.5 |
| 50 Sn | 118.69 | tetr | 7.30 | 505.1 |
| 51 Sb | 121.75 | rhomb | 6.69 | 903.6 |
| 55 Cs | 132.90 | bcc | 1.87 | 301.6 |
| 56 Ba | 137.34 | bcc | 3.58 | 983 |
| 57 α-La | 138.91 | db cph | 6.16 | 1193 |
| 58 Ce | 140.12 | fcc | 6.77 | 1068 |
| 59 Pr | 140.91 | db cph | 6.77 | 1208 |
| 60 Nd | 144.24 | db cph | 7.00 | 1297 |
| 61 Pm | (147) | | | |
| 62 Sm | 150.35 | rhomb | 7.54 | 1345 |
| 63 Eu | 151.96 | bcc | 5.25 | 1099 |
| 64 Gd | 157.25 | cph | 7.89 | 1585 |
| 65 Tb | 158.92 | cph | 8.25 | 1629 |
| 66 Dy | 162.50 | cph | 8.56 | 1680 |
| 67 Ho | 164.93 | cph | 8.80 | 1734 |
| 68 Er | 167.26 | cph | 9.06 | 1770 |
| 69 Tm | 168.93 | cph | 9.32 | 1818 |
| 70 Yb | 173.04 | fcc | 6.96 | 1097 |
| 71 Lu | 174.97 | cph | 9.85 | 1925 |
| 72 Hf | 178.49 | cph | 13.3 | 2495 |
| 73 Ta | 180.95 | bcc | 16.6 | 3270 |
| 74 W | 183.85 | bcc | 19.3 | 3670 |
| 75 Re | 186.2 | cph | 21.04 | 3455 |
| 76 Os | 190.2 | cph | 22.6 | 2980 |
| 77 Ir | 192.2 | fcc | 22.5 | 2715 |
| 78 Pb | 195.09 | fcc | 21.45 | 2042 |
| 79 Au | 196.97 | fcc | 19.32 | 1336 |
| 80 Hg | 200.59 | rhomb | 13.546 | 234.3 |
| 81 Tl | 204.37 | cph | 11.85 | 576 |
| 82 Pb | 207.19 | fcc | 11.34 | 600.6 |
| 83 Bi | 208.98 | rhomb | 9.80 | 544.5 |
| 84 Po | (210) | cubic (simple) | 9.32 | 520 |
| 87 Fr | (223) | | | |
| 88 Ra | (226) | | ~5 | 975 |
| 89 Ac | (227) | fcc | 10 | 1325 |
| 90 Th | 232.04 | fcc | 11.72 | 1965 |

## Table XV. *Cont'd*

| Element and atomic number | Atomic weight | Crystal structure | Density (g/cm³) | Melting point (°K) |
|---|---|---|---|---|
| | | At 293°K | | |
| 91 Pa | (231) | tetr | 15.37 | 1850 |
| 92 U | 238.03 | ortho | 19.05 | 1405.5 |
| 93 Np | (237) | ortho | 20.45 | 912 |
| 94 α-Pu | 239.1 | monocl | 19.82 | 913 |
| 95 Am | (241) | db cph | 13.67 | 1267 |
| 96 Cm | (244) | db cph | ~13.3 | 1615 |
| 97 Bk | (247) | | | |
| 98 Cf | (249) | | | |
| 99 Es | (254) | | | |
| 100 Fm | (253) | | | |
| 101 Md | (256) | | | |
| 102 (No) | (256) | | | |
| 103 Lw | (257) | | | |
| 104 | (260) | | | |

### Properties of Some Nonmetallic Elements

| | | | | |
|---|---|---|---|---|
| 5 B | 10.81 | tetr | 2.34 | 2500 |
| | | β-rhomb | 2.34 | |
| 6 C | 12.011 | (gr) hex | 2.26 | ~3900 |
| | | diam | 3.51 | |
| 14 Si | 28.086 | diam | 2.33 | 1696 |
| 32 Ge | 72.59 | diam | 5.35 | 1232 |
| 34 Se (gray) | 78.96 | hex | 4.81 | 493 |
| 50 Sn (gray) | 118.69 | diam | 5.75 | |
| 52 Te | 127.60 | hex | 6.24 | 724 |

The atomic weights are based on the 1961 carbon-12 scale [A. E. Cameron and E. Wichers, *J. Am. Chem. Soc.* **84**, 4175 (1962)]. Those of the radioactive elements refer to the isotopes of longest known half-life, with the exceptions of Pm, Po, Am, and Cm, where the isotopes given are the best-investigated ones. The atomic weight given for Pu is that which is fairly commonly met with in research work.

The density of solid Hg at 227°K is 14.24 g/cm³; the value in the table is that of the liquid at 293°K.

### Table XVI. Conversion Tables Between the Kelvin, Celsius, Fahrenheit, and Rankine Temperature Scales

| °K | °C | °F | °R |
|---|---|---|---|
| 0 | −273.15 | −459.67 | 0 |
| 50 | −223.15 | −369.67 | 90 |
| 100 | −173.15 | −279.67 | 180 |
| 150 | −123.15 | −189.67 | 270 |
| 200 | −73.15 | −99.67 | 360 |
| 250 | −23.15 | −9.67 | 450 |
| 255.37 | −17.78 | 0 | 459.67 |
| 273.15 | 0 | 32 | 491.67 |
| 300 | 26.85 | 80.33 | 540 |
| 350 | 76.85 | 170.33 | 630 |
| 373.15 | 100 | 212 | 671.67 |
| 400 | 126.85 | 260.33 | 720 |
| 450 | 176.85 | 350.33 | 810 |
| 500 | 226.85 | 440.33 | 900 |
| 1000 | 726.85 | 1340.33 | 1800 |
| 1500 | 1226.85 | 2240.33 | 2700 |
| 2000 | 1726.85 | 3140.33 | 3600 |
| 3000 | 2726.85 | 4940.33 | 5400 |
| 4000 | 3726.85 | 6740.33 | 7200 |

The Kelvin absolute scale of temperature is used throughout the book. The absolute zero on the Celsius scale adopted by the International Committee on Weights and Measures in 1954 is −273.15°C. This is equivalent to −459.67°F.

# References

*Monographs, Books, and Reviews* to which frequent reference is made:

M1. A. N. Gerritsen, "Metallic Conductivity, Experimental Part," in: S. Flügge (ed.), *Handbuch der Physik, Vol. 19* (Springer-Verlag, Berlin, 1956), p. 137.

M2. E. Grüneisen, *Ergebn. exakt. Naturw.* **21**, 50 (1945).

M3. H. Jones, "Theory of Electrical and Thermal Conductivity in Metals," in: S. Flügge (ed.), *Handbuch der Physik, Vol. 19* (Springer-Verlag, Berlin, 1956), p. 227.

M4. D. K. C. MacDonald, "Electrical Conductivity of Metals and Alloys at Low Temperatures," in: S. Flügge (ed.), *Handbuch der Physik, Vol. 14* (Springer-Verlag, Berlin, 1956), p. 137.

M5. W. Meissner and B. Voigt, "Messungen mit Hilfe von flüssigem Helium. XI: Widerstand der reinem Metalle in tiefen Temperaturen," *Ann. Physik* **7** (5), 761–797 (1930).

M6. W. Meissner and B. Voigt, "Messungen mit Hilfe von flüssigem Helium. XI: Widerstand der reinem Metalle in tiefen Temperaturen," *Ann. Physik* **7** (5), 892–936 (1930).

M7. N. F. Mott and H. Jones, *The Theory of the Properties of Metals and Alloys* (Oxford, 1936; Dover, 1958).

M8. J. L. Olsen, *Electron Transport in Metals* (Interscience, New York and London, 1962).

M9. G. K. White, *Experimental Techniques in Low Temperature Physics* (Oxford, 1959).

M10. G. K. White and S. B. Woods, "Electrical and Thermal Resistivities of the Transition Elements at Low Temperatures," *Phil. Trans. Roy. Soc. (London), Ser. A* **251**, 273–302 (1959).

M11. A. H. Wilson, *The Theory of Metals*, ed. 2 (Cambridge, 1953).

M12. J. M. Ziman, *Electrons and Phonons* (Oxford, 1960).


*Other Monographs and Books:*

M13. P. W. Bridgman, *The Physics of High Pressures* (Bell, London, reprinted 1958).

M14. L. Brillouin, *Die Quantenstatistik und Ihre Anwendung auf die Elektronentheorie der Metalle* (Springer-Verlag, Berlin, 1931).

M15. A. J. Dekker, *Solid State Physics* (MacMillan, London, 1958).

M16. W. Ehrenberg, *Electric Conduction in Semiconductors and Metals* (Oxford, 1958).

M17. D. C. Gall, *Direct and Alternating Current Potentiometer Methods* (Pitman, London).

M18. S. Gygax and J. L. Olsen, *Superconductivity for Engineers* (Plenum, New York and London, 1966 or 1967).

M19. F. E. Hoare, L. C. Jackson, and N. Kurti, *Experimental Cryophysics* (Butterworths, London, 1961).

M20. W. Hume-Rothery, *Atomic Theory for Students of Metallurgy*, ed. 3 (Institute of Metals, London, 1960).

M21. *International Critical Tables, Vol. 6* (Published for N. R. C. by McGraw-Hill, New York, 1929).

M22. C. Kittel, *Introduction to Solid State Physics*, ed. 2 (Wiley, 1956).

M23. Landolt-Börnstein, *Zahlenwerte und Funktionen, Vol. 2*, Part 6, ed. 6 (Springer-Verlag, Berlin, 1959).

M24. F. A. Laws, *Electrical Measurements* (McGraw-Hill, New York, 1938).

M25. E. A. Lynton, *Superconductivity* (Methuen, London, 1962).

M26. W. Meissner, "Elektronenleitung, Galvanomagnetische, und verwandte Effekte," *Handbuch der Experimentalphysik, Vol. 11*, Part 2 (Leipzig, Akademi Verlagsgesellschaft, 1935), p. 338.

M27. K. Mendelssohn, *Cryophysics* (Interscience, New York and London, 1960).

M28. E. H. Putley, *The Hall Effect and Related Phenomena* (Butterworths, London, 1960).

M29. A. C. Rose-Innes, *Low Temperature Techniques* (English University Press, London, 1964).

M30. H. M. Rosenberg, *Low Temperature Solid State Physics* (Oxford, 1963).

M31. R. B. Scott, *Cryogenic Engineering* (Van Nostrand, Princeton, 1959).

M32. R. A. Smith, *Semiconductors* (Cambridge, 1959).

M33. A. H. Sully, *Manganese* (Butterworths, London, 1955).

M34. *Temperature: Its Measurement and Control in Science and Industry, Vol. 1* (Reinhold, New York, 1941).

M35. *Temperature: Its Measurement and Control in Science and Industry, Vol. 2*, H. C. Wolfe (ed.) (Reinhold, New York, 1955).

M36. *Temperature: Its Measurement and Control in Science and Industry, Vol. 3*, Part 1, F. G. Brickwedde (ed.) (Reinhold, New York, 1962).

M37. *Temperature: Its Measurement and Control in Science and Industry, Vol. 3*, Part 2, I. A. Dahl (ed.) (Reinhold, New York, 1962).

*All Other References:*

40. S. C. Abrahams, *J. Phys. Chem. Solids* **24**, 589 (1963).

41. H. K. Adenstedt, *Trans. Am. Soc. Metals* **44**, 949 (1952).

42. B. N. Aleksandrov and I. G. D'yakov, *Zh. Experim. i Teor. Fiz. (USSR)* **43**, 852 (1962) [*Sov. Phys. JETP* (Engl. transl.) **16**, 603 (1963)].

43. N. E. Alekseevskii and Yu. P. Gaidukov, *Zh. Experim. i Teor. Fiz. (USSR)* **36**, 447 (1959) [*Sov. Phys. JETP* (Engl. transl.) **9**, 311 (1959)].

44. N. E. Alekseevskii and Yu. P. Gaidukov, *Zh. Experim. i Teor. Fiz. (USSR)* **38**, 1720 (1960) [*Sov. Phys. JETP* (Engl. transl.) **11**, 1242 (1960)].

45. P. Alley and B. Serin, *Phys. Rev.* **116**, 334 (1959).

46. J. K. Alstad, R. V. Colvin, and S. Legvold, *Phys. Rev.* **123**, 418 (1961).

47. J. K. Alstad, R. V. Colvin, S. Legvold, and F. H. Spedding, *Phys. Rev.* **121**, 1637 (1961).

48. G. S. Anderson, S. Legvold, and F. H. Spedding, *Phys. Rev.* **109**, 243 (1958).

49. J. Appel, *Phys. Rev.* **122**, 1760 (1961).

50. J. Appel, *Phys. Rev.* **125**, 1815 (1962); *Phil Mag.* **8** (8), 1071 (1963).
51. S. Arajs, *J. Appl. Phys.* **32**, 97 (1961).
52. S. Arajs and R. V. Colvin, *J. Less-Common Metals* **4**, 572 (1962).
53. S. Arajs and R. V. Colvin, *J. Less-Common Metals* **7**, 54 (1964).
54. S. Arajs and R. V. Colvin, *Phys. Stat. Sol.* **6**, 797 (1964).
54a. S. Arajs and R. V. Colvin, *Phys. Rev.* **136**, A439 (1964).
55. S. Arajs, R. V. Colvin, and M. J. Marcinkowski, *J. Less-Common Metals* **4**, 46 (1962).
55a. S. Arajs and G. R. Dunmyre (to be published).
56. G. P. Arnold, C. E. Olsen, and N. G. Nerenson, *J. Appl. Phys.* **35**, 1031 (1964).
57. J. G. Aston, E. Willinghanz, and G. H. Messerly, *J. Am. Chem. Soc.* **57**, 1642 (1935).
58. J. D. Babbitt and K. Mendelssohn, *Phil. Mag.* **20** (7), 1025 (1935).
59. W. G. Baber, *Proc. Roy. Soc.* (*London*), *Ser. A* **158**, 383 (1937).
60. M. Bailyn, *Phys. Rev.* **120**, 381 (1960).
60a. D. E. Baker, *J. Less-Common Metals* **8**, 435 (1965).
61. A. S. Balchan and H. G. Drickamer, *Rev. Sci. Instr.* **32**, 308 (1961).
62. C. R. Barber, in: K. Mendelssohn (ed.), *Progress in Cryogenics, Vol. 2* (Heywood, London, 1960), p. 147.
63. C. R. Barber, A. Gridley, and J. A. Hall, *J. Sci. Instr.* **32**, 213 (1955).
64. J. Bardeen, *Phys. Rev.* **52**, 688 (1937).
65. C. S. Barrett, M. H. Mueller, and R. L. Hittermann, *Phys. Rev.* **129**, 625 (1963).
66. Z. S. Basinski, J. S. Dugdale, and A. Howie, *Phil. Mag.* **8** (8), 1989 (1963).
66a. J. Baum, D. F. Brewer, J. G. Daunt, and D. O. Edwards, *Phys. Rev. Letters* **3**, 127 (1959).
67. C. P. Bean, R. W. Deblois, and L. B. Nesbitt, *J. Appl. Phys.* **30**, 1976 (1959).
68. R. V. Bellau and B. R. Coles, *Proc. Phys. Soc.* **82**, 121 (1963).
69. G. J. van den Berg, Thesis, University of Leiden (1938).
70. G. J. van den Berg, *Physica* **14**, 111 (1948).
71. G. J. van den Berg, in: C. J. Gorter (ed.), *Progress in Low Temperature Physics, Vol. 4* (North-Holland, Amsterdam, 1964), p. 194.
72. T. G. Berlincourt, *Phys. Rev.* **114**, 969 (1959).
73. R. Berman, *Phil. Mag.* **42** (7), 642 (1951).
74. R. Berman, J. C. F. Brock, and D. J. Huntley, *Cryogenics* **4**, 233 (1964).
75. W. C. Black, W. R. Roach, and J. C. Wheatley, *Rev. Sci. Instr.* **35**, 587 (1964).
76. M. Blackman, *Proc. Phys. Soc.* (*London*), *Ser. A* **64**, 681 (1951); S. Flügge (ed.), *Handbuch der Physik, Vol. 7*, Part 1 (Springer-Verlag, Berlin, 1955), p. 325.
77. C. Blake, C. E. Chase, and E. Maxwell, *Rev. Sci. Instr.* **29**, 715 (1958).
78. J. S. Blakemore, *Rev. Sci. Instr.* **33**, 106 (1962).
79. F. J. Blatt, *Phys. Rev.* **99**, 1708 (1955).
80. F. J. Blatt and H. G. Satz, *Helv. phys. acta* **33**, 1007 (1960).
81. F. Bloch, *Z. Physik* **52**, 555 (1928); **53**, 216 (1929); **59**, 208 (1930).
82. W. Boas and J. K. Mackenzie, in: B. Chalmers (ed.), *Progress in Metal Physics, Vol. 2* (Interscience, New York, and Butterworths, London, 1950), p. 90.
83. H. J. Born, S. Legvold, and F. H. Spedding, *J. Appl. Phys.* **32**, 2543 (1961).
84. E. S. Borovik, V. G. Volotskaya, and N. Ya Fogel', *Zh. Experim. i Teor. Fiz.* (*USSR*) **45**, 46 (1963) [*Sov. Phys. JETP* (Engl. transl.) **18**, 34 (1964)].
85. C. C. Bradley, T. E. Faber, E. G. Wilson, and J. M. Ziman, *Phil. Mag.* **7** (8), 865 (1962).

86. F. J. Bradshaw and S. Pearson, *Proc. Phys. Soc. (London), Ser. B* **69**, 441 (1956).
87. A. D. Brailsford and A. W. Overhauser, *J. Phys. Chem. Solids* **15**, 140 (1960).
88. P. W. Bridgman, *Proc. Am. Acad. Arts Sci.* **56**, 104 (1921); **60**, 385 (1925).
89. P. W. Bridgman, *Proc. Am. Acad. Arts Sci.* **60**, 305 (1925).
89a. P. W. Bridgman, *Proc. Am. Acad. Arts Sci.* **60**, 423 (1925).
90. P. W. Bridgman, *Proc. Am. Acad. Arts Sci.* **68**, 27, 37, 95 (1933).
90a. M. B. Brodsky, *Phys. Rev.* **137**, A1423 (1965).
90b. T. Broom, *Proc. Phys. Soc.* **65B**, 871 (1952).
91. T. Broom, *Advan. Phys. (Phil. Mag. Suppl.)* **3**, 26 (1954).
92. T. Broom and R. K. Ham, *Vacancies and Other Point Defects in Metals and Alloys* (Institute of Metals, London, 1958), p. 41.
93. H. Bross and A. Holz, *Phys. Stat. Sol.* **3**, 1141 (1963).
94. F. Brunke, *Ann. Physik* **21** (5), 139 (1934).
95. H. G. van Bueren, *Z. Metallk.* **46**, 272 (1955); *Imperfections in Metals* (North-Holland, Amsterdam, 1960).
96. F. P. Bundy and H. M. Strong, in: F. Seitz and D. Turnbull (eds.), *Solid State Physics, Vol. 13* (Academic Press, New York, 1962), p. 81.
97. J. W. Cable, R. M. Moon, W. C. Koehler, and E. O. Wollan, *Phys. Rev. Letters* **12**, 553 (1964).
98. R. G. Chambers, *Proc. Roy. Soc. (London), Ser. A* **202**, 378 (1950).
99. R. G. Chambers, in: W. A. Harrison and M. B. Webb (eds.), *The Fermi Surface* (Wiley, New York, 1961), p. 100.
100. S. H. Christie, *Phil. Trans. Roy. Soc. (London), Ser. A* **123**, 95 (1833).
101. N. Clayton and J. E. Enderby, Unpublished work (1961).
102. J. R. Clement and E. H. Quinnell, *Phys. Rev.* **79**, 1028 (1950); *Rev. Sci. Instr.* **23**, 213 (1952).
103. B. R. Coles, *Advan. Phys. (Phil. Mag. Suppl.)* **7** (8), 40 (1958).
104. E. W. Collings and F. T. Hedgcock, *Phys. Rev.* **126**, 1654 (1962).
105. J. G. Collins and J. M. Ziman, *Proc. Roy. Soc. (London), Ser. A* **264**, 60 (1961).
106. R. V. Colvin and S. Arajs, *J. Appl. Phys.* **34**, 286 (1963).
107. R. V. Colvin and S. Arajs, *Phys. Stat Sol.* **4**, 37 (1964).
108. R. V. Colvin, S. Legvold, and F. H. Spedding, *Phys. Rev.* **120**, 741 (1960).
109. J. G. G. Conybeare, *Proc. Phys. Soc.* **49**, 29 (1937).
110. J. W. Corbett, R. B. Smith, and R. M. Walker, *Phys. Rev.* **114**, 1452, 1460 (1959).
111. P. Cotti, J. L. Olsen, J. G. Daunt, and M. Kreitman, *Cryogenics* **4**, 45 (1964); also P. Cotti, *Proceedings of the International Conference on High Magnetic Fields* (MIT, Cambridge, Mass., 1961), p. 539.
112. A. H. Cottrell, *Vacancies and Other Point Defects in Metals and Alloys* (Institute of Metals, London, 1958), p. 1.
113. R. S. Crisp and W. G. Henry, *Cryogenics* **4**, 361 (1964).
114. A. J. Croft, E. A. Faulkner, J. Hatton, and E. F. W. Seymour, *Phil. Mag.* **44** (7), 289 (1953).
115. M. A. Curry, S. Legvold, and F. H. Spedding, *Phys. Rev.* **117**, 953 (1960).
116. N. E. Cusack, *Rep. Progr. Phys.* **26**, 361 (1963).
117. J. K. Darby and N. H. March, *Proc. Phys. Soc.* **84**, 591 (1964).
118. K. B. Das and A. N. Gerritsen, *J. Appl. Phys.* **33**, 3301 (1962).
119. S. B. Das and A. N. Gerritsen, *Phys. Rev.* **135**, A1081 (1964).
120. J. G. Daunt, in: H. C. Wolfe (ed.), *Temperature: Its Measurement and Control in Science and Industry, Vol. 2* (Reinhold, New York, 1955), p. 327.

121. T. M. Dauphinée, in: F. G. Brickwedde (ed.), *Temperature: Its Measurement and Control in Science and Industry*, Vol. *3*, Part 1 (Reinhold, New York, 1962), p. 269.

122. T. M. Dauphinée, C. G. M. Kirby, and H. Preston-Thomas, *Rev. Sci. Instr.* **31**, 258 (1960).

123. T. M. Dauphinée and H. Preston-Thomas, *Rev. Sci. Instr.* **25**, 884 (1954).

124. T. M. Dauphinée and H. Preston-Thomas, *Rev. Sci. Instr.* **31**, 253 (1960).

125. T. M. Dauphinée and S. B. Woods, *Rev. Sci. Instr.* **26**, 693 (1955).

126. D. D. Davis and R. M. Bozorth, *Phys. Rev.* **118**, 1543 (1960).

127. L. Davis, *Phys. Rev.* **56**, 93 (1939).

128. A. J. Dekker, *Physica* **25**, 1244 (1959).

129. A. Desalvo, P. Gondi, F. A. Levi, and F. Zignani, *Nuovo Cimento* **31** (10), 904 (1964).

130. H. van Dijk, in: F. G. Brickwedde (ed.), *Temperature: Its Measurement and Control in Science and Industry*, Vol. *3*, Part 1 (Reinhold, New York, 1962), p. 173.

131. R. B. Dingle, *Proc. Roy. Soc. (London)*, Ser. A **201**, 545 (1950).

132. A. C. Downing, *J. Sci. Instr.* **25**, 230 (1948).

133. P. Drude, *Ann. Physik* **1** (4), 566, 1900; **7** (4), 687 (1902).

134. C. V. Drysdale, *Phil. Mag.* **17** (6), 402 (1909); *Proc. Phys. Soc.* **21**, 561 (1907-1909); *J. Inst. Elec. Eng. (London)* **68**, 339 (1930).

135. J. S. Dugdale, *Science* **134**, 77 (1961).

136. J. S. Dugdale and D. Gugan, *Proc. Roy. Soc. (London)*, Ser. A **241**, 397 (1957).

137. J. S. Dugdale and D. Gugan, *Proc. Roy. Soc. (London)*, Ser. A **254**, 184 (1960).

138. J. S. Dugdale and D. Gugan, *Cryogenics* **2**, 103 (1961).

139. J. S. Dugdale and D. Gugan, *Proc. Roy. Soc. (London)*, Ser. A **270**, 186 (1962).

140. J. S. Dugdale and D. Gugan, *J. Sci. Instr.* **40**, 28 (1963).

141. J. S. Dugdale, D. Gugan, and K. Okumura, *Proc. Roy. Soc. (London)*, Ser. A **263**, 407 (1961).

142. J. S. Dugdale and D. Phillips, *Proc. Roy. Soc. (London)*, Ser. A **287**, 381 (1965).

143. R. J. Elliott and F. A. Wedgwood, *Proc. Phys. Soc.* **81**, 846 (1963).

144. R. O. Elliott and C. E. Olsen, *J. Appl. Phys.* **35**, 1925 (1964).

145. R. O. Elliott, C. E. Olsen, and S. E. Bronisz, *Phys. Rev. Letters* **12**, 276 (1964).

146. R. O. Elliott, C. E. Olsen, and J. Louie, *J. Phys. Chem. Solids* **23**, 1029 (1962).

147. H. D. Erfling, *Ann. Physik* **37** (5), 162 (1940).

148. I. Estermann and J. E. Zimmerman, *J. Appl. Phys.* **23**, 578 (1952).

149. A. Eucken and G. Gehlhoff, *Verhandl. Deut. Physik Ges.* **14**, 169 (1912).

150. J. P. Evans, in: F. G. Brickwedde (ed.), *Temperature: Its Measurement and Control in Science and Industry*, Vol. *3*, Part 1 (Reinhold, New York, 1962), p. 285.

151. P. de Faget de Casteljau and J. Friedel, *J. Phys. Radium* **17**, 27 (1956).

152. E. Fawcett, *Advan. Phys. (Phil. Mag. Suppl.)* **13**, 139 (1964).

153. E. S. Fisher and H. J. McSkimin, *Phys. Rev.* **124**, 67 (1961).

154. K. Försvoll and I. Holwech, *Phys. Letters* **3**, 66 (1962).

155. K. Försvoll and I. Holwech, *Phil. Mag.* **9**, 435 (1964).

156. K. Försvoll and I. Holwech, *Phil. Mag.* **10**, 181 (1964).

157. V. Frank and O. G. Jeppeson, *Phys. Rev.* **89**, 1153 (1953).

158. B. Frankenhauser and D. K. C. MacDonald, *J. Sci. Instr.* **26**, 145 (1949).

159. S. A. Friedberg, in: H. C. Wolfe (ed.), *Temperature: Its Measurement and Control in Science and Industry, Vol. 2* (Reinhold, New York, 1955), p. 359.
160. J. Friedel, *Can. J. Phys.* **34**, 1190 (1956).
161. A. N. Friedman and S. H. Koenig, *IBM J. Res. Develop.* **4**, 158 (1960).
162. K. Fuchs, *Proc. Cambridge Phil. Soc.* **34**, 100 (1938).
163. G. T. Furukawa, M. L. Reilly, and W. G. Saba, *Rev. Sci. Instr.* **35**, 113 (1964).
164. D. C. Gall, *Electrican* **90**, 360 (1923).
165. C. F. Gallo, B. S. Chandrasekhar, and P. H. Sutter, *J. Appl. Phys.* **34**, 144 (1963).
166. R. I. Garber and I. A. Gindin, *Usp. Fiz. Nauk* **74**, 31 (1961) [*Sov. Phys.-Usp.* (Engl. transl.) **4**, 405 (1964)].
167. T. H. Geballe, D. N. Lyon, J. M. Whelan, and W. F. Giauque, *Rev. Sci. Instr.* **23**, 489 (1952).
168. P. G. de Gennes and J. Friedel, *J. Phys. Chem. Solids* **4**, 71 (1958).
169. A. N. Gerritsen, *Physica* **19**, 61 (1953); **25**, 489 (1959).
170. A. N. Gerritsen and J. O. Linde, *Physica* **17**, 573 (1951).
171. A. N. Gerritsen and J. O. Linde, *Physica* **18**, 877 (1952).
172. H. Gestenkorn, *Ann. Physik* **10** (6), 49 (1952).
173. A. Giansoldati and J. O. Linde, *J. Phys. Radium* **16**, 341 (1955).
174. W. F. Giauque, R. M. Buffington, and W. A. Schulze, *J. Am. Chem. Soc.* **49**, 2343 (1927).
175. W. F. Giauque, L. Johnston, and M. Kelly, *J. Am. Chem. Soc.* **49**, 2367 (1927).
176. W. F. Giauque, J. W. Stout, and C. W. Clark, *J. Am. Chem. Soc.* **60**, 1053 (1938).
177. A. Gmelin, *Compt. rend. acad. sci.* (*Paris*) **259**, 3459 (1964).
178. E. Goens and E. Grüneisen, *Ann. Physik* **14**, 164 (1932).
179. J. M. Goode, *J. Chem. Phys.* **26**, 1269 (1957).
180. D. A. Goodings, *Phys. Rev.* **132**, 542 (1963); *J. Appl. Phys.* **34**, 1370 (1963).
181. B. A. Green, *Rev. Sci. Instr.* **32**, 364 (1962).
182. R. W. Green, S. Legvold, and F. H. Spedding, *Phys. Rev.* **122**, 827 (1961).
183. E. Grüneisen, *Ann. Physik* **16** (5), 530 (1933).
184. E. Grüneisen, *Ann. Physik* **40** (5), 543 (1941).
185. E. Grüneisen and H. K. Adenstedt, *Ann. Physik* **31** (5), 714 (1938).
186. E. Grüneisen and H. D. Erfling, *Ann. Physik* **38** (5), 399 (1940).
187. E. Grüneisen and J. Gielessen, *Ann. Physik* **26** (5), 449 (1936).
188. E. Grüneisen and E. Goens, *Z. Physik* **26**, 250 (1924).
189. E. Grüneisen and E. Goens, *Z. Physik* **44**, 615 (1927).
190. E. Grüneisen and H. Reddemann, *Ann. Physik* **20** (5), 843 (1934).
191. K. A. Gschneidner, R. O. Elliott, and V. O. Struebhing, *Plutonium 1960* (Cleaver-Hume, London, 1961), p. 134.
192. A. I. Gubanov, *Zh. Experim. i Teor. Fiz.* (*USSR*) **26**, 139 (1954); **30**, 862 (1956); **31**, 462 (1956) [*Sov. Phys. JETP* (Engl. transl.) **1**, 364 (1955); **3**, 854 (1957); **4**, 465 (1957)]. *Zh. Tekhn. Fiz.* (*USSR*) **26**, 8 (1956); **27**, 3 (1957) [*Sov. Phys.-Tech. Phys.* (Engl. transl.) **1**, 1605 (1956); **2**, 1 (1957)].
193. A. Guntz and W. Broniewski, *Compt. rend. acad. sci.* (*Paris*) **147**, 1474 (1908).
194. W. J. de Haas and P. A. van Alphen, *Proc. Acad. Sci. Amsterdam* **33**, 1106 (1930); *Leiden Commun.* No. 212a.
195. W. J. de Haas and J. H. de Boer, *Physica* **1**, 609 (1933–1934).
196. W. J. de Haas, J. H. de Boer, and G. J. van den Berg, *Physica* **1**, 1115 (1933–1934).

197. M. L. Hackspill, *Compt. rend. acad. sci.* (*Paris*) **151**, 305 (1910).
198. P. Haen and G. T. Meaden, *Cryogenics* **5**, 194 (1965).
199. P. Haen and L. Weil, *Cryogenics* **5**, 46 (1965).
200. H. T. Hall, *Rev. Sci. Instr.* **29**, 267 (1958); **31**, 125 (1960).
201. P. M. Hall, S. Legvold, and F. H. Spedding, *Phys. Rev.* **116**, 1446 (1959).
202. P. M. Hall, S. Legvold, and F. H. Spedding, *Phys. Rev.* **117**, 971 (1960).
203. F. S. Ham and D. C. Mattis, *IBM J. Res. Develop.* **4**, 143 (1960).
204. A. F. A. Harper, W. R. G. Kemp, P. G. Klemens, R. J. Tainsh, and G. K. White, *Phil. Mag.* **2** (8), 577 (1957).
205. W. A. Harrison, *J. Phys. Chem. Solids* **5**, 44 (1958).
206. A. Hasegawa, *J. Phys. Soc. Japan* **19**, 504 (1964).
207. F. T. Hedgcock and W. B. Muir, *Phys. Rev.* **136**, A561 (1964).
208. F. T. Hedgcock, W. B. Muir, and E. Wallingford, *Can. J. Phys.* **38**, 376 (1960).
209. D. E. Hegland, S. Legvold, and F. H. Spedding, *Phys. Rev.* **131**, 158 (1963).
210. R. A. Hein, R. Mayelsky, R. C. Miller, and J. K. Hulm, *Bull. Am. Phys. Soc.* **9**, 268 (1964).
211. W. G. Henry and P. A. Schroeder, *Can. J. Phys.* **41**, 1076 (1963).
212. A. V. Hill, *J. Sci. Instr.* **25**, 225 (1948).
213. J. D. Hill, *J. Sci. Instr.* **36**, 369 (1959).
214. F. E. Hoare and J. C. Matthews, *Proc. Roy. Soc.* (*London*), *Ser. A* **212**, 137 (1952).
215. L. Holborn, *Ann. Physik* **59** (4), 145 (1919).
216. E. W. Hornung and D. N. Lyon, *Rev. Sci. Instr.* **32**, 684 (1961).
217. W. V. Houston, *Z. Physik* **48**, 449 (1928); *Phys. Rev.* **34**, 279 (1929).
218. A. Howie, *Phil. Mag.* **5** (8), 251 (1960).
219. R. P. Hudson, in: F. E. Hoare, L. C. Jackson, and N, Kurti, *Experimental Cryophysics* (Butterworths, London, 1961), p. 233.
220. J. K. Hulm, *Proc. Phys. Soc.* **64B**, 207 (1951).
221. J. K. Hulm and B. B. Goodman, *Phys. Rev.* **106**, 659 (1957).
222. S. C. Hunter and F. R. N. Nabarro, *Proc. Roy. Soc.* (*London*), *Ser. A* **220**, 542 (1953).
223. E. S. Itskevich, *Zh. Experim. i Teor. Fiz.* (*USSR*) **42**, 1173 (1962) [*Sov. Phys. JETP* (Engl. transl.) **15**, 811 (1962)].
224. W. Jaeger and H. Steinwehr, *Ann. Physik* **45** (4), 1089 (1914).
225. B. W. James and B. Yates, *J. Sci. Instr.* **40**, 193 (1963).
226. N. R. James, S. Legvold, and F. H. Spedding, *Phys. Rev.* **88**, 1092 (1952).
227. J.-P. Jan, in: F. Seitz and D. Turnbull (eds.), *Solid State Physics, Vol. 5* (Academic Press, New York, 1957), p. 1.
228. C. H. Johansson and J. O. Linde, *Ann. Physik* **25** (5), 1 (1936).
229. H. Jones and C. Zener, *Proc. Roy. Soc.* (*London*), *Ser. A* **145**, 268 (1934).
230. M. C. Jones and E. H. Sondheimer, *Phys. Letters* **11**, 122 (1964).
231. E. Justi, *Phys. Z.* **41**, 486, 563 (1940).
232. E. Justi and I. Ascherman, *Phys. Z.* **43**, 207 (1947).
233. E. Justi and H. Kramer, *Phys. Z.* **41**, 196 (1940).
234. T. Kasuya, *Progr. Theor. Phys.* (*Kyoto*) **16**, 58 (1956).
235. T. Kasuya, *Progr. Theor. Phys.* (*Kyoto*) **22**, 227 (1959).
236. W. H. Keesom and J. N. van den Ende, *Leiden Commun.* No. 203c (1929).
237. F. M. Kelly, *Can. J. Phys.* **32**, 81 (1954).
238. F. M. Kelly and D. K. C. MacDonald, *Can. J. Phys.* **31**, 147 (1953).
239. W. R. G. Kemp, P. G. Klemens, A. K. Sreedhar, and G. K. White, *Phil. Mag.* **46** (7), 811 (1955).
240. W. R. G. Kemp, P. G. Klemens, R. J. Tainsh, and G. K. White, *Acta met.* **5**, 303 (1957).

241. W. R. G. Kemp, P. G. Klemens, and G. K. White, *Austral. J. Phys.* **9**, 180 (1956).
242. V. I. Khotkevich and M. Y. Zabara, *Cryogenics* **3**, 33 (1963).
243. E. King and J. A. Lee, *Cryogenics* **3**, 177 (1963).
244. E. King, J. A. Lee, K. Mendelssohn, and D. A. Wigley, *Proc. Roy. Soc.* (*London*), *Ser. A* **284**, 325 (1965).
245. A. Kjekshus and W. B. Pearson, *Can. J. Phys.* **40**, 98 (1962).
246. P. G. Klemens and G. C. Lowenthal, *Austral. J. Phys.* **14**, 352 (1961).
247. B. Knook, Thesis, University of Leiden (1962).
248. B. Knook and G. J. van den Berg, in: R. O. Davies (ed.), *Proceedings of the Eighth Low Temperature Physics Conference, London, 1962* (Butterworths, London, 1963), p. 239.
249. M. Kohler, *Ann. Physik* **32** (5), 211 (1938).
250. M. Kohler, *Ann. Physik* **6** (6), 18 (1949).
251. M. Kohler, *Z. Physik* **126**, 495 (1949).
252. H. Kojima, R. S. Tebble, and D. E. G. Williams, *Proc. Roy. Soc.* (*London*), *Ser. A* **260**, 237 (1961).
253. J. Kondo, *Progr. Theor. Phys.* (*Kyoto*) **32**, 37 (1964).
254. E. Krautz and H. Schultz, *Z. Naturforsch.* **9a**, 125 (1954); **12a**, 710 (1957).
255. J. E. Kunzler, T. H. Geballe, and G. W. Hull, in: F. G. Brickwedde (ed.), *Temperature: Its Measurement and Control in Science and Industry, Vol. 3,* Part 1 (Reinhold, New York, 1962), p. 391; *Rev. Sci. Instr.* **28**, 96 (1957).
256. N. Kurnakow and A. J. Nikitinski, *Z. anorg. allgem. Chem.* **88**, 151 (1914).
257. R. Lallement, *J. Phys. Chem. Solids* **24**, 1617 (1963).
258. R. Lallement, *Phys. Letters* **6**, 182 (1963).
259. L. D. Landau and I. Ya. Pomeranchuk, *Zh. Experim. i Teor. Fiz.* (*USSR*) **7**, 379 (1937).
260. A. W. Lawson, in: B. Chalmers (ed.), *Progress in Metal Physics, Vol. 6* (Interscience, New York, and Butterworths, London, 1956), p. 1.
261. J. A. Lee, *Progress in Nuclear Energy, Vol. 3* (International Conference on the Peaceful Uses of Atomic Energy, Series 5, Geneva, 1961), p. 453.
262. J. A. Lee, R. O. A. Hall, E. King, and G. T. Meaden, *Plutonium 1960* (Cleaver-Hume, London, 1961), p. 39.
263. J. A. Lee, G. T. Meaden, and K. Mendelssohn, *Cryogenics* **1**, 52 (1960).
264. R. G. Leffler and D. J. Montgomery, *Phys. Rev.* **126**, 53 (1962).
265. E. J. Lewis, *Phys. Rev.* **34**, 1575 (1929).
266. I. M. Lifshitz, M. Y. Azbel', and M. I. Kaganov, *Zh. Experim. i Teor. Fiz.* (*USSR*) **31**, 63 (1956) [*Sov. Phys. JETP* (Engl. transl.) **4**, 41 (1957)].
267. J. O. Linde, *Ann. Physik* **14** (5), 353 (1932); **15**, 219 (1932).
268. J. O. Linde, Thesis, Lund (1939).
269. P. Lindenfeld, in: F. G. Brickwedde (ed.), *Temperature: Its Measurement and Control in Science and Industry, Vol. 3,* Part 1 (Reinhold, New York, 1962), p. 399.
270. M. D. Liston, *Electronics* (January 1954).
271. M. D. Liston, C. E. Quinn, W. E. Sargeant, and G. G. Scott, *Rev. Sci. Instr.* **17**, 194 (1946).
272. S. H. Liu, *J. Appl. Phys.* **35**, 1087 (1964); IBM Research Paper RC-1082 (1963).
273. E. C. Lloyd, V. O. Hutton, and D. P. Johnson, *J. Res. Natl. Bur. Std.* **63C**, 59 (1959).
274. J. M. Lock, *Proc. Phys. Soc.* **70B**, 566 (1957).
275. H. London, *Proc. Roy. Soc.* (*London*), *Ser. A* **176**, 522 (1940).
276. W. B. H. Lord, *Metall. Revs.* **8**, 277 (1963).

277. H. A. Lorentz, *Proc. Acad. Sci. Amsterdam* **7**, 438, 585, 684 (1904-1905).
278. L. Lorenz, *Ann. Physik* **13** (3), 422 (1881).
279. O. V. Lounasmaa, *Phil. Mag.* **3** (8), 652 (1958).
280. O. V. Lounasmaa, *Phys. Rev.* **133**, A219 (1964).
281. M. S. Lubell and B. S. Chandrasekhar, *Rev. Sci. Instr.* **35**, 906 (1964).
282. B. Luthi, *Helv. phys. acta* **33**, 161 (1960).
283. B. Luthi and P. Wyder, *Helv. phys. acta* **33**, 667 (1960).
284. D. K. C. MacDonald, *J. Sci. Instr.* **24**, 232 (1947).
285. D. K. C. MacDonald, *Nature* **163**, 637 (1949).
286. D. K. C. MacDonald, *Phil. Mag.* **43** (7), 479 (1952).
287. D. K. C. MacDonald and K. Mendelssohn, *Proc. Roy. Soc.* (*London*), *Ser. A* **202**, 503 (1950).
288. D. K. C. MacDonald and K. Mendelssohn, *Proc. Roy. Soc.* (*London*), *Ser. A* **202**, 523 (1950).
289. D. K. C. MacDonald and W. B. Pearson, *Proc. Roy. Soc.* (*London*), *Ser. A* **219**, 373 (1953).
290. D. K. C. MacDonald and K. Sarginson, *Proc. Roy. Soc.* (*London*), *Ser. A* **203**, 223 (1950).
291. D. K. C. MacDonald, G. K. White, and S. B. Woods, *Proc. Roy. Soc.* (*London*), *Ser. A* **235**, 358 (1956).
292. A. R. Mackintosh, *Phys. Rev. Letters* **9**, 90 (1962).
293. A. R. Mackintosh, *Phys. Letters* **4**, 140 (1963).
294. I. Mannari, *Progr. Theor. Phys.* (*Kyoto*) **22**, 335 (1959).
295. B. T. Matthias, in: C. J. Gorter (ed.), *Progress in Low Temperature Physics*, *Vol. 2* (North-Holland, Amsterdam, 1957), p. 138.
296. B. T. Matthias, T. H. Geballe, and V. B. Compton, *Rev. Mod. Phys.* **35**, 1 (1963).
297. B. T. Matthias, T. H. Geballe, V. B. Compton, E. Corenzwit, and G. W. Hull, *Rev. Mod. Phys.* **36**, 155 (1964), plus the attendant discussion.
298. A. Matthiessen, *Ann. Physik Chem.* (Pogg. Folge) **110**, 190 (1860). A. Matthiessen and G. Vogt, *Ann. Physik. Chem.* (Pogg. Folge) **122**, 19 (1864).
299. C. R. Maxwell, *J. Chem. Phys.* **17**, 1288 (1949).
300. C. J. McHargue and H. L. Yakel, *Acta met.* **8**, 637 (1960).
302. J. C. McLennan, C. D. Niven, and J. O. Wilhelm, *Phil. Mag.* **6** (7), 666 (1928).
303. G. T. Meaden, D. Phil. Thesis, Oxford (1961). (Published by Micromethods Ltd., East Ardsley, Wakefield, England, as Microfiche O/N 8605.)
304. G. T. Meaden, *Proc. Roy. Soc.* (*London*), *Ser. A* **276**, 553 (1963).
305. G. T. Meaden, *Cryogenics* **4**, 105 (1964).
305a. G. T. Meaden, *J. Less-Common Metals* **9**, 392 (1965).
306. G. T. Meaden, Unpublished work.
307. G. T. Meaden and J. A. Lee, *Cryogenics* **1**, 33 (1960).
308. G. T. Meaden and J. A. Lee, *Cryogenics* **2**, 182 (1962).
308a. G. T. Meaden and P. Pelloux-Gervais, *Cryogenics* **5**, 227 (1965).
309. G. T. Meaden and P. Pelloux-Gervais (to be published, 1966).
310. G. T. Meaden and T. Shigi, *Cryogenics* **4**, 90 (1964).
311. C. J. Meechan, *Atomics International Quarterly Progress Report: Solid State Physics* (1955), p. 20.
312. W. Meissner, *Z. Physik* **38**, 647 (1926).
313. W. Meissner, H. Franz, and H. Westerhoff, *Ann. Physik* **13** (5), 555 (1932).
314. J. Meixner, *Ann. Physik* **38** (5), 609 (1940).
315. K. Mendelssohn, *Can. J. Phys.* **34**, 1315 (1956).
316. E. Mendoza and J. G. Thomas, *Phil. Mag.* **42** (7), 291 (1951).

317. H. Miwa, *Progr. Theor. Phys.* (*Kyoto*) **28**, 208 (1962); *Technical Report of the Institute for Solid State Physics, Tokyo,* Series A, No. 69 (1963).
318. H. Montgomery, *Proc. Roy. Soc.* (*London*), *Ser. A* **244**, 85 (1958).
319. R. M. Moon, J. W. Cable, and W. C. Koehler, *J. Appl. Phys.* **35**, 1041 (1964).
320. N. F. Mott, *Proc. Phys. Soc.* **46**, 680 (1934).
321. N. F. Mott, *Proc. Roy. Soc.* (*London*), **146**, 465 (1934).
322. N. F. Mott, *Proc. Phys. Soc.* **47**, 571 (1935).
323. N. F. Mott, *Proc. Cambridge Phil. Soc.* **32**, 281 (1936).
324. N. F. Mott, *Proc. Roy. Soc.* (*London*), *Ser. A* **153**, 699 (1936).
325. N. F. Mott, *Advan. Phys.* (*Phil. Mag. Suppl.*) **13**, 325 (1964).
326. N. F. Mott and K. W. H. Stevens, *Phil. Mag.* **2** (8), 1364 (1957).
327. E. F. Mueller, *Natl. Bur. Std. Bull.* **13**, 547 (1916-1917).
328. W. B. Muir, *Rev. Sci. Instr.* **35**, 408 (1964).
329. J. L. Nichols, *J. Appl. Phys.* **26**, 470 (1955).
330. H. E. Nigh, S. Legvold, and F. H. Spedding, *Phys. Rev.* **132**, 1092 (1963).
331. K. Niira, *Phys. Rev.* **117**, 129 (1960).
332. A. L. Norbury, *Trans. Faraday Soc.* **17**, 257 (1921).
333. L. Nordheim, *Ann. Physik* **9** (5), 607 (1931).
334. L. Nordheim, *Act. sci. et ind.* No. 131 (Hermann, Paris, 1934).
335. J. L. Olsen, *Helv. phys. acta* **31**, 713 (1958).
336. J. L. Olsen, *Electron Transport in Metals* (Interscience, New York and London, 1962). (See Table A-3, p. 107.)
337. M. Olsen-Bär, D. Phil. Thesis, Oxford (1956).
338. M. Olsen-Bär and R. W. Powell, *Proc. Roy. Soc.* (*London*), *Ser. A* **209**, 542 (1951).
339. H. K. Onnes and G. Holst, *Leiden Commun.* No. 142a (1914); *Proc. Amst. Soc.* **17**, 508 (1915).
340. H. K. Onnes and W. Tuyn, *Proc. Acad. Amsterdam* **25**, 443 (1923).
341. H. K. Onnes and W. Tuyn, *Leiden Commun. Suppl.* No. 58 (1926).
342. M. P. Orlova, in: F. G. Brickwedde (ed.), *Temperature: Its Measurement and Control in Science and Industry, Vol. 3,* Part 1 (Reinhold, New York, 1962), p. 345.
343. A. W. Overhauser and A. Arrott, *Phys. Rev. Letters* **4**, 226 (1960).
344. J. Owen, M. E. Browne, W. D. Knight, and C. Kittel, *Phys. Rev.* **102**, 1501 (1956).
345. D. H. Parkinson and L. M. Roberts, *Proc. Phys. Soc.* **68B**, 386 (1955).
346. J. Pascal, J. Morin, and P. Lacombe, *Compt. rend. acad. sci.* (*Paris*) **256**, 4899 (1963); *J. Nucl. Mater.* **13**, 28 (1964).
347. W. Paul, in: R. S. Bradley (ed.), *High Pressure Physics and Chemistry, Vol. 1* (Academic Press, London and New York, 1963), p. 299.
348. W. B. Pearson, *Phil. Mag.* **46** (7), 911, 920 (1955).
349. R. Peierls, *Ann. Physik* **4** (5), 121 (1930).
350. V. P. Peshkov and K. N. Zinoveva, *Rept. Progr. Phys.* **22**, 504 (1959).
351. M. L. Picklesimer and S. T. Sekula, *Phys. Rev. Letters* **9**, 254 (1962).
352. A. B. Pippard, *Phil. Trans. Roy. Soc.* (*London*), *Ser. A,* **250**, 325 (1957).
353. A. B. Pippard and G. T. Pullan, *Proc. Cambridge Phil. Soc.* **48**, 188 (1952).
354. I. Ya. Pomeranchuk, *Zh. Experim. i Teor. Fiz.* (*USSR*) **33**, 992 (1958) [*Sov. Phys. JETP* (Engl. transl.) **8**, 693 (1959)].
355. H. H. Potter, *Proc. Phys. Soc.* **49**, 671 (1937).
356. E. V. Potter, H. C. Lukens, and R. W. Huber, *Trans. Met. Soc. AIME* **185**, 399 (1949).
357. R. L. Powell, M. D. Bunch, and R. J. Corruccini, *Cryogenics* **1**, 139 (1961).
358. R. L. Powell, M. D. Bunch, and E. F. Gibson, *J. Appl. Phys.* **31**, 504 (1960).

359. R. L. Powell, W. M. Rogers, and D. O. Coffin, *J. Res. Nat. Bur. Std.* **59**, 349 (1957); see also R. L. Powell, H. M. Roder, and W. J. Hall, *Phys. Rev.* **115**, 214 (1959).

360. R. L. Powell, W. M. Rogers, and H. M. Roder, *J. Appl. Phys.* **28**, 1282 (1957).

361. R. W. Powell, *Proc. Roy. Soc. (London), Ser. A* **209**, 525 (1951).

362. R. W. Powell, *Phil. Mag.* **44** (7), 645 (1953).

363. R. W. Powell, Private communication (1964); see also R. J. Tainsh and G. K. White, *Can. J. Phys.* **42**, 208 (1964).

363a. R. W. Powell and B. W. Jolliffe, *Phys. Letters* **14**, 171 (1965).

364. R. W. Powell and R. P. Tye, *J. Less-Common Metals* **3**, 226 (1961); **5**, 297 (1963).

365. R. W. Powell, R. P. Tye, and M. J. Woodman, *Platinum Metals Rev.* **6**, 138 (1962).

366. R. W. Powell, R. P. Tye, and M. J. Woodman, *J. Less-Common Metals* **5**, 49 (1963).

367. R. W. Powell, M. J. Woodman, and R. P. Tye, *Phil. Mag.* **7** (8), 1183 (1962).

368. J. S. Preston, *J. Sci. Instr.* **23**, 173 (1946).

369. P. J. Price, *IBM J. Res. Develop.* **4**, 152 (1960).

370. S. V. Radcliffe and J. S. White, *J. Sci. Instr.* **38**, 363 (1961).

371. K. Rausch, *Ann. Physik* **1** (6), 190 (1947).

372. A. R. Regel', *J. Tech. Phys. (Moscow)* **18**, 1510 (1948).

373. R. Reich, *Compt. rend. acad. sci. (Paris)* **258**, 2814, 3298 (1964).

374. R. Reich, J. Bonmarin, and A. Peyron, *Compt. rend. acad. sci. (Paris)* **258**, 3014 (1964).

375. R. Reich and V. Q. Kinh, *Compt. rend. acad. sci. (Paris)* **256**, 156 (1963).

376. R. Reich and V. Q. Kinh, *Compt. rend. acad. sci. (Paris)* **256**, 4432 (1963).

377. R. Reich, V. Q. Kinh, and J. Bonmarin, *Compt. rend. acad. sci. (Paris)* **256**, 5558 (1963).

378. *Rev. Sci. Instr.* **26**, 698 (1955); **28**, 497, 1070 (1957); **30**, 557 (1959).

379. E. Rinck, *Compt. rend. acad. sci. (Paris)* **192**, 421 (1931).

380. E. Rinck, *Compt. rend. acad. sci. (Paris)* **193**, 1328 (1931).

381. E. Rinck, *Compt. rend. acad. sci. (Paris)* **234**, 845 (1952).

382. A. T. Robinson and J. E. Dorn, *J. Metals (Trans.)* **3**, 457 (1951).

383. H. J. M. van Rongen, B. Knook, and G. J. van den Berg, *Proceedings Ninth Low Temperature Physics Conference* (Columbus, 1964).

384. H. M. Rosenberg, *Phil. Trans. Roy. Soc. (London), Ser. A* **247**, 441 (1955).

385. E. Rosenbohm, *Physica* **6**, 337 (1939).

386. T. A. Sandenaw, *J. Phys. Chem. Solids* **23**, 1241 (1962).

387. T. A. Sandenaw and R. B. Gibney, *J. Phys. Chem. Solids* **6**, 81 (1958).

388. J. E. Schirber and C. A. Swenson, *Phys. Rev. Letters* **2**, 296 (1959); *Phys. Rev.* **123**, 1115 (1961).

389. F. Schodey, W. R. Hosler, and M. L. Cohen, *Phys. Rev. Letters* **12**, 474 (1964).

390. L. Schubnikov and W. J. de Haas, *Proc. Acad. Amsterdam* **33**, 350 (1930); *Leiden Commun.* No. 207c.

391. L. Schubnikov and W. J. de Haas, *Proc. Acad. Amsterdam* **33**, 363 (1930); *Leiden Commun.* No. 207d.

392. O. Sckell, *Ann. Physik* **6** (5), 932 (1930).

393. J. A. Seitchik, A. C. Gossard, and V. Jaccarino, *Phys. Rev.* **136**, A1119 (1964).

394. F. Seitz, *Rev. Mod. Phys.* **34**, 656 (1962).

395. E. E. Semenenko and A. I. Sudovtsov, *Zh. Experim. i Teor. Fiz.* (*USSR*) **42**, 1022 (1962) [*Sov. Phys. JETP* (Engl. transl.) **15**, 708 (1962)].
396. E. E. Semenenko, A. I. Sudovtsov, and A. D. Shvets, *Zh. Experim. i Teor. Fiz.* (*USSR*) **42**, 1488 (1962) [*Sov. Phys. JETP* (Engl. transl.) **15**, 1033 (1962)].
397. E. E. Semenenko, A. I. Sudovtsov, and N. V. Volkenshtein, *Zh. Experim. i Teor. Fiz.* (*USSR*) **45**, 1387 (1963) [*Sov. Phys. JETP* (Engl. transl.) **18**, 957 (1964)].
398. C. W. Siemens, *Proc. Roy. Soc.* (*London*), *Ser. A* **19**, 351 (1871).
399. R. E. Skochdopole, M. Griffel, and F. H. Spedding, *J. Chem. Phys.* **23**, 2258 (1955).
400. G. A. Slack, *Phys. Rev.* **122**, 1451 (1961).
401. F. E. Smith, *Phil. Mag.* **24** (6), 541 (1912).
402. A. Sommerfeld, *Z. Physik* **47**, 1 (1928).
403. A. Sommerfeld and H. Bethe, *Handbuch der Physik*, Vol. *24/2* (Springer-Verlag, Berlin, 1933), p. 333.
404. E. H. Sondheimer, *Phys. Rev.* **80**, 401 (1950).
405. E. H. Sondheimer, *Proc. Roy. Soc.* (*London*), *Ser. A* **203**, 75 (1950).
406. E. H. Sondheimer, *Advan. Phys.* (*Phil. Mag. Suppl.*) **1**, 1 (1952).
407. E. H. Sondheimer and A. H. Wilson, *Proc. Roy. Soc.* (*London*), *Ser. A* **190**, 435 (1947).
408. J. C. Southard and D. H. Andrews, *J. Franklin Inst.* **207**, 323 (1929).
409. F. H. Spedding, A. H. Daane, and K. W. Herrmann, *J. Metals* **9**, 895 (1957); also F. H. Spedding, K. W. Herrmann, and A. H. Daane, *Trans. Met. Soc. AIME* **209**, 895 (1957).
410. F. H. Spedding, J. J. Hanak, and A. H. Daane, *Trans. Met. Soc. AIME* **212**, 949 (1952).
411. H. Stehle and A. Seeger, *Z. Physik* **146**, 217, 242 (1956).
412. D. L. Strandburg, S. Legvold, and F. H. Spedding, *Phys. Rev.* **127**, 2046 (1962).
413. A. I. Sudovtsov and E. E. Semenenko, *Zh. Experim. i Teor. Fiz.* (*USSR*) **31**, 525 (1956) [*Sov. Phys. JETP* (Engl. transl.) **4**, 592 (1957)].
413a. L. J. Sundström, *Phil. Mag.* **11**, 657 (1965).
414. B. Svensson, *Ann. Physik* **14** (5), 699 (1932).
415. B. Svensson, *Ann. Physik* **25** (5), 263 (1936).
416. C. A. Swenson, *Phys. Rev.* **100**, 1607 (1955).
417. C. A. Swenson, in: F. Seitz and D. Turnbull (eds.), *Solid State Physics*, Vol. *11* (Academic Press, New York, 1960), p. 41.
418. C. S. Taylor, L. A. Willey, D. W. Smith, and J. D. Edwards, *Metals and Alloys* **9**, 189 (1938).
419. J. B. Taylor, S. L. Bennett, and R. D. Heyding, *J. Phys. Chem. Solids* **26**, 69 (1965).
420. M. A. Taylor and C. H. L. Smith, *Physica* **28**, 453 (1962).
421. I. M. Templeton, *J. Sci. Instr.* **32**, 172 (1955).
422. I. M. Templeton, *J. Sci. Instr.* **32**, 314 (1955); *Solid State Electronics* **1**, 258 (1960).
423. M. W. Thompson, *J. Sci. Instr.* **34**, 515 (1957).
424. E. A. Turov, *Izv. Akad. Nauk SSSR, Ser. Fiz.* **19**, 474 (1955) (*Columbia Tech. Transl.* p. 426).
425. E. A. Turov, *Fiz. Metall. Metallovedinie* **6**, 203 (1958) [*Phys. Metals Metallog.* (Engl. transl.) **6**, 13 (1958)]; also Sh. Sh. Abel'skii and E. A. Turov, *Fiz. Metall. Metallovedinie* **10**, 801 (1960) [*Phys. Metals Metallog.* (Engl. transl.) **10**, 1 (1960)].
426. W. Tuyn and H. K. Onnes, *Proc. Acad. Sci. Amsterdam* **26**, 504 (1933).

427. R. P. Tye, *J. Less-Common Metals* **3**, 13 (1961).
428. W. W. Tyler and A. C. Wilson, *Phys. Rev.* **89**, 870 (1953).
429. F. I. Vasenin, *Zh. Tekhn. Fiz.* **25**, 1190 (1955).
430. W. Voigt, *Lehrbuch der Kristallphysik* (Teubner, Leipzig, 1928), p. 959.
431. N. V. Volkenshtein and V. E. Startsev, *Zh. Experim. i Teor. Fiz.* (*USSR*) **46**, 457 (1964) [*Sov. Phys. JETP* (Engl. transl.) **19**, 308 (1964)].
432. R. J. Wasilewski, *Trans. Met. Soc. AIME* **224**, 5 (1962).
433. R. J. Weiss and A. S. Marotta, *J. Phys. Chem. Solids* **9**, 302 (1959).
434. G. K. White, *Austral. J. Phys.* **6**, 397 (1953).
435. G. K. White, *Proc. Phys. Soc.* **A66**, 559 (1953).
436. G. K. White and S. B. Woods, *Can. J. Phys.* **33**, 58 (1955).
437. G. K. White and S. B. Woods, *Phil. Mag.* **1** (8), 846 (1956).
438. G. K. White and S. B. Woods, *Can. J. Phys.* **35**, 248 (1957).
439. G. K. White and S. B. Woods, *Can. J. Phys.* **35**, 346 (1957).
440. G. K. White and S. B. Woods, *Can. J. Phys.* **35**, 656 (1957).
441. G. K. White and S. B. Woods, *Can. J. Phys.* **35**, 892 (1957).
442. G. K. White and S. B. Woods, *Rev. Sci. Instr.* **28**, 638 (1957).
443. G. K. White and S. B. Woods, *Can. J. Phys.* **36**, 875 (1958).
444. G. K. White and S. B. Woods, *Phil. Mag.* **3** (8), 342 (1958).
445. G. Wiedemann and R. Franz, *Ann. Physik* **89** (2), 497 (1853).
446. W. Wien, *Sitzgsber. Preuss. Akad. Wiss. Berlin, Sitz. Berlin* **5**, 184 (1913).
447. D. A. Wigley, D. Phil. Thesis, Oxford (1963).
448. D. A. Wigley, *Proc. Roy. Soc.* (*London*), *Series A* **284**, 344 (1965).
449. M. K. Wilkinson, W. C. Koehler, E. O. Wollan, and J. W. Cable, *J. Appl. Phys.* **32**, 48S (1961).
450. A. H. Wilson, *Proc. Roy. Soc.* (*London*), *Ser. A* **167**, 580 (1938).
450a. J. Wittig, *Phys. Rev. Letters* **15**, 159 (1965); *Phys. Letters* **17**, 187 (1965).
451. A. D. B. Woods, B. N. Brockhouse, R. H. March, A. T. Stewart, and R. Bowers, *Phys. Rev.* **128**, 1112 (1962).
452. S. B. Woods, *Can. J. Phys.* **34**, 223 (1956).
453. M. Yaqqu, *Cryogenics* **1**, 101 (1960).
454. K. Yosida, *Phys. Rev.* **107**, 396 (1958).
455. V. B. Zernov and Y. V. Sharvin, *Zh. Experim. i Teor. Fiz.* (*USSR*) **36**, 1038 (1959) [*Sov. Phys. JETP* (Engl. transl.) **9**, 373 (1959)].
456. J. M. Ziman, *Proc. Roy. Soc.* (*London*), *Ser. A* **226**, 436 (1954).
457. J. M. Ziman, *Phil. Mag.* **3** (8), 1117 (1958).
458. J. M. Ziman, *Phil. Mag.* **6** (8), 1013 (1961).
459. J. E. Zimmerman, *Rev. Sci. Instr.* **32**, 402 (1961).

# Author Index

The numbers in bold type refer to the reference numbers used in this book, while those in parentheses refer to the pages on which these references are cited.

# Subject Index

## A

AC bridges and potentiometers: 161-162; induction methods 162-164
Actinides: 48-54; general properties 48; see also under individual metals
Actinium (Ac): 12, 48, 57
Adiabatic demagnetization cryostats: 174
Alkalis: 14-21, 76-78, 93-94, Table VI; effect of pressure 128-130; specimen fabrication 164; see also under individual metals
Alloys: 110-120; dilute 113-115; nondilute 115-117; disordered solid solutions 115-117; dilute transition-metal alloys 83-84, 115; nondilute transition-metal alloys 118-120; alloys with resistance minimum 82-84; Linde–Norbury rule 113-115; Mott's rule 113; Nordheim's rule 113; superconducting alloys 58, 178; Al–rich alloys 115; Au–rich alloys 113-115; $Au_3Mn$, AuMn 120; Cu–Au system 113, 115-117; Cu–rich alloys 111-115; $Cu_3Au$, CuAu 117; Cu–Ni (2), 118-119; dilute Mn in Au 83-84; Ni–Cr alloys 120, Table XI; noble metal–Pd alloys 119; miscellaneous important alloys, Table XI
Aluminum (Al): 26
Aluminum: magnetoresistivity size effect 140-141
Aluminum: alloys 115
Americium (Am): 12, 54
Amplifier, DC chopper: 158, (162)
Amplifier, galvanometer: 156-157

Amplitude of lattice vibrations $(\overline{x^2})$: 72, 126
Anisotropy in resistivity: 8-11, Table III
Annealing: (117), 121-123
Anomalous skin effect: 141-142
Antiferromagnetism: 8, 33-35, 86-88, 120; see also rare earths
Antimony (Sb): 28-29, 57
Arsenic (As): 28-29, 57
Atomic ordering: 116-117, 120
Atomic weights of metals and semiconductors, Table XV

## B

Bands: 68
Barium (Ba): 24
Berkelium (Bk): 54
Beryllium (Be): 22-23, 57
Bismuth (Bi): 28-29, 57
Bloch theory: 65-75
Bloch–Grüneisen function: see Grüneisen–Bloch function
Bloch waves: 65
Boiling points of gases: 175, Table XIII
Boltzmann transport equation: 70
Bragg relation: 67
Brasses, resistivity: Table XI; as low-temperature thermometers 178
Bridges, AC: 162; direct-reading platinum thermometer 183; Kelvin double 149; Mueller, Smith 149-150; Wheatstone 144-147, 149, 150 (sensitivity 145-147)
Brillouin zones: 67-69; magnetic 87-88
Bronze: as low-temperature thermometer 178

211

Magnetic ordering: 8, 33-36, 86-88, 120

Magnetoresistivity, electrical: 131-137; cryostat for measuring 172-174; Cu or Bi probes for field measurement 3; Fermi surface determination 132, 136-137; in high fields 132, 135-137; Kohler's rule 132-135; polar diagrams 134-135; size effect 139-141

α-Manganese (Mn): 35, 88, 178

α-Manganese (Mn): alloys with gold: 83-84, 120

β-Manganese: 35, 184

γ-Manganese: 35

Manganin: resistivity (26), 120, Table XI; thermal conductivity 165-166, Table XII; as thermometer 178

Matthiessen's rule: 5, 7-8, 82, 113; deviations 82, 113, 123, 177

Mean free path: 63, 64-65, 137-141

Melting, effect on the resistivity: 93-94, Table VI

Melting points of metals and semiconductors: Table XV

Melting points of solids as fixed points: 175-176, Table XIII (and XIV)

Mercury (Hg): 25-26

β-Mercury: 26

Metals: characteristics 1, 3, 5, 59-60; general properties Table XV; of the periodic system 3-6, 12-58, Tables I and II; see also under individual elements and properties

Methods of measuring electrical resistance: 143-168; AC bridges 162; AC potentiometers 161-162; DC bridges 144-151; DC potentiometers 151-156; four-terminal resistors 147-149; induction methods 162-164

Minimum, resistance: 22, 23, 82-84; Kondo's theory 84

Molybdenum (Mo): 34

Monel: Table XI

Monovalent metals: 14-22, 68, 75-78; effect of pressure 126-130; see also alkali and noble metals and individual elements

Mott's rule: 113

Multiply connected Fermi surface: 136

**N**

Néel temperature: 33

Neodymium (Nd): 42

Neptunium (Np): 51-52, 92

Nickel (Ni): 37, 86

Nickel–chromium alloys: 120, Table XI

Nickel–copper alloys: (2), 118-119, Table XI

Niobium (Nb): 32; as leads wire 167; $Nb_3Sn$ 58; Nb–25% Zr 174

Noble metals: 22, 78, 83-84, 92-93; effect of pressure 128-130; see also under copper, silver, and gold

Noble metals – palladium alloys: 119

Norbury – Linde rule: 113-115

Nordheim's concentration rule: 113

Normal processes: 72-73

**O**

Ohm, old International: 25

Ohm's law: 6-7, 62

Open orbits: 136

Ordering, atomic: 116-117, 120

Ordering, magnetic: 8, 33-36, 86-88, 120

Oscillatory magnetic effects: 29, 136-137

Osmium (Os): 36-37

**P**

Palladium (Pd): 38, 86, 92

Palladium – noble metal alloys: 119

Parasitic thermal emfs, elimination or reduction: (147), 154-155, 158-161

Penetration depth: 141

Perfect conductor: 66

Periodic table: Table I

Phase transformations: 13; see also resistivity graphs of Ce and Pu

Phonon, definition: 66

Platinum (Pt): 38, 89, 92, 176-177

Platinum resistance thermometer: 176-177; calibration 177; measurement 183

α-Plutonium: 52-54, 123-124

β-Plutonium: 53-54

δ-Plutonium: 53-54

Point defects: resistivity of interstitials and vacancies 123; see also defects, dislocations, and irradiation damage